# Operating Techniques for the Tractor-Loader-Backhoe

# Revised

by Gary J. Ober

**Equipment Training Resources**

**EQUIPMENT TRAINING RESOURCES**

Equipment Training Resources
**8340 Chimineas Ave.
Northridge, CA 91325
(818) 349-1230 • FAX (818) 349-1241**

For our complete catalog of heavy equipment safety and
training products, visit our website at **www.equiptrain.com**

Library of Congress Catalog Card Number: 99-66158

Published by
Equipment Training Resources
8340 Chimineas Ave.
Northridge, CA  91325
(818) 349-1230      FAX (818) 349-1241
www.equiptrain.com

ISBN 0-911785-01-9

Published in Northridge, California
Printed and bound in U.S.A.

# Table of Contents

# Introduction

The tractor-loader-backhoe (or "TLB" as I'll call it here) is a highly versatile, productive piece of equipment. It's ideal for most of the trenching that's done on a building site. It's perfect for loading soil and heavy objects into a truck. It handles light demolition well. And, of course, it backfills trenches and does minor grading much faster than could be done by hand.

## What You Need to Know

This book isn't a technical manual. And it doesn't cover any particular type of TLB. The various manufacturers have all the technical manuals you'll need on the equipment they manufacture and sell. Nor does this book recommend one brand of TLB over any other. They're all good. What this book does is explain in the most concise and direct way possible what you should know for safety and productivity of the TLB. Without this information, you may not be aware of the potential for accidents, and the safety hazards that can cause serious damage to people or property.

I've written this book for both the beginning and the experienced operator. It begins with the basics, of course. But there's plenty of useful information in later chapters for even veteran operators. And I've never met an operator who couldn't learn a little more or get rid of a few bad habits. Certainly I haven't stopped learning about the TLB. In fact, during the writing and illustrating of this revised edition, my own knowledge has been stretched into new areas of understanding, and that information is presented in this book for all to learn from. This highly technical information has been distilled into easy to understand terms, and generously illustrated for your ease of understanding and for safe operation of these machines in the future.

## Steps Toward Your Goal

As you read through the first chapters, you may feel that my descriptions seem to cover a series of unrelated subjects and procedures. Be patient – and learn these important principles as they are presented. As you read further, you will notice that each bit of information becomes a part of a larger process.

Later sections of this book emphasize the more technical aspects and difficult job situations, such as: tight work space, working around utilities, precision excavation and many more complicated tasks. Although many jobs do not demand the highest degree of operating skills, mastering the machine provides safety as well as the necessary skills to do precision work.

Learn the more demanding tasks and everything else will seem like a piece of cake. That's why I've emphasized techniques and work procedures that cover "worst-case" situations.

## Get Started Right

A word to beginners: There's no substitute for practice, practice and more practice. Just reading this book isn't enough. It's practicing what you've learned here that makes you an expert. With time, operating a backhoe safely and productively will become as natural to you as driving a car or tying your shoe.

And don't be discouraged when you run into difficulty. The TLB is among the most difficult pieces of heavy equipment to operate. There are two reasons: First, it's really two machines in one, with separate controls and operating principles for each. Second, the TLB is used for so many different tasks and procedures, that there's a lot to learn. No matter how experienced you are, there's always another job yet to be attempted and mastered. And remember, it is the operator's job to find an intelligent, safe, workable solution to the job at hand.

---

### Instructors, please note...

The Answer Key on pages 285–296 is perforated for easy removal, if desired. If you choose to remove these pages, please return them to the students at the end of the course as they are an excellent review of the material.

---

### IMPORTANT

These machines are commonly called on for wide range of tasks, procedures, and applications. Because of these wide ranging uses, I have used terminology that will convey the exact thought of the author to the reader.

When **"TLB"** is used in this book, I am referring to the machine in general.

When the word **loader** is used in this book, I am referring to the machine **being used as a loader**, moving on the site and **using the loader bucket** to perform work. The machine could be grading, leveling, moving material, or loading trucks.

When the word **backhoe** is used in this book, I am referring to the machine **being used as a backhoe**, with the stabilizers down and the machine in a set position.

---

# 1. TLB Dimensions and Stability

**dimensions** 1. measure of the size and mass of an object, such as length, height, width and weight.

**stability** 1. the state or quality of being stable.

## General

The modern tractor-loader-backhoe is the most versatile machine on today's construction site. It can dig trenches, carry heavy materials in bulk, transport large objects, and work the earth in whatever way required for all modern construction, demolition or excavation projects. It has become a common sight on city streets as well as in rural locations.

Like any piece of complicated machinery, the TLB requires a skilled operator who is proficient in the use and control of the machine's various functions. Becoming a skilled TLB operator requires a thorough understanding of the machine's capabilities, the principles behind its operation, and thousands of hours of practice.

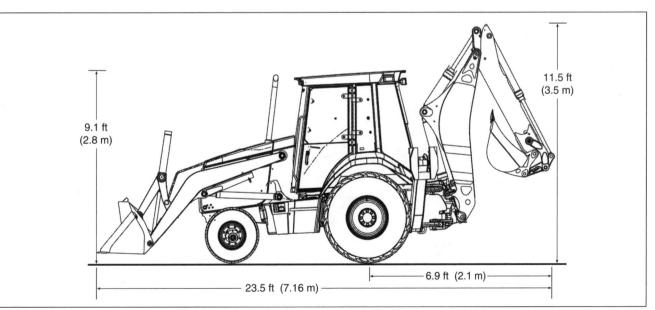

9.1 ft
(2.8 m)

11.5 ft
(3.5 m)

6.9 ft (2.1 m)

23.5 ft (7.16 m)

**Fig 1-1**  *Typical dimensions of a TLB*

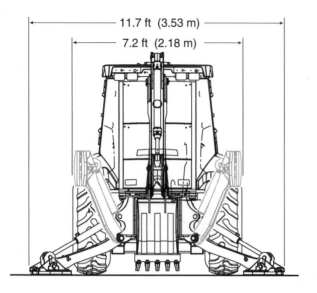

**Fig. 1-2** *Typical rear view of TLB*

The primary step toward this understanding between man and machine is in learning the TLB's dimensions. The TLB is generally more difficult to maneuver than other types of heavy equipment because it is over-long, over-high, and over-wide. Depending on the make and model, the TLB usually has an overall length of twenty-three feet with the boom drawn in. With the boom extended, the machine may stretch out to a length of thirty-five feet or more. It is at least twelve feet high with the backhoe in transport position. With the two stabilizer arms lowered, the TLB takes up twelve feet from side to side. In short, the TLB can be an awk-

ward machine. Depending on the operator's skill, however, this awkwardness can be minimized and even made to work to their advantage. One way operators can do this is by understanding the TLB's weight distribution.

## Weight Distribution

The TLB consists of three major components: 1) the tractor itself, which houses the diesel-powered engine, the hydraulic pump and the cab; 2) the front loader assembly; and 3) the backhoe assembly, mounted on the rear. Because of the flexibility of these components, particularly the backhoe itself, how the machine's seven tons are distributed frequently plays a major role in the planning and completion of many jobs.

Approximately one-third of the total weight of the TLB is in the two-ton backhoe assembly, whose main components include the boom, the crowd (or stick), the bucket and the stabilizer units (see Fig. 1-2). Because of its location high above the ground and far behind the wheelbase, the TLB's weight transfers the entire machine's center of gravity upward as well as to the rear, when compared to other machines. This, in turn, makes the machine lighter on the front end and somewhat top-heavy. The positioning of this weight when maneuvering around a jobsite is a concern for all operators, since each job presents different demands.

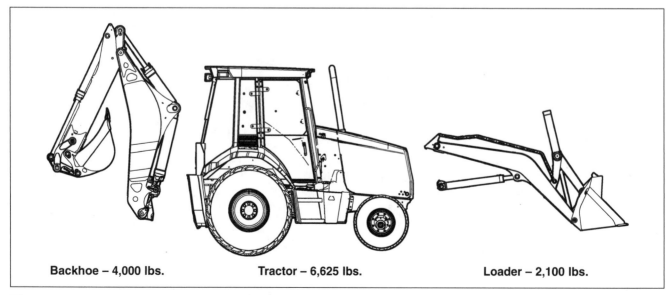

**Backhoe – 4,000 lbs.**       **Tractor – 6,625 lbs.**       **Loader – 2,100 lbs.**

**Fig. 1-3** *Typical gross weight of TLB components*

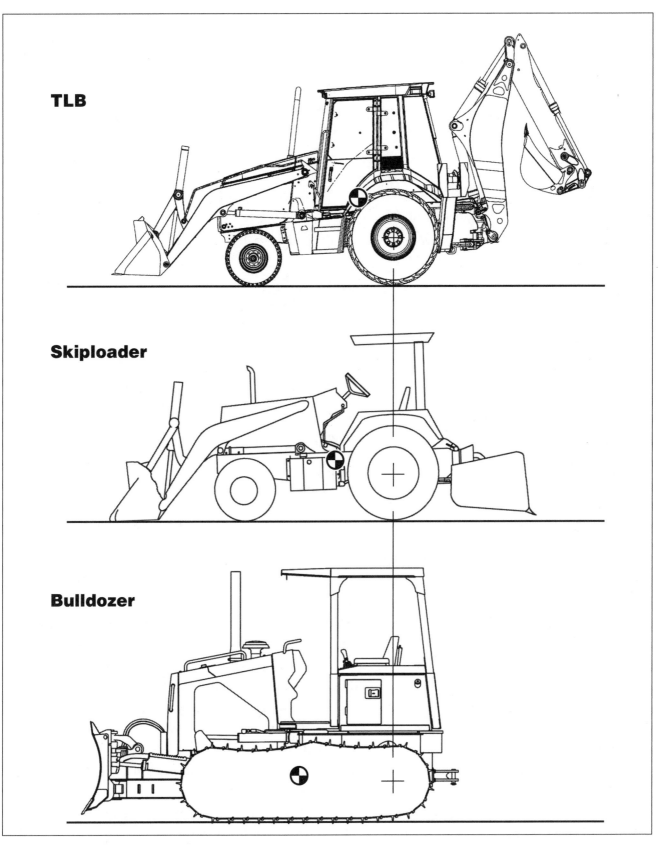

**TLB**

**Skiploader**

**Bulldozer**

**Fig. 1-4**   *Center of gravity comparison*

*"The high weights involved in operating heavy equipment bring with them the unbending laws of physics."* — Gary J. Ober 1999

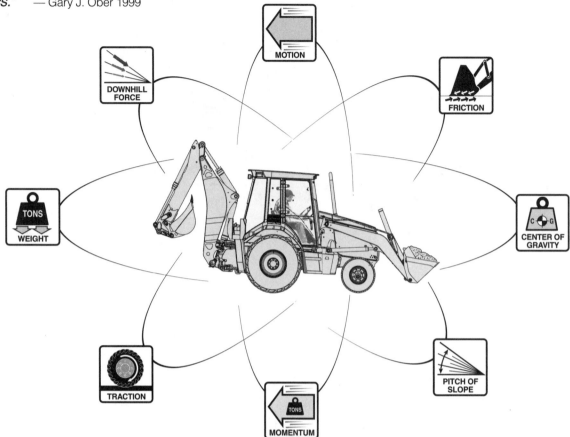

## Universal Forces and Principles

Operating a TLB, or any other type of heavy equipment, is a construction trade that is unique in the industry. This is because of the great weights involved with the equipment and the materials being handled. The high weights involved in operating "heavy" equipment bring with them the unbending laws of physics.

If we were to look at a TLB in operation strictly from a physics viewpoint, it would be: a very **HEAVY MACHINE**… **MOVING** around the job site… and moving very **HEAVY** materials.

The weight of a working TLB can vary from 14,000 to well over 25,000 lb. That's 7 to 12 tons of machine and materials, working and moving through a busy job site, all day, every day.

In order for this to be accomplished **with safety and productivity,** the operator must understand the **UNIVERSAL FORCES AND PRINCIPLES** that govern weight and movement.

*UNIVERSAL FORCES AND PRINCIPLES* apply to operating the TLB in the following ways:

1. There are physical **forces and principles** that act on a TLB.

2. These forces have both a **constant and a variable** effect on the machine.

3. These forces have a strong effect on the **control and safety** of the machine.

4. These forces can and must be **limited, controlled and counteracted** by the operator for safety and control.

In order for you to safely move both machine and materials, you must first understand the **UNIVERSAL FORCES AND PRINCIPLES** and how they relate to operating heavy equipment.

4

In order to fully understand these forces, we need to understand that each of them has both a **constant** and a **variable** effect on the machine.

### *How can something be both constant and variable at the same time?*

The forces of physics are **constant** in how they affect our world. From the scale of a molecule to the scale of the universe, the same physical laws apply to all things at all times.

**All** of these forces and principles are **variable** when the machine is in motion. The forces change in magnitude and have a wide variety of effects on the machine. The changes occur in the amount of force acting on the machine, and these changes can also have an effect on the safe operation of the machine.

☞ *Remember:* Understanding and applying these principles is the **basis for safe operating procedures** when dealing with any great weight such as the TLB.

 **Weight**

> **weight** – 1. a measure of the heaviness or mass of an object 2. the downward force exerted on an object by gravity.

According to physics, the earth exerts a downward force on all objects. This downward force is called gravity and produces what we commonly think of as weight. Weight is something that we all know about. However, most of us have never experienced handling the high weights involved in operating heavy equipment.

Weight is a force that has a **constant** effect on all objects. However, there are several ways that the weight of the machine is **variable** during the course of a normal day's operation, and this can also effect the operation of a TLB.

*1. WORKING WEIGHT* – The "working weight" of the machine includes the weight of the machine plus the weight of the materials that are being handled. The working weight of the machine changes every time that the backhoe or loader picks up or dumps a bucket of material.

*2. ATTACHMENTS* – Many of the attachments that are used with the TLB can change the weight and balance of the machine.

*3. WEIGHT DISTRIBUTION* is another important aspect of TLB operation. The TLB is a very "flexible" machine that changes shape as it works. These changes will effect the "center of gravity" of the machine.

☞ *Important:* The great weight of the TLB also dictates that the other forces and principles acting on the machine will also be of great magnitude.

 **Motion**

> **motion** – 1. the action or process of change of position. 2. the act of moving a machine or materials. 3. a requirement for performing and completing any work task.

In the study of physics, this is usually referred to as the "velocity" or speed of an object. However, as it relates to operating "heavy" equipment, a better term to use is motion.

The combination of motion with other forces (such as weight), must be properly managed by the TLB operator for the controlled and safe operation of the machine.

Motion in an object does not happen on its own. It only occurs when there is a force acting on that object. For the TLB, motion can be generated in several ways.

*Natural Physical Forces* – Gravity, motion and momentum are examples of the most important naturally occurring forces.

*Machine Made Forces* – The diesel engines of the TLB produce power in the form of torque. This power is harnessed by the torque converter and transmission to propel the drive wheels. The engine power is also converted to hydraulic power and used for the backhoe, the loader lift and dump functions.

***Man Made Forces*** – Man made forces are generated biologically in the form of MUSCLE POWER. Man can use his muscles to pick up and move objects.

Successful operators combine their intelligence with the control of their hands and feet to perform complex movements. In this manner, muscle power on the machine controls provides the motion necessary to harness the power of the machine.

Another important aspect of motion is that it actually is work. By that we mean that motion is necessary to start, do and finish any task performed by man or machine. Without motion, nothing is being done and no work is being completed.

## The Work Motion Cycle

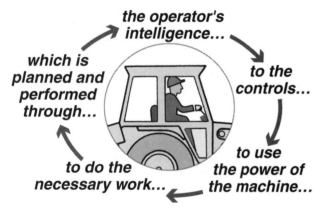

*the operator's intelligence...*

*to the controls...*

*to use the power of the machine...*

*to do the necessary work...*

*which is planned and performed through...*

As we can see here, motion is a requirement of all work and when the machine is put into motion, the other UNIVERSAL FORCES AND PRINCIPLES will then be activated and become a factor in all procedures.

☞***REMEMBER:*** Only the knowledge and skill of the operator can maintain safety when this heavy machine is in motion.

## Momentum

> **momentum** – 1. the result of the weight of an object combined with motion.

☞ *Weight + Motion = Momentum*

When the physical forces of weight and motion are combined, the resulting force is momentum. The strength of the force is determined by how heavy the object is and the speed of the object.

To give you an idea of the power of momentum, think of this simple act. If you placed a hammer on your thumb, the weight of the hammer would not cause any pain. However, if you lift the hammer only three or four inches above your thumb and let it drop, the weight combined with the motion of the hammer will produce **momentum**, and a totally different result.

A hammer may weigh about l lb. Think about the consequences of motion in a TLB which weighs up to 25,000 lb. It does not take much imagination to understand that such a weight, even when moving slowly, could inflict tremendous damage to a person or property.

Momentum, on a hill for example, if not slowed and controlled by the operator can overpower the braking system of almost any type of heavy equipment.

Momentum can become a stronger force than the traction available to control the machine.

Momentum is a very powerful force. It is a force that can act on its own or it can combine with other forces. When momentum and other forces combine (such as combining with downhill force), they can become stronger than the forces that are keeping the machine under control. Loss of control, with the possibility of personal injury or property damage may be the result.

Here are some methods for the operator to use to control momentum in every day situations.

☞ The loader should **always go down a hill in the same gear that it takes to go up the hill.** This will provide engine braking, and will keep the machine at a controllable speed. Use the brakes to prevent the engine from over-revving as this could damage the engine.

☞ When on a hill, **never allow the transmission to be shifted into neutral!** This is because the machine will instantly gain speed and momentum to a point that the brakes or the available traction may not be able to slow or control the machine.

## Pitch of Slope

**pitch of slope** – 1. an incline upward or downward
2. an inclined surface or stretch of ground
3. a deviation from level or the amount of deviation

☞ *NOTE:* "Pitch of slope" can also be referred to as gradient, grade, or degree of slope.

The pitch of slope in the work area can be critical to the safety of any job site. When very low, the pitch of the slope will have little or no influence on the machine. However, in a steeper area, the pitch of the slope can have extreme influence on the machine and the safety of the job.

For example, when there is no slope…such as on flat level ground, there will be no affect on the machine, and normal operating procedures can be followed.

A minor slope such as 2 to 5 percent can have a minor effect on the machine but is generally not a problem.

A steeper slope such as 10% to 15 % will have a great effect on the machine and can become dangerous if not properly handled by the operator.

In general, the steeper the work area, the greater the danger. This danger applies not only to the work phase of the job, but also to before and after the work, such as transporting the machine, and the loading and unloading of the transport vehicle.

☞ *REMEMBER:* At any given moment on the job site, the pitch of slope in the work area will have a great effect on the safety of the job site.

### How are slopes measured?

Slopes are not only a major safety factor in all TLB operations, they are also commonly specified in the building plans and for trenching and grading operations.

*"Not in Degrees"* – When someone who is not familiar with common construction procedures thinks of a "slope", they will usually think of an angle measured in "degrees". The most commonly expressed angles are 90 degrees, such as the corner of any square or rectangle, and 45 degrees, such as the cuts at the corner of any picture frame.

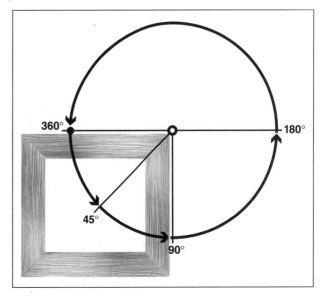

**Fig. 1-5** *Commonly-used angles shown in degrees.*

On the job, however, degrees are rarely used in layout procedures, and are **generally not used in describing slopes in construction.**

Slopes that are specified in common construction are usually measured in one of two ways:

**1) percent (%)**

**2) ratio**

**Percent –** Percent (%) is a measurement that is most commonly used when specifying lower angle slopes such as parking lots, streets, drainage channels, sewer systems, driveways and highways. The word percent, which actually means "per hundred", can also be expressed by the symbol (%). To understand this form of measurement, think "per hundred" when you see the word, or the symbol (%). So, a one percent (1%) slope would be , "1 ft. per hundred ft." and would rise or fall 1 foot vertical for every 100 feet horizontal. Accordingly, a 20% slope would be "20 ft. per hundred ft.", and would rise or fall 20 feet in 100 feet horizontal.

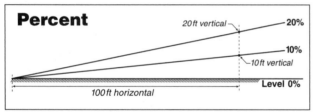

**Fig. 1-6**

For most construction applications, it is the lower gradient slopes (nearly flat) that are usually measured and specified in percent.

Sewer and drain lines that depend on gravity flow, for example, are installed with a specified pitch or "gradient" to maintain flow. In addition, the surface drainage of streets, parking lots, and other areas are designed to specific gradients. The slopes of these sewer and drain structures are generally between one and five percent.

**Ratio –** Ratio is a form of measurement such as 1:1, 2:1, 5:1, etc. This form of measurement is commonly used in trenches, excavations, and land grading when steeper slopes are needed. Some examples include; sloping trenches and excavations for safety purposes, cut or fill slopes between building pads, and other applications where steeper slopes are specified. The ratio is

expressed in a "horizontal to vertical", such as "2:1", or as spoken, "two to one".

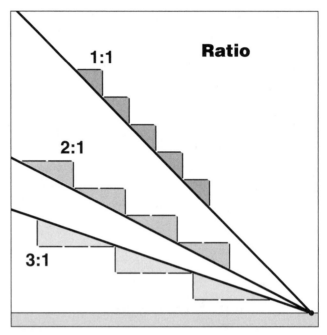

**Fig. 1-7**
*1:1, or "one to one," is 1 foot horizontal to 1 foot vertical*
*2:1, or "two to one," is 2 feet horizontal to 1 foot vertical*
*3:1, or "three to one," is 3 feet horizontal to 1 foot vertical*

## General Slope Information

Here are some slopes that are commonly called for in general grading and trenching procedures.

**0.0%        100:0        0 degrees**
Level No slope

Required for grading large areas such as building pads, as well as footings, underground electrical vaults, and septic tanks.

**0.24%        100:0.33        0.14 degrees**
Very close to level. This slope will fall only three inches in 100 feet, or about 3/8 of an inch in 10 feet. This is the minimum slope required for common sewer pipe installations.

**1%        100:1        0.57 degrees**
Commonly used for drainage on paved surfaces such as parking lots.

**2%        50:1        1.14 degrees**
Commonly specified for providing "sheet flow" drainage in large "flat" areas and around houses to provide positive drainage and to prevent ponding of water.

***10%        10:1        5 degrees***

Beginning in this range of gradient, care should be used to maintain stability of the TLB. From this point steeper, the stability concerns become greater, and operator awareness and safety planning become the #1 filter for every move made by the machine.

***20%        5:1        11 degrees***

Normal working limits of the TLB. Experienced operators (2 years or more) using proper technique can usually work safely on slopes up to this gradient. In climates that do not get snow and ice dangers (high traction situations), 20% is generally the steepest grade recommended for drive ways, access roads, and shuttle routes.

***50%        2:1        26.6 degrees***

Commonly used slope for stability between building pads. Loader backhoes are almost never used on a slope this steep.

***75%        1½:1        37 degrees***

Common slope for "cut" slopes in stable materials. Steep slopes that are difficult but possible to walk on.

***100%        1:1        45 degrees***

Commonly used in temporary excavations as per OSHA regulations. In most cases a 1:1 slope is difficult or impossible for a person to transverse up, down, or across. Too steep for normal operations of any type of equipment or persons.

***133%        ¾:1        53 degrees***

Very steep. To the human eye (especially from the bottom), this slope looks almost vertical. A ¾:1 slope is often used in stable soils for sloping temporary excavations when specified by the engineer, or competent person (see sloping illustration on page 63).

***Vertical***

Vertical is straight up and down, and an example is a trench side dug by the backhoe.

The ratio of a vertical slope is 0:1, or, 0 feet horizontal to 1 foot vertical.

The percent of a vertical slope does not exist. This is because a vertical line will never get 100 feet away from the point of origin in the horizontal direction.

The angle of a vertical is 90 degrees from horizontal.

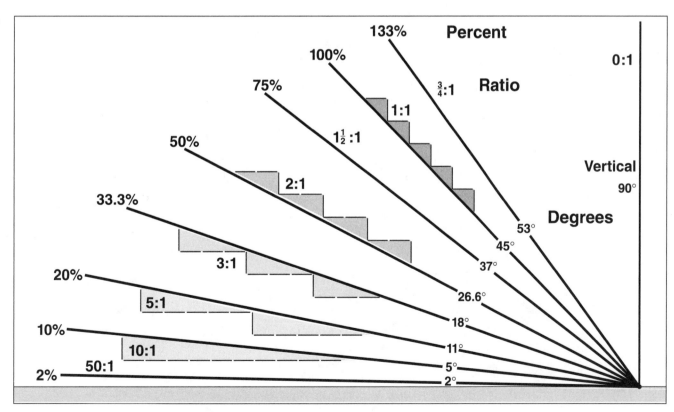

**Fig. 1-8** *Pitch of Slope – cross reference*

## Downhill Force – Force Down the Plane

> **downhill force** – the variable force on an object that is produced by the weight of the object and the pitch of slope.

☞ *Weight x Pitch of Slope = Downhill Force*

In physics, this force is usually referred to as "the force down the plane." For our purposes, **downhill force** is the best description.

A well known example of downhill force is demonstrated when riding a bicycle. When on a downhill, the downhill force propels the bike and rider. On an uphill, the rider will have to work hard to overcome the downhill force. The power (or strength) of the downhill force varies greatly and is determined by the weight of the object and the pitch of the slope it is resting (or moving) on. As the slope becomes steeper, and the weight becomes greater, the strength of force acting on the object in the downhill direction increases greatly.

Figures 1-9 through 1-12 should help to clarify these factors.

☞ **NOTE:** To get the most out of these examples, imagine that you are the man who is pushing and controlling the wheelbarrow.

**Fig. 1-9** *When pushing a wheelbarrow with medium weight up a slope, the downhill force will provide extra resistance. The same weight on the same down-slope – will produce an equal downhill force – that will pull the wheelbarrow forward.*

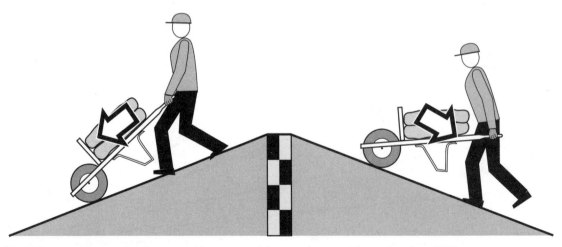

**Fig. 1-10** *When pushing a wheelbarrow with same weight up a steeper slope, the downhill force will be stronger and will require more effort to go up. When going down this steeper slope, downhill force will propel the wheelbarrow in a more powerful way.*

Downhill force applies to the TLB in exactly the same way – except for one thing. With all of that weight, the power of the downhill force will be about 50 times stronger!

It is also important to understand that even almost level surfaces exert downhill force. For a practical demonstration of this, place a ball bearing on a level glass surface (a picture frame with glass will work well) and try to adjust the glass so that it is level. Notice how the ball will immediately roll to the downhill side if not perfectly level. Here you can see how sensitive downhill force is, especially when there is very low friction between the objects.

## Traction

> **traction** – 1. adhesive friction, related to propelling or stopping a machine, such as a tire on a road.

Traction is the friction between the tires and the ground that is required to propel or stop the loader. The amount of traction available at any given time is determined by two factors: the type and condition of the ground surface, and the amount of weight pressing the surfaces together.

For example, a man pushing a heavy wheelbarrow on an uphill requires traction between his boots

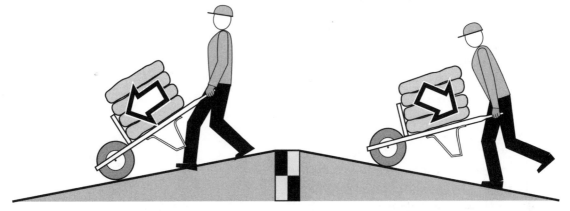

**Fig. 1-11** *When pushing a wheelbarrow with heavy weight up a slope, the downhill force will produce a more powerful resistance than the lower weight. This heavier weight on the same down slope will produce a stronger downhill force that will pull harder on the wheelbarrow, and may not be controllable.*

**Fig. 1-12** *With this heavier weight and steeper slope, the downhill force may be so strong you may not be able to push it up the slope. If you were on top, trying to come down, you would be unable to control or stop the wheelbarrow because the downhill force has become stronger than the traction available to stop the object.*

and the ground surface. If the ground surface happens to be muddy and slippery, the available traction may not be enough to propel the wheelbarrow.

The same is true for the TLB. The amount of traction available determines the amount of "forward driving force" for the machine to do work, and the stopping power available to control the machine.

☞ **REMEMBER:**
*Loss of Traction = Loss of Control*

In most situations, the traction available is usually not a problem. However, this varies from site to site and can also change as the job progresses. Obviously, wet, muddy, snowy, or icy conditions will provide less traction for the machine. The results of poor traction conditions could be: 1) the machine can not effectively move around the job site, or, 2) all control over the machine is lost. In addition, traction can change from very good to extremely dangerous over a period of a couple hours, or in as little as a few seconds if the area becomes wet.

It is important to remember that the more weight on the drive wheels, the more traction there is available. If the weight on the tires is decreased, the available traction will be less. The only exception to this rule is when the ground is unable to support the existing weight of the machine (such as soft ground or mud where the machine will sink and become stuck).

Fig. 1-13

## Friction

> **friction** – 1. a force that acts to resist or retard motion between two objects that are in contact.
> 2. creates resistance in varying degrees to all procedures that involve digging, cutting, or bucket loading.

Friction occurs on the loader or backhoe bucket at the teeth, or cutting edge. If the friction is great, it will rob the power of the machine, and can slow or stop the bucket. The operator needs to be aware of the friction on the cutting tool and constantly adjust the tool so that friction is kept to a minimum.

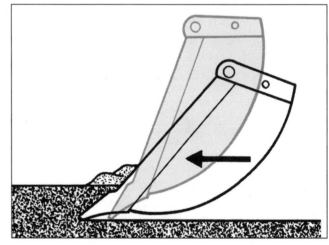

Fig. 1-14

High friction situations such as hard ground are not uncommon, and can be overcome by the operator using techniques that **concentrate the power of the machine in a smaller section of the cutting edge** (Fig. 1-13), **or reposition the cutting edge to present a sharper tool angle**. (Fig. 1-14)

## Center of Gravity

**center of gravity** – 1. an imaginary point within or near an object that represents the balance point of that object. 2. the position within or near an object that represents the "center of the weight" of that object.

Discussion of the center of gravity (COG) is, in some ways, a continuation on the subject of weight, and is basic to safety because it answers a very important question: ***Will I be involved in a rollover accident during the next procedure that I perform?***

As we discussed earlier in this chapter, moving the machine and **handling high weights can present many dangers**. However, **none are more important** than understanding and maintaining **the stability of the machine**.

In the most basic sense, maintaining stability will prevent the machine and operator from being involved in a rollover accident. However, stability and weight distribution will affect other factors such as traction, motion and momentum. In essence, **the control of the machine is affected in many ways by the stability of the machine.**

The study of center of gravity is complex, and even more so with the TLB because the two separate machines each pose their own problems and restrictions. However, we have taken these complex forces and principles and broken them down into **four elements of stability** – 1. Location and Movement of Center of Gravity, 2. Base of a Machine, 3. Vertical Line, and 4. Weight Transfer & Contact Surfaces. Using these four elements on the job will clarify the safe and unsafe procedures.

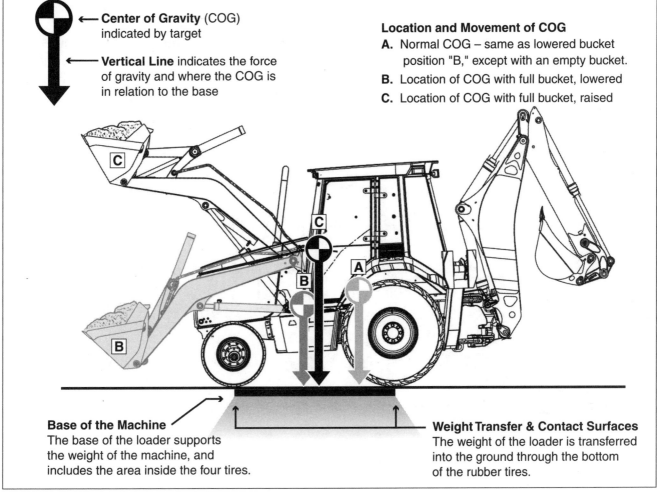

**Center of Gravity** (COG) indicated by target

**Vertical Line** indicates the force of gravity and where the COG is in relation to the base

**Location and Movement of COG**
A. Normal COG – same as lowered bucket position "B," except with an empty bucket.
B. Location of COG with full bucket, lowered
C. Location of COG with full bucket, raised

**Base of the Machine**
The base of the loader supports the weight of the machine, and includes the area inside the four tires.

**Weight Transfer & Contact Surfaces**
The weight of the loader is transferred into the ground through the bottom of the rubber tires.

**Fig. 1-15** *The four elements of stability.*

**1. Location and movement of the Center of Gravity –** To a greater degree than any type of heavy equipment, the unique "flexibility" of TLB, and the weight of the loads it handles, causes the center of gravity of the machine to move. The high weight of the loader arms or the backhoe assembly and the weight of the materials being handled cause instant and critical changes in the location of the COG.

In fact, there is no other type of heavy equipment that has so much movement of the center of gravity while the machine is in operation. These changes in location of the COG are extremely important to safe operation because with every change in location of the COG there is a corresponding change in the stability of the machine.

**2. Base of the machine –** The base of the machine acts as a foundation as it carries the working weight of the machine, and transfers that weight into the ground. The base is determined by what parts of the machine are transferring the weight into the ground at any given time.

For example, **when using the loader**, the weight is transferred into the ground through the tires. In this case, the area within the tires represents the base of the machine. (Fig. 1-16A)

**Base when using the backhoe –** When the backhoe is being used, the machine should be supported by the stabilizers and the loader bucket. In this situation, the base of the machine is comprised of the area that is within the stabilizers and the loader bucket. (Fig. 1-16B)

Notice the difference in the size of the base when the machine is supported either on the tires or by the stabilizers and the loader bucket. The base is much larger and much more stable when set up for backhoe operations. (Fig. 1-16C)

Because of this large base when using the tripod set-up (see chapter 7), the backhoe is generally quite stable, as long as it is positioned on stable ground and operated in a proper manner.

**Base when using the loader –** Because of the size, shape, and weight distribution of the TLB, safe operation of the loader has its own unique requirements. Here are some examples of how stability of the loader can be affected.

• The base of the loader is much smaller than the backhoe's, and therefore provides much less stability.

• The base during loader operation is not as solid as the stabilizers and the loader bucket (that support the machine during backhoe operations), but springy and bouncy because of the rubber tires.

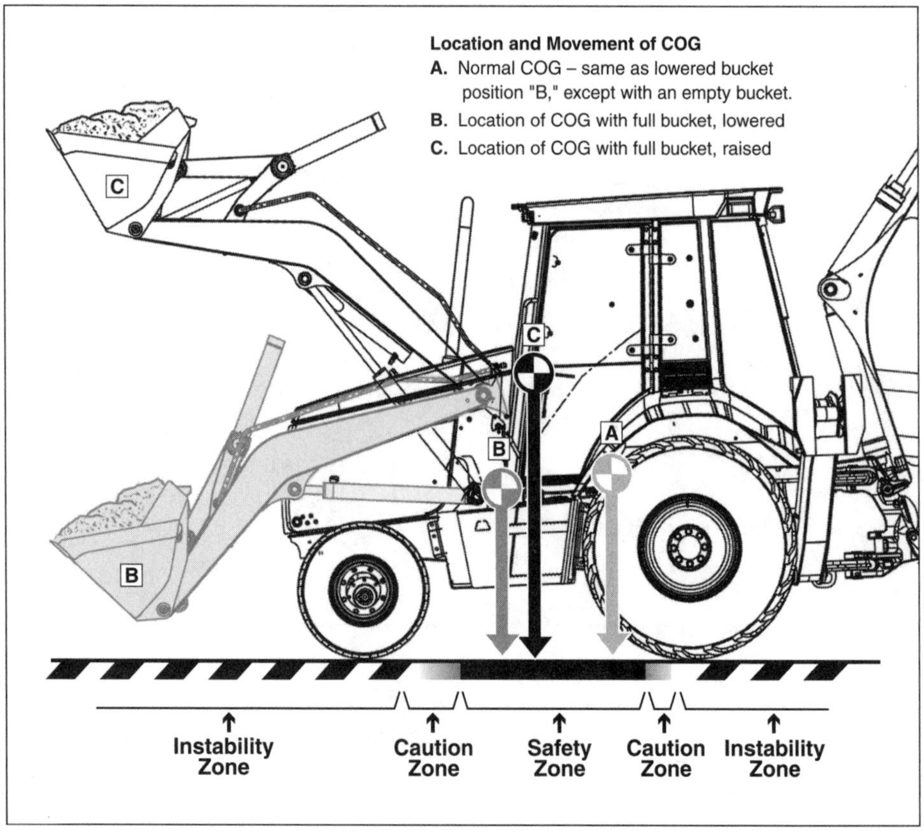

**Location and Movement of COG**
A. Normal COG – same as lowered bucket position "B," except with an empty bucket.
B. Location of COG with full bucket, lowered
C. Location of COG with full bucket, raised

Instability Zone    Caution Zone    Safety Zone    Caution Zone    Instability Zone

**Fig. 1-17**

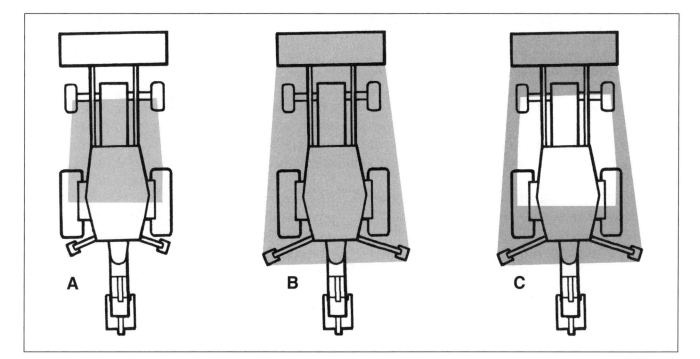

**Fig. 1-16**
*A. Base of the machine when using the loader.*
*B. Base of the machine when using the backhoe.*
*C. Notice the greater size of the base when using the backhoe in a proper tripod setup.*

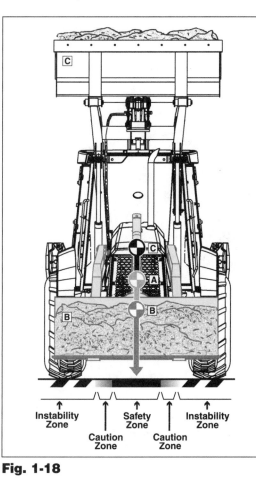

**Fig. 1-18**

In order to prevent dangerous situations and rollover accidents, operators need to be aware of the three zones within the base of the TLB. These zones are the **safety zone**, the **caution zone**, and the **instability zone**. These zones indicate the relative safety associated with various positions of the COG. If the center of gravity is directly above the safety zone, the machine is in a stable position. If it is above the caution zone, you may be getting close to an unstable condition, and caution must be used. In the instability zone, momentary changes in the operating surface or machine dynamics could result in machine instability.

There is one other element needed to complete the relationship between the COG and the base and that is the vertical line.

**3. Vertical Line –** The vertical line (through the center of gravity) is an imaginary line that:

• Passes through the center of gravity

• Represents the force of gravity

• And shows the exact direction of that force.

The vertical line (VL also) points down on the base zones to indicate the safety of the situation.

The vertical line acts as if it were a pendulum attached to the COG of the machine. As the center of gravity moves, the VL moves with it, and as the machine crosses various sloped areas, the VL will always hang straight down (in a plumb position) from the COG.

**Q: *Why are the safe and caution zones so small compared to the base of the loader?***

**A:** *Because there are other factors that can lower the stability of the TLB.*

***4. Weight Transfer & Contact Surfaces –*** For machine stability, it is also important to consider the tires of the machine and the ground conditions of the area where the tires make contact.

**How will the tire react to the extreme weight that is being placed on it when on a side-slope?**

Pneumatic rubber tires can change shape depending on the load on the tire at any given time. When on a side-slope, for example, weight will be reduced on the uphill tire, and added to the downhill tire. This weight transfer can easily put 75% (or more) of the weight of the machine onto one tire.

The result of this great weight on one side of the machine will cause the tire to "squat", or squeeze down, while the tire on the other side of the machine will raise up to more of a "no load" profile. This change in tire shape will move the COG down the hill slightly, and can effectively increase the slope angle. In addition, the extreme weight on the slope can deform, or "roll," the tire in a sideways direction. This slight sideshift will also shift the COG down the hill, and can create enough momentum to cause the machine to roll over.

The ground conditions under the machine are an important factor to consider, and with the same kinds of concerns as with the tires, namely the extreme weight.

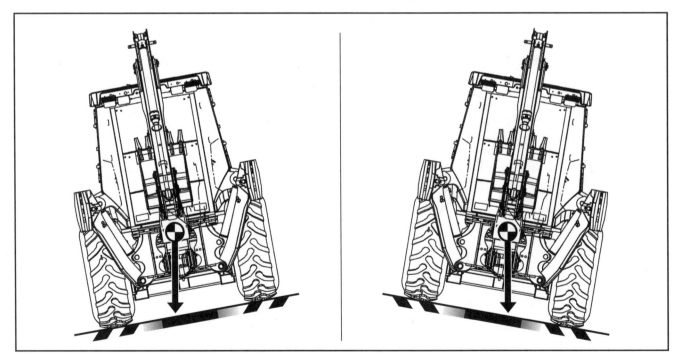

**Fig. 1-19** *The vertical line passes through the center of gravity, represents the force of gravity, and shows the exact direction of that force. The vertical line also points down onto the base "zones" to illustrate changes in stability.*

### How will the ground react to the extreme weight that is being placed on it?

In most situations, the ground will compress, and the tire will sink into the ground. As the tire sinks-in on the downhill side, the lean angle is increased, and the stability is decreased. When on a side-slope with the loader, the weight that is transferred to the downhill side can reduce stability in three different ways:

1. **Tire squat** will increase the lean of the machine to the downhill side.

2. **Tire roll** will permit the machine to slide side-ways several inches. This slight sideways movement can provide enough momentum to further reduce stability.

3. **The ground** can compress and permit the tire to sink in which will increase the lean of the machine.

We have explained these factors in detail to show how this machine will tend to increase the effective slope angle. It is important to remember that all three usually occur in combination, and can take a seemingly stable position into an unstable one instantly.

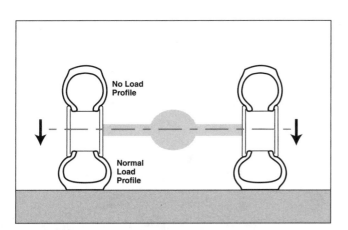

**Fig. 1-20** *This illustration shows the natural flex that occurs to the rear tires of the loader under normal loads, and also the profile with no load.*

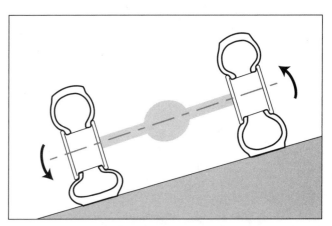

**Fig. 1-21** *When the machine is on a side-slope, the machine's weight will transfer to the downhill side. This will cause the downhill tire to squat, and the uphill tire to approach a no-load profile.*

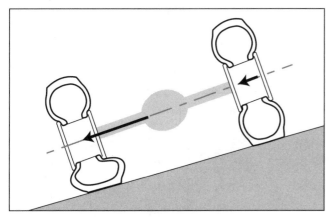

**Fig. 1-22** *Tire roll will permit the machine to slide sideways several inches. This slight sideways movement can provide enough momentum to further reduce stability.*

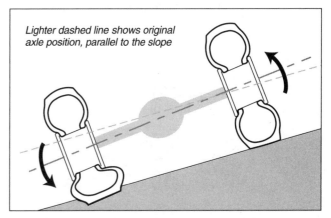

**Fig. 1-23** *The ground can compress and the tire can sink in. This will also increase the lean angle of the machine, and combine with tire squat and roll to increase the chance of a rollover.*

## Important Factors Relating to Center of Gravity

### Position of COG

The weight and position of the backhoe is an important factor in the TLB's stability. The structure of the backhoe, the hydraulic cylinders and the bucket are very heavy. The position of this heavy structure (high off the ground and far outside the wheelbase of the machine) moves the center of gravity higher as well as to the rear of the machine. In addition, there are many different machine designs and attachments commonly used with the TLB. These different configurations will cause variations in the COG of these machines.

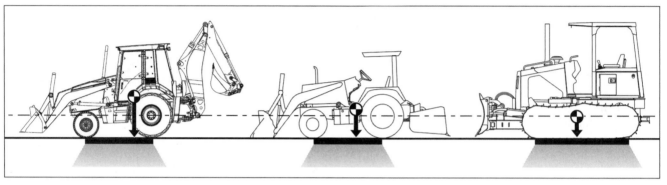

**Fig. 1-24** *The weight and position of the backhoe assembly moves the COG high and to the rear when compared with other machines.*

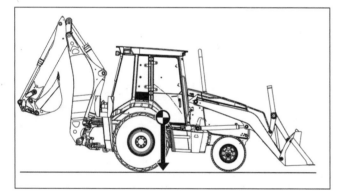

**Fig. 1-25** *Typical COG of a two-wheel drive TLB.*

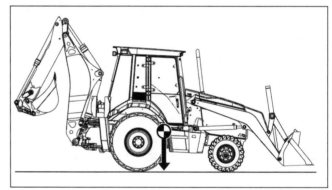

**Fig. 1-26** *Typical COG of a four-wheel drive TLB.*

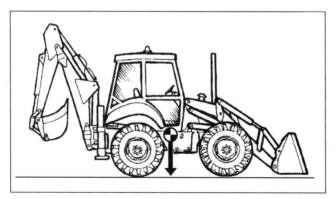

**Fig. 1-27** *Typical COG of a quad-wheel drive TLB.*

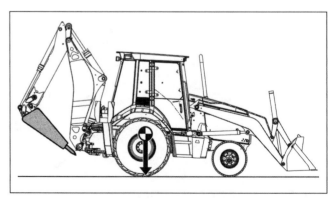

**Fig. 1-28** *Typical COG of a two-wheel drive TLB with a concrete breaker attachment.*

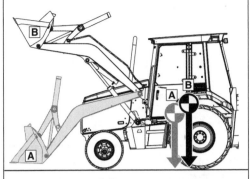

**Fig. 1-29** *Typical COG of a TLB with the bucket lowered (A), and with the bucket raised (B).*

## Movement of COG

The center of gravity of the TLB does not stay in the same position all the time. The flexibility of the machine and the weight of the loads that it handles will cause movement in the COG.

The loader, for example, can raise the loader arms and bucket high off the ground.

The backhoe can stretch out far behind the machine and swing from side to side.

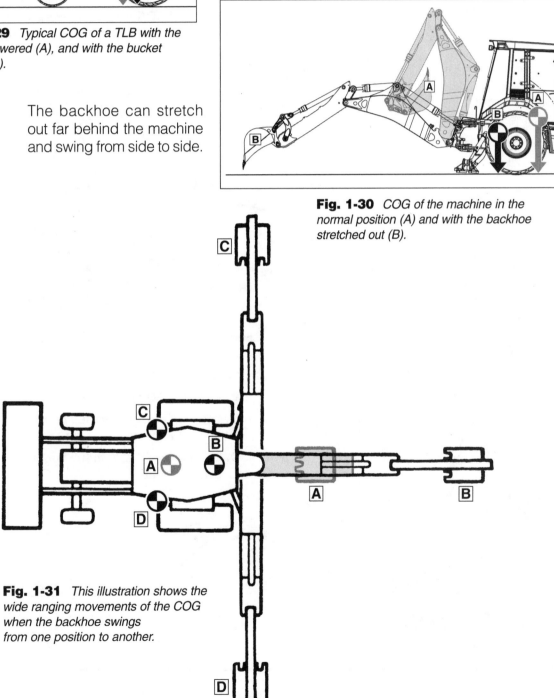

**Fig. 1-30** *COG of the machine in the normal position (A) and with the backhoe stretched out (B).*

**Fig. 1-31** *This illustration shows the wide ranging movements of the COG when the backhoe swings from one position to another.*

## Weight of Materials and COG

Every time the loader or the backhoe picks up a bucket of material, the location of the COG will change.

☞ As a rule of thumb, always keep the loader bucket as low as possible, especially when carrying a load.

Carrying a full bucket in the lowered position can help stabilize the machine by moving the COG forward and lower as in (B)

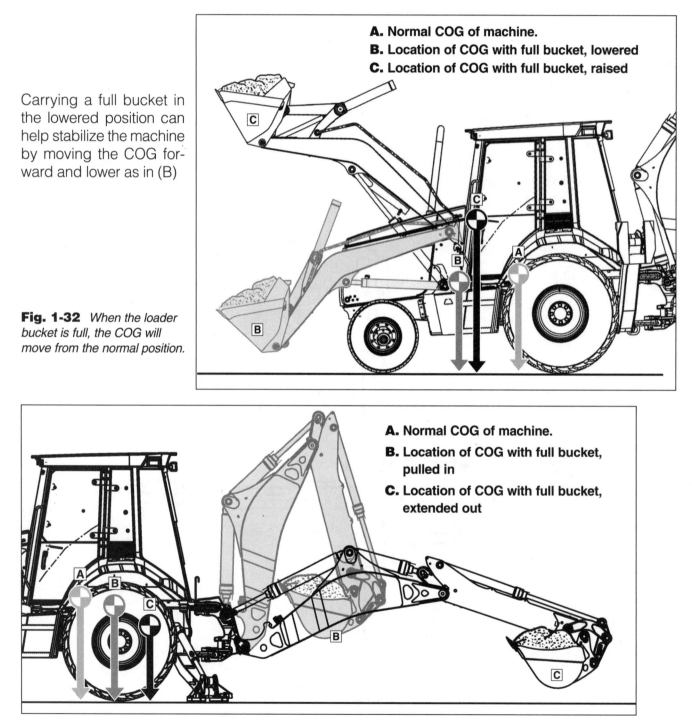

**A. Normal COG of machine.**

**B. Location of COG with full bucket, lowered**

**C. Location of COG with full bucket, raised**

**Fig. 1-32** *When the loader bucket is full, the COG will move from the normal position.*

**A. Normal COG of machine.**

**B. Location of COG with full bucket, pulled in**

**C. Location of COG with full bucket, extended out**

**Fig. 1-33** *When the backhoe bucket is full, the COG will move to a different position.*

## Affect of Slopes on COG

### Pitch of Slope

The slope of the work area will have an effect on the stability of the machine.

**Fig. 1-34** *Loader going down a 20% slope*

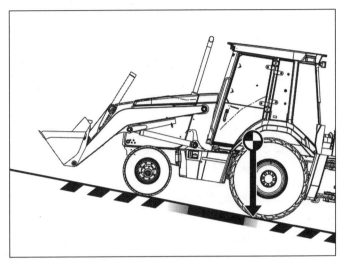

**Fig. 1-35** *Loader going up a 20% slope*

## Altering Dimensions

The unique flexibility of the TLB can be used to enhance machine stability. Swinging the backhoe to one side will make an important difference in the COG by moving it to that side of the machine.

This movement can either reduce or improve the stability of the machine. A skilled operator will use this movement of the COG to their advantage.

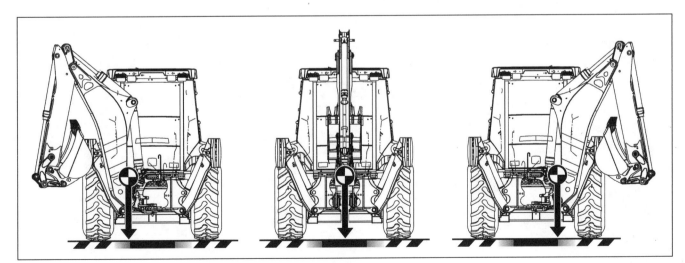

**Fig. 1-36** *When positioned on level ground, the backhoe can swing to either side with the COG remaining in the safe zone, just at the edge of the caution zone.*

## Fig. 1-37 – 10% Slope

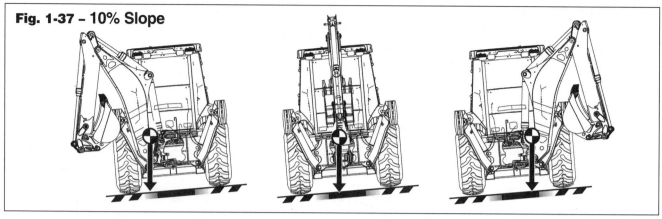

A. Even on a minor slope, this machine is at the limit of stability, and if the tire pressure was low, the machine could roll over.

B. Stable position

C. Stable position

## Fig. 1-38 – 20% Slope

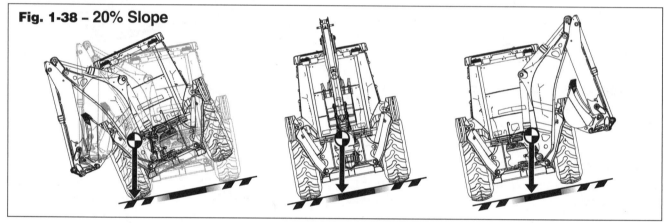

A. This machine is "on the way"

B. If sitting in a stationary position, this machine would be stable. However, if it was working and moving, great caution must be used because any kind of a bump could push it into the danger zone.

C. Stable position

## Fig. 1-39 – 30% Slope

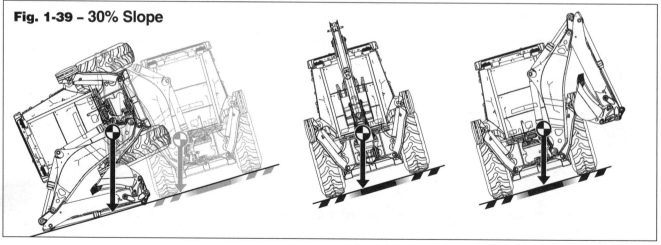

A. This situation could have been avoided if the operator had swung the backhoe to the uphill side.

B. At the edge of stability. In this situation, lower the downhill stabilizer until it is just off the ground. This will prevent a rollover by providing a larger base if the machine starts to lean too far.

C. This machine is in a stable position, but any slope this steep warrants extreme caution at any time.

## Truck Loading

Truck loading is a very common task for the loader, and it always requires the loader to lift heavy loads high into the air. When a heavy load is lifted using the loader, the COG also moves to a higher position.

It is at this time that the loader is the most sensitive and reactive (like the ball bearing) to any base that is not level, to changes in the operating surface, sudden acceleration or deceleration, or too rapid steering movement.

## Problem Situations

**Fig. 1-40**
*Instability* –
*If attempting to load a truck in this situation, the loader would remain stable until the load was dumped into the truck, and then instantly become unstable.*

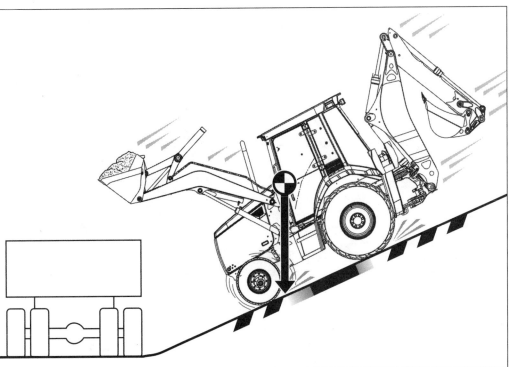

**Fig. 1-41**
*Traction* – *If attempting to load a truck on a downhill, the COG is transferred forward, and into the instability zone in the base. The problem here is not that the machine might rollover, but that the machine cannot be controlled (stopped) due to lack of traction, downhill force, and then momentum. With the brakes and tires locked, the loader may hit the truck.*

## Attachments

There are dozens of types of attachments that are commonly used with the TLB. Many of these attachments will not change the COG to a great degree.

Others, such as a concrete breaker, will result in a considerable change in the COG. In fact, the COG of many TLBs with a concrete breaker attached will be in the caution zone while on flat ground.

**Fig. 1-42** *Backhoe with concrete breaker installed moving up a 15% slope*

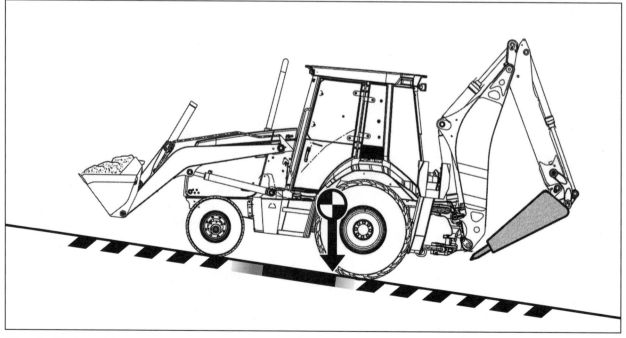

**Fig. 1-43** *A machine with a concrete breaker attached will often need to be stabilized with weight in the loader bucket to maneuver, even on minor slopes.*

## COG Wrapup

As we can see from these many examples, the movement and dynamics of center of gravity are important underlying factors to machine control and general safety.

As the operator, you must be aware of the changes in the center of gravity, understand how they can affect the stability of the machine, and **counteract these changes as necessary to maintain stability.**

In addition, you also must be able to recognize any unsafe procedure or situation, and **stop all operations until a safe procedure is determined.**

## Summary

The information in this chapter describes the underlying principles of safe and controlled operation of these machines.

☞ *Remember* – It is the operator's responsibility to recognize any unsafe procedure or situation, and stop all operations until a safe procedure is determined.

As a TLB operator, it is your responsibility to:

• Determine the safety of the work area, and if the TLB can perform the desired task in a safe manner.

• Take into account the existing factors of any given job.

• Formulate a plan of how to proceed with the job in a safe manner.

By understanding and applying the forces and principles presented in this chapter, you can evaluate jobsite situations, and plan all procedures to ensure safety in all operations.

## Questions – Chapter 1  **TLB Dimensions**

*Notes:* _____

_____

_____

_____

_____

_____

_____

_____

_____

_____

_____

_____

_____

_____

_____

_____

_____

_____

_____

_____

_____

_____

_____

_____

_____

_____

_____

_____

**1. On a two-wheel drive TLB, about how much of the machine's weight is in the backhoe assembly?**

_____ a. 1/2

_____ b. 1/4

_____ c. 1/5

_____ d. 1/3

**2. Because of its location, high above the ground and far behind the wheelbase, the weight the backhoe attachment transfers the machine's center of gravity upward as well as to the rear when compared to other machines.**

_____ a. True

_____ b. False

**3. Why should the operator alter the TLB's dimensions?**

_____ a. To improve stability

_____ b. To improve safety

_____ c. To improve maneuverability

_____ d. All of the above

**4. A 32% slope will rise how many feet vertical in 100 ft. horizontal?**

_____ a. 3.2 ft

_____ b. 6.4 ft

_____ c. 32 ft

_____ d. 320 ft

**5. On a two-wheel drive machine, why is it important to keep as much weight and traction as possible on the rear wheels?**

_____ a. They can take more weight

_____ b. They are bigger

_____ c. The brakes are only on the rear wheels

_____ d. All of the above

**6. If you must drive up or back down a grade with the backhoe on the downward end, you should:**

_____ a. Go as slowly as possible

_____ b. Lower the backhoe

_____ c. Go as fast as possible

_____ d. Stabilize the front wheels by filling the loader bucket with dirt or heavy material

**7. Raising the loader bucket will**

_____ a. Shorten the machine

_____ b. Shift the weight up and to the rear

_____ c. Decrease the TLB's stability

_____ d. All of the above

**8. Features such as 4 wheel-drive, and large front tires tend to destabilize the TLB.**

_____ a. True

_____ b. False

**9. A machine with a hydraulic breaker attached to the backhoe will have _____ weight on the front tires?**

_____ a. Less

_____ b. More

_____ c. The same

_____ d. None of the above

**10. A ¾:1 slope is commonly used in stable soils for sloping temporary excavations, when specified by the engineers.**

_____ a. True

_____ b. False

**11. Operating a TLB (or any kind of heavy equipment) is a construction trade that is unique in the industry, because**

_____ a. It is powered by a diesel engine

_____ b. It is two machines in one

_____ c. Because of the high weight involved

_____ d. Because it has many different controls

_____
_____
_____
_____
_____
_____
_____
_____
_____
_____
_____
_____
_____
_____
_____
_____
_____
_____
_____
_____
_____
_____
_____
_____
_____
_____
_____
_____
_____
_____

**12. The Universal Forces and Principles are**

_____ a. Constant

_____ b. Variable

_____ c. Both of the above

_____ d. None of the above

**13. A slope that rises 1 ft. vertical for every 10 ft. horizontal is expressed as**

_____ a. 1%

_____ b. 2%

_____ c. 10%

_____ d. 100%

**14. The great weight of the TLB dictates that the other forces and principles acting on the machine will be minimal.**

_____ a. True

_____ b. False

**15. When weight and motion are combined the result is**

_____ a. Downhill force

_____ b. Traction

_____ c. Momentum

_____ d. All of the above

**16. When momentum and downhill force combine, they can become stronger than the forces that are keeping the machine under control.**

_____ a. True

_____ b. False

**17. Which of the following are true of a 2:1 slope?**

_____ a. Commonly used slope for stability between building pads

_____ b. Loader backhoes are almost never used on a slope this steep

_____ c. A 2:1 slope is a 1 ft rise for every two feet horizontal

_____ d. All of the above

**18. Downhill force is the result of the combination of weight and momentum.**

_____ a. True

_____ b. False

**19. When on a downhill, a bicycle rider will be propelled by the center of gravity.**

_____ a. True

_____ b. False

**20. When operating a TLB, a loss of traction would result in**

_____ a. Reduced productivity

_____ b. Loss of control

_____ c. Loss of safety

_____ d. All of the above

**21. Friction usually occurs between the bucket (or cutting-edge) and the ground.**

_____ a. True

_____ b. False

**22. Raising the loader bucket or extending the backhoe will move the center of gravity toward the rear of the machine.**

_____ a. True

_____ b. False

**23. The power or strength of downhill force is determined by the weight of the object and the slope it is resting on.**

_____ a. True

_____ b. False

**24. A 1:1 slope is commonly used in temporary excavations as per OHSA regulations.**

_____ a. True

_____ b. False

_____
_____
_____
_____
_____
_____
_____
_____
_____
_____
_____
_____
_____
_____
_____
_____
_____
_____
_____
_____
_____
_____
_____
_____

**25. There are _____ universal forces and principles that determine the safe operation of a TLB.**

_____ a. 2

_____ b. 4

_____ c. 8

_____ d. 10

**26. On flat, level ground, downhill force is an important consideration for the operator to consider when planning the job.**

_____ a. True

_____ b. False

**27. A 100% slope equals _____ degrees.**

_____ a. 180

_____ b. 90

_____ c. 45

_____ d. 30

**28. A 1% slope is commonly used for drainage on paved surfaces such as parking lots.**

_____ a. True

_____ b. False

**29. A 50% slope is equal to a 1:1 slope.**

_____ a. True

_____ b. False

**30. A 2% slope is commonly required for sheet flow drainage such as grading around houses to ensure positive drainage.**

_____ a. True

_____ b. False

**31. On a 20% slope, how much vertical rise would there be when the horizontal measurement was 100 feet?**

_____ a. 2 ft

_____ b. 5 ft

_____ c. 20 ft

_____ d. 50 ft

**32. The center of gravity of an object is determined by:**

_____ a. The weight of the object

_____ b. The shape of the object

_____ c. How the weight is distributed

_____ d. All of the above

**33. When using the loader, the base of the machine is the entire area inside of where the tires contact the ground.**

_____ a. True

_____ b. False

**34. The vertical line indicates the force of gravity and where the COG is in relation to the base.**

_____ a. True

_____ b. False

**35. The high weights involved in operating heavy equipment**

_____ a. Should not concern the operator

_____ b. Are no different than driving a car

_____ c. Require a high-horsepower machine

_____ d. Bring with them the unbending laws of physics

# 2. Machine Control

> **control** 1. to exercise authority over. 2. power to regulate, direct, or dominate.

The subject of this chapter is Machine Control. It is designed to present the necessary information for an operator to master the controls of the TLB. The goal of this information is to help a person achieve the highest level of operator skills.

*What are the mental and physical requirements for a person to reach the highest level of operator skills?*

## Mental Requirements

Learn and understand the wide ranging knowledge required for backhoe operation. This information includes the manufacturer-supplied operator's manual for the machine you are operating. In addition, the contents of this book covers wide ranging subjects such as: fundamentals, forces, principles, techniques and procedures. The information contained within these categories will provide the basis for the many years of learning that is required to operate these machines in a professional manner.

## Physical Requirements

During normal backhoe procedures, expert, professional-level backhoe operators think about the safety and execution of the job. At the same time, their hands are controlling the backhoe, the bucket and performing the job at hand. The motion of their hands is automatic and without need of conscious attention from the operator. This level of expertise should be the goal of every person becoming an operator of any type of heavy equipment.

To master the controls of the TLB, an operator will need hundreds of hours of practice. In order to get the most out of the practice time, they should strive for smoothness in all machine movements. The operator can then use that knowledge and skill to take command of the machine for safety and productivity.

### *What exactly does this mean?*

The operator will use the controls of the machine…

To direct the power of the engine…

Through the transmission or hydraulic system…

To move the machine and materials…

In a smooth, precise, controlled and therefore safe manner.

## Machine Controls

The common controls on a TLB include the loader and backhoe controls.

*Loader controls* of most TLBs are similar in design, but there are some variations in systems and locations. These controls include: the steering wheel, brakes, throttle, gear selector, forward/reverse control, loader lift and bucket control.

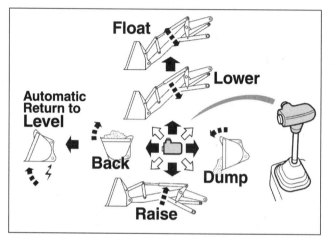

**Fig 2-1** *Loader bucket control*

*Backhoe controls* include: the hand throttle, stabilizer controls, boom, stick or crowd, bucket, swing, extension control, auxiliary control, as well as the loader lift and bucket controls.

TLBs are commonly produced in four different control configurations. These four systems include: 4-lever, two different 2-lever patterns, and 3-lever with foot swing.

Because of the wide-ranging differences in the design features, the controls of loader backhoes vary from one machine to another. This is another example of why the operator's manual provided by the manufacturer must be basic knowledge of every operator. At the time of this writing, there were over 15 different manufacturers of these machines worldwide. With an average of 5 or more models each, there are easily 75 different models of loader-backhoes out there being operated every day. With this wide variety of machines and designs, operators need to understand what can be expected when changing from one machine to another, and how to maintain control and safety at all times.

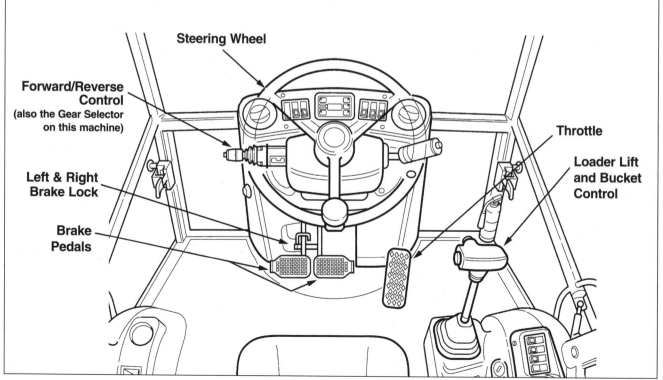

**Fig 2-2** *Loader controls*

## Machine Response
### What exactly is meant by "machine response"?

Machine response is how the machine reacts to operator input. The physical and mechanical makeup of all machines varies from manufacturer to manufacturer and, even within one make and model, there will be differences.

The machine that you operate today may respond differently than the last machine that you operated. There can be many differences from one machine to another, and here are a few examples:

• Quicker **OR** slower

• Smooth **OR** jerky

• More power **OR** less power

• Heavy in the rear **OR** balanced on all 4 wheels

• Brakes that grab or lock easily **OR** brakes that are weak and hard to lock up

• As you expected **OR** different than you expected

The first step to learning to control a machine, is to understand that...***Different machines respond differently!***

This is especially important when you get on a machine that you have never operated. Keep in mind that it will probably not respond like the last machine that you operated!

### Why are there such great differences in machine response?

The response of any machine is caused by two major factors that are unique to every machine:

1. Machine size and weight distribution

2. Mechanical response

## Dimensions

This applies to the size and weight of the machine, the center of gravity of the machine and how that weight is distributed to the ground. Every model of machine has its own unique weight distribution. This, combined with differences in mechanical response, handling characteristics, and any attachments, can cause response to differ from one machine to another.

☞ *Remember* – The weight, distribution, and center of gravity will vary from machine to machine. That difference will cause variations in how the machine moves, steers and handles.

## Mechanical Response

The mechanical response of any machine is affected by many different mechanical systems and controls. Engineers from many companies have used varying approaches to the design of all of the major components. Here are some examples of major machine components that have an impact on how a machine responds to operator input.

The **engine** power curve differs greatly from one manufacturer to another. Some engines raise and lower RPM (revolutions per minute) quickly and precisely, while other engines raise and lower RPM slowly and usually with lower RPM torque. Both types of power delivery have advantages and disadvantages in different situations.

For example, the quick and instant type of power response is sometimes better for tight maneuvering of the loader, such as loading a truck in a tight working area. The engine that produces high torque at a lower RPM will perform better when maximum forward driving force is needed, such as loading the loader bucket or pushing or pulling at maximum power.

**Transmissions** vary in the gear ratios and how the torque converters transmit the power to the tires.

The **brakes** of different machines vary in how powerful they are as well as the pedal pressure needed to apply.

**Hydraulic systems** vary greatly in design, speed of operation, and power available to the ground engaging tools.

The **hydraulic controls** of different machines may have varying response. Each will respond somewhat differently.

The **steering** of these machines varies in design.

*Standard two-wheel drive* – From the late '50s until the mid '80s almost all TLBs were two-wheel drive. Over the years, many improvements and innovations were introduced, but the drive system designs generally remained unchanged throughout this period.

*Four-wheel drive* – Since the mid '80s, four wheel drive has become very popular. This feature adds greatly to the machine's maneuverability on slopes and soft conditions such as sand or mud.

As we can see, the wide variations in the design of these machines will cause many differences in the machine's performance and response. Keep this in mind when you begin to operate any machine that is new to you.

## Older Machines

Here are some examples of how the age and maintenance history of the machine will have an effect on your ability to control the machine.

Older machines may exhibit some of these characteristics:

- The hydraulic controls will be "sloppier" with excessive free play in the linkages

- Brakes are usually weaker

- Parking brake may not be maintained or properly adjusted

- Worn swing bushings can allow "slop" in the backhoe boom, and drift of the boom back and forth

- Worn steering linkages will cause slop in the steering

- Broken seat mechanism could cause unwanted seat movement

The bottom line...***Don't expect an old machine to respond the same as a new machine.***

*What determines how and when a machine begins to feel less responsive, loose and "old"?*

A *well-maintained* machine could begin getting "old" at around eight years of age (this varies).

A *poorly-maintained* machine could begin to show "old" characteristics as early as two years of age or at any time after (this varies).

Keep in mind that as machines age, the response of some mechanical systems will change. Older machines in particular will vary greatly due to general wear and tear. Broken or missing parts, weaker hydraulic power, poor or worn brakes, repairs and modifications, bucket or attachment changes, and many other maintenance related items can contribute to **poor machine response**.

Poor machine response is when the machine does not do what you are telling it to do!

Here are a few examples:

- Push the brakes hard and the machine does not stop.

- Stop the backhoe swing straight with the machine and it continues to drift to the left.

This type of situation can be one of the most frustrating situations for an operator and can also be a safety concern. It is a good thing that these types of situations do not happen very often, however they *DO* occur, and every operator should be aware that they can happen at any time when operating. These types of incidents are usually the result of an aging machine that has been poorly maintained. Here are a few examples that show how a machine can "take on a mind of its own" and can move, without the operator's input.

- Control valves and hydraulic cylinders that leak internally and cause unwanted machine movement.

- Worn brakes that were not strong enough to stop the machine.

- Worn out hydraulic linkages and controls that stick or bind, and do not function properly.

- Worn hydraulic kickout mechanism that will grab and pull the control lever against the lever stop. This usually results in the loader bucket rolling up all the way, or the loader lift control stuck until the loader arms are fully raised!

The practical aspects of **Machine Response** information come when you are climbing into the seat of an unfamiliar machine. This could be as a beginning operator, just learning how to operate, or an expert operator starting on a new machine.

In either case, it will take time and effort to gain complete control of the machine.

Some expert operators have reported that after changing from one machine to another (with identical controls) it takes about two weeks of full time operation to fully master that particular machine.

☞ **NOTE** – Don't "horse" the older machine. Do not push it into full power situations, because something will break. Most parts of old machines are worn, stressed, weakened, and even cracked. Hydraulic hoses degrade over time. Worn or damaged rubber, damaged and rusted steel braiding, and pinched or pulled hoses are causes of hose failure which is common on older machines.

Operate the older machine in a more gentle way to avoid overstressing the individual parts which could result in more frequent breakdowns.

☞ **IMPORTANT:** If you ever find a mechanical problem on any machine that could compromise safety, notify your supervisor immediately, and **take necessary action to maintain safety at all times.**

# Loader Control

☞ **NOTE:** *The following information on the brake system applies to two wheel drive machines and (to a lesser extent) to four-wheel-drive machines and late model machines designed with four large equal-size tires.*

## Brakes

A major aspect of loader control is in using the brakes for more than simply stopping the machine. Skillfully using the brakes will allow the operator to exercise the highest level of control over the machine. When expertly used, the independent brakes of the TLB can be used to assist steering and control of the machine, as well as to stop it.

**Brake System** – Modern two-wheel-drive TLBs are equipped with a system that provides independent braking for each of the rear wheels. The controls of this system consist of two brake pedals located next to each other. This design allows the operator to control one or both of the brake pedals with one foot. On most machines the left foot controls the brakes while the right foot controls the engine speed.

These left and right brake pedals are equipped with a mechanical locking device. (See Fig. 2-2) This device is designed to lock the right and left brake pedals together to apply both brakes at the same time. When unlocked, the brakes can be applied individually.

In some situations, such as high speed travel, it is almost always better to have the brakes locked together. However, there are situations when the opposite is true. As an operator you must clearly understand and implement the safest method for each working situation.

If the brake system is out of adjustment or functioning improperly, the machine should be taken out of service until repaired.

When operating a machine for the first time, the operator should check to see if the brakes are properly adjusted.

***Brake Adjustment Test*** – Improper adjustment can be determined by performing a simple test.

1) Unlock the locking device to allow the brake pedals to move individually.

2) Center your foot over the pedals and apply equal pressure to both pedals at the same time.

3) Check to see if the pedals are aligned and flat.

4) Apply higher pressure back and forth between the pedals by moving your knee to the right and to the left. Repeat this knee rocking motion several times.

If the brakes are properly adjusted, the pedals will remain flat. If they are improperly adjusted, or functioning improperly, one pedal will depress further than the other.

☞Always notify your supervisor when the machine's brakes are out of adjustment, or not functioning properly. In this situation, the machine should be taken out of service.

When brakes are out of adjustment and the pedals are locked together, only one brake will engage when the pedals are depressed. In this situation, the brakes' stopping power is reduced and they no longer aid in controlling the machine. This is one area that must be clearly understood.

Driving a machine on public streets or highways is commonly referred to as "roading" the machine. A TLB has inherent dangers that the operator must be aware of and know how to deal with before driving a TLB on a road or highway.

***Operations with the Brakes Unlocked*** – When operating the machine with the brakes unlocked there are also some things to watch for.

The dangers around operating with unlocked brakes are usually caused by operator error, or being unfamiliar with the machine. These include; hitting one brake instead of two, hitting the wrong pedal, or the foot slipping on wet or muddy surfaces to the wrong pedal.

When operating the machine with the brakes unlocked the operator must: 1) be experienced

and 2) apply the brakes in an exact and precise manner.

***To Lock or Not to Lock*** – There are four main factors that must be considered before deciding if the brakes should or should not be locked together.

• **Skill Level** – Skill level ranges from beginners to experts. Beginners should move the machine slowly and with the brakes locked for the greatest safety.

• **Experience** – As the operator logs more seat time on the same machine, he or she becomes more familiar, or "in tune," with the machine. Time in the seat is the only thing that provides the operator with the skill needed to react to a given situation instantly and in a safe and effective manner. The more seat time an operator has on a machine, the more likely they are to unlock the brakes for better machine control.

• **Machine age and condition** – As an operator, you will work on many machines, ranging from a factory fresh, brand new item, to an old or poorly maintained TLB. You must be aware that the age and condition of the machine will have a great effect on the brake's operation. On an older machine, the operator should check the brakes for equal adjustment. If the adjustment is unequal, the operator must leave them unlocked to permit an equal and controlled application.

• **Speed of Operation** – The speed of the machine when it is working is an important factor when considering whether to lock or unlock the brakes. Slow speed operation is usually aided by using the brakes for assistance in steering and control.

At higher speeds, it is critical that the brakes are applied evenly and equally to gain the maximum stopping power. In higher speed situations, such as roading the machine down the highway (if the machine's brakes are adjusted properly), it is usually advantageous to have the brakes in the locked position.

The work of the TLB covers an almost infinite variety of jobs and job sites. For safety's sake, the operator must weigh these factors to maintain the greatest control of the machine in all work site situations.

## On the Job

The following are examples of "on-the-job" situations. Most of these situations happen when the TLB "gets light" on the front end, therefore reducing or eliminating traction to the front tires.

The following examples show common TLB tasks and **situations that are made safer and more efficient by using the brakes** to control the machine.

*Cleanup* – When using the loader to clean paved surfaces, the front tires are often barely touching the ground, or off the ground completely. With little or no traction on the front tires, steering is lost. At this point, the brakes are the only effective means of steering the machine.

*Reduced Traction Conditions* – These include ice, snow, wet or muddy conditions. As traction is reduced on the front tires, the steering control of the machine is also reduced.

*Grading* – During grading operations, the loader bucket is often used to backdrag the area in the "float" position or with down pressure applied. Again, less weight on the front tires and therefore less traction and control.

*Maneuvering in Tight Areas* – When maneuvering in a tight area, you may need to "assist" the front tires to turn the machine in a tighter circle than it would naturally.

*Loading and Unloading* – Loading and unloading the machine is one of the more difficult and hazardous procedures faced by an operator. The uphill slope required to get the machine onto a truck or trailer will increase the weight on the rear wheels and decrease the weight on the front wheels. It is not uncommon for the front wheels to come off the ramp surface several inches. In this situation, the only real steering control over the machine is through the brakes. Because of the technical control skills required for this procedure, only experienced operators with highly developed braking skills should attempt to load or unload a TLB.

*Side Sloped Areas* – When operating the machine across a slightly sloped area, the machine will tend to drift sideways down the slope, or up the slope. Apply the brake on the uphill side as needed to keep the machine on the desired path.

*Transfer Power for Increased Traction* – This is another weight transfer situation that occurs on side slopes. When the machine is traveling on a side slope, the weight can shift off of the uphill tire and reduce its traction. Often, this tire will start to slip and spin due to the lack of traction. When it spins, the forward driving torque is removed from the downhill tire, and the forward motion of the machine will stop. By applying the brake on the uphill side, the power is shifted to the downhill side and forward driving force is maintained.

*Moving Objects Sideways* – Backhoe buckets and concrete or rocks can be moved sideways for short distances using the loader bucket.

## Loader Summary

Controlling the TLB means the operator knows how to make the machine perform exactly as he wants it to, regardless of any external conditions. When an operator masters total control of his machine, common job site hazards and obstacles no longer prevent him from performing the work efficiently. Anything less can result in injuries, property damage, or both.

One common element that should be present in every TLB operation is "smoothness." It is impossible to place too much emphasis on this basic concept. Smoothly operating the TLB should be the constant goal of every operator. Smooth operation will contribute to a longer machine life. It will also enhance the operator's efficiency, allowing faster and more precise operation.

Control comes into play during the two basic areas of machine operation; namely, maneuvering the machine and hydraulic control.

Again, the emphasis must be placed on control. Anyone can get on a machine and drive it around a job site, but it takes a skilled operator to exercise total control over it. In the previous chapter we discussed several variable factors that affect the TLB's handling, such as weight distribution and how it can change during operation. A working knowledge of these factors and how to manipulate them is essential to TLB control.

## Hydraulic Control

The TLB's hydraulic system controls the movements of the backhoe itself, as well as the side-mounted stabilizers and the loader bucket in the front. Its heart is a pump and fluid reservoir located in the tractor. Without getting into a long essay on the principles of hydraulics, the basic idea is that fluid is pumped through the system at a flow ranging from fifteen to thirty-five gallons per minute.

## Backhoe Control

The backhoe part of the machine is powered and controlled completely by means of hydraulics, which is a different way than most people are used to. Loaders and other types of heavy equipment use their drive wheels to control and direct their force, but on the backhoe this force is controlled strictly through the hydraulic system.

The typical hydraulic system for one of these machines consists of a pump, a reservoir, various valves, hydraulic cylinders, and many hoses and pipes to connect all of the parts.

The hydraulic pump is the heart of the system, and it is usually powered directly off of the engine. **The speed of the pump is in direct relation to the speed of the engine.** If the engine is idling, the pump speed will be quite slow and with much less power than normal operating RPM (revolutions per minute). Operating the backhoe at the proper RPM is a critical part of machine control, as well as safety.

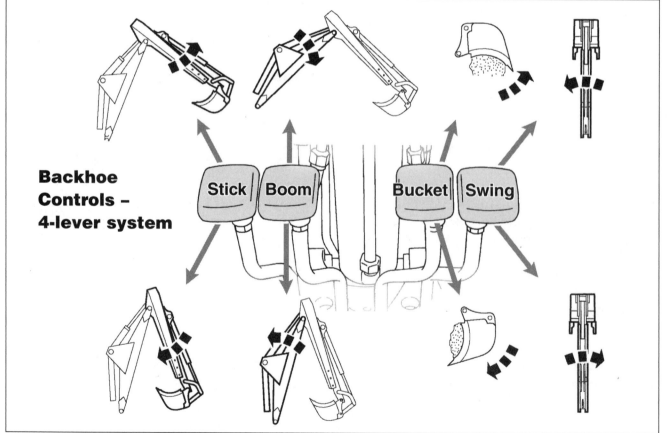

**Backhoe Controls – 4-lever system**

Stick   Boom   Bucket   Swing

**Fig. 2-3**

***How does the operator control the RPM?***
The speed and power of the hydraulics is directly related to the RPM of the engine. If high speed and power are desired, such as working in an open area, with no people around and no chance of underground utilities in the area, then the engine could be set at a high RPM for fast and powerful operation of the backhoe.

The operator will set the RPM for the given situation by setting the hand throttle to the desired RPM. The hand throttle is designed to hold the engine at any RPM that the operator desires, from an idle to the maximum RPMs. The device will hold the RPMs at the same setting until the operator changes it. It is important to note that the hand throttle is to be used only when operating the backhoe. The hand throttle is not to be used when operating the loader, and should be set to idle during all loader operations.

***What is normal operating RPM?*** – In most backhoe operating situations, the throttle is set at about 75% open. In the open area situation

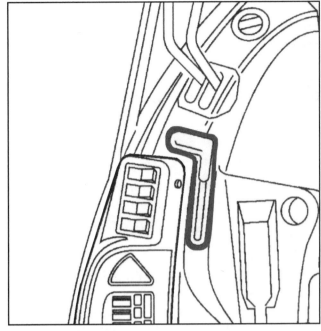

**Fig. 2-4**  *Hand throttle when operating backhoe*

described above, the operator may want to open the throttle up to 90% or even wide open for more power and speed. There are also times when the operator would want to lower the power and speed

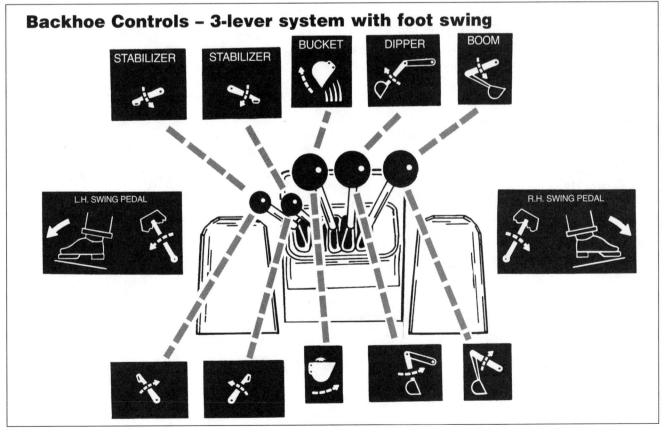

**Fig. 2-5**

of the backhoe. By lowering the speed of the engine, the power available to the hydraulics is also lowered. A slower, gentler, and more easily controlled movement of the bucket can then be achieved. Tight working conditions or the possibility of utilities in the area are good reasons to slow down and maintain better, more precise control over the machine.

The operator controls the backhoe with six valves located at the rear of the tractor. These valves control the four basic hoe motions – the crowd or "stick," the boom, the bucket and the swing – as well as the two stabilizers.

Depending on how they are manipulated, these valves send hydraulic fluid through the system to the function or functions the operator wants to actuate. As resistance is built up in the hydraulic cylinders, the force necessary to move the various parts of the machine is created. This force may reach several tons, particularly when the boom, stick and bucket are manipulated simultaneously to perform the most common backhoe operation – digging.

Since all power and movement is controlled through these valves, the operator must become proficient in opening and closing them. This will determine how much force or speed is used to perform whatever task the operator faces. Each

control is separate from the other, yet all are inter-related because they draw their power from the oil flow of the same pump. Therefore, if two or more valves are opened simultaneously, the oil will flow to the one with the least resistance. If all four main backhoe controls were actuated at once, the flow each would receive would be about one-fourth as much as each function would receive if it were operated alone. So, much of what it takes to control the backhoe depends on the correct diverting of hydraulic fluid from point to point.

Once the operator learns to operate the backhoe's hydraulics smoothly, and to go through the digging cycles with fluid-like precision, he has taken a big step toward total backhoe control.

The smooth operator will bring the boom from the spoil pile to the trench and back again in sweeping, continuous arcs. Contrast this type of motion with the jerky, stop-and-go right angle movements of the beginning operator, and the benefits of practicing smoothness at all times are better appreciated.

To better illustrate the concept of smooth operation, we rigged a backhoe with a series of lights, and then took a number of time-exposures, while operating the backhoe (Figs. 2-8 and 2-9). The lights indicate the path of movement followed by the bucket, and give some idea of how the back-

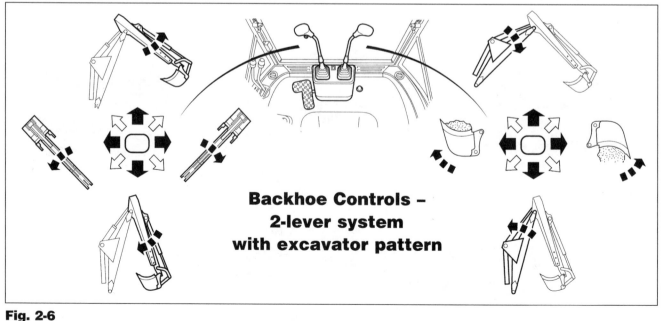

**Backhoe Controls – 2-lever system with excavator pattern**

**Fig. 2-6**

hoe should be controlled, with the emphasis on smoothness.

It's impossible to learn how to be smooth from the pages of this or any other book or training manual. Control can only be mastered by making a concentrated effort to be smooth at all times while practicing at the backhoe's controls.

The way to master smooth operation is through a technique called "feathering." This is simply the opening and closing of the valves in combination, in such a way that the flowing style mentioned earlier is created. The beginning operator, using one function at a time, will find the machine rough, jerky and frustrating (Fig. 2-10, 2-11). High productivity will be impossible to achieve at first. Once he learns how to combine the hydraulic functions in a smooth way, however, he will be able to control the backhoe as he desires, and productivity will rise to the level expected from professional operators. Again, this skill cannot be learned from a book, but only through practice and constant striving for smoothness.

One illustration of the use of feathering would be to swing the hoe across from left to right (or vice versa), carrying a load. As the bucket nears the end of the arc, start to extend the stick, which will then divert flow from the swing to the stick and thus slow the swing. Then, at the end of the arc, roll the bucket outward, which means three functions are now in use. As the swing comes to a stop, bring the swing control back in the opposite direction; as the bucket reaches the end of its outward roll and the bucket lever is released, more power will come back to the swing and it will slowly, smoothly start back in the other direction.

One final note, hydraulics systems are becoming more sophisticated all the time. Recent developments include electro-hydraulic controls and limiting devices, which enhance precise operation. Also, an array of highly-engineered valve stacks further aid smoothness. Other examples of common valves found on TLBs include flow control valves and proportional priority flow divider valves, relief valves, and pressure reducing valves. All of these contribute to increased operator control, ease of operation and protection against hydraulic system damage.

In addition, some backhoe models now feature two-lever systems replacing the four-lever systems, combining two functions in each lever or "joystick." The advantages of the two-lever system include less operator fatigue and increased control when using all four functions at once, which is much more difficult on four-lever models.

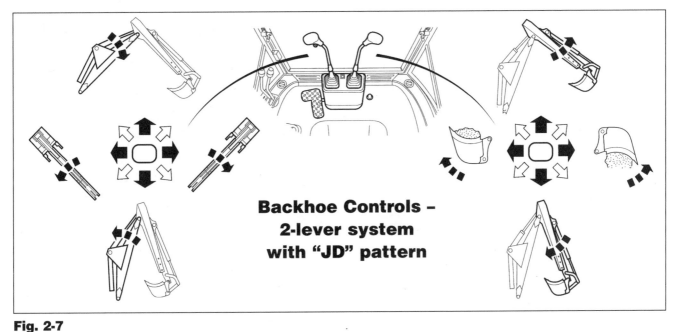

**Backhoe Controls –
2-lever system
with "JD" pattern**

**Fig. 2-7**

**Fig. 2-8** *By following the path of the lights, the viewer can trace the smooth, flowing digging cycle from right to left in the top photo, and from left to right in the photo below.*

**Fig. 2-9**

**Fig. 2-10** *When contrasted to the photos on the facing page, these show clearly the jerky, inefficient digging motion common to beginning operators.*

**Fig. 2-11**

## Practice Exercises

As mentioned earlier, machine control is not enhanced simply by reading this book. It is gained through practice, with an emphasis on smoothness. Here are some exercises that will help the beginning operator achieve smooth backhoe operation.

*"Floating the Bucket"* – This exercise will teach the operator the most important basic motion of backhoe operation, the digging motion. When properly performed, the basic digging motion of the backhoe will move the bucket in long, level passes. The ability to perform this movement smoothly is essential to backhoe operation and is required in all precision excavations. How easy it is to perform depends on the hardness of the soil. If soil is hard, it will be fairly easy; if it is soft, muddy or sandy, it will become very difficult. A good operator must be able to handle all soil conditions, whether hard, soft or in-between. This exercise will teach the operator how to control the backhoe in the most difficult situations.

The object of this exercise is to follow the contour of the ground with the bucket teeth raised one inch above the surface. Extend the backhoe out all the way and lower it to within about an inch of the ground. Now, by raising the boom and pulling in the stick at the same time, the teeth will follow the contour of the ground while remaining just barely above it. When the bucket reaches the nearest position, reverse the procedure and extend the stick while lowering the boom. Practice this procedure in both directions until it becomes easy and speed is increased.

*"Open Area Smoothness"* – To further help the beginner understand backhoe control basics, it is helpful to separate job functions into two categories. The first category includes jobs which don't require precision digging or spoil placement. These may include any task in an open area with plenty of swing room for operating the boom and without height or exact spoil placement restrictions; any time the operator practices in an open area; and when digging large excavations.

In these situations the operator is not required to maintain precise machine control, because there is nothing within the backhoe's reach that can be damaged. The machine can be operated at maximum speed and efficiency. These are excellent opportunities for the operator to practice and concentrate on developing a perfectly flowing, smooth digging cycle (Fig. 2-8). The beginner can work on mastering the art of feathering the controls, enhancing smoothness. The best thing about this kind of practice is that it can be done on the job, as long as it is safe. Because there are no obstacles or restrictions, this general digging motion is easiest for the beginning operator to perform – yet in reality, it is not at all easy and usually takes hundreds of hours to become accustomed to. When it gradually comes naturally to the operator, however, they can then begin concentrating on the more difficult tasks.

The second category of basic backhoe functions are the more difficult jobs that usually make up about 80 percent of all tasks performed by the TLB. These jobs include obstacles and restrictions which demand a higher degree of control to prevent damage to the area or structures in the area. These restrictions can include: houses and buildings; lawns, trees or bushes; delicate concrete, asphalt or masonry surfaces; trenches or other excavations; existing footings; building materials piled on the site; cars and trucks; and stakes, hubs or other surveyors' markings.

Another set of obstacles exist underground. Transportation systems for gas, water, sewage, electricity, telephone wires, and cable television can pose problems, as can oil, steam, and cold and hot water lines. On some job sites, everything from gases and chemicals to beer or grape juice can be piped underground.

Some jobs may include only a few of these restrictions, while others are so complicated that safe, damage-free TLB operation can be next to impossible. However, it is the operator's job to control the machine in such a manner that damage will be prevented. It is also his responsibility to know when job site conditions are so restrictive that damage could be unavoidable. In these cases, the operator must inform those in charge of the job, or, as a last resort, he should know when a job shouldn't even be attempted.

To help the beginning operator gain the type of control necessary in these difficult situations, the following exercise may be practiced.

*"Dipping Water"* – To practice this exercise, some source of water will be needed. This could include a stream, pond or similar source that will allow the operator to move the water about without causing problems and one which allows easy, safe access to the TLB.

The object of this exercise is simple: dip the water with the backhoe bucket, swing it to the side and dump it, simulating the act of digging. The beginner (and even many experienced operators) will have a hard time avoiding splashing or spilling the water at first. As smoothness and control increase, however, the operator will be able to keep the "load" in the bucket and avoid splashing or spilling.

Unlike the "open area" exercise where the operator can work at full speed without worrying about restrictions, this exercise simulates working in extremely tight situations, where one quick or thoughtless move could cause damage or other accidents. It simulates the kind of situation where every move must be planned and executed carefully, with the utmost in precision. By practicing swinging in both directions, this exercise is an excellent way to gain the control necessary for most on-the-job situations.

Practicing these exercises and striving for smooth, controlled TLB operation while off the job will enable the beginning operator to develop the confidence necessary to perform the duties expected while on the job.

# Questions – Chapter 2 **Machine Control**

*Notes:* _____

_____

_____

_____

_____

_____

_____

_____

_____

_____

_____

_____

_____

_____

_____

_____

_____

_____

_____

_____

_____

_____

_____

_____

_____

_____

_____

_____

_____

_____

**1. One common element that should be present in every TLB operation is smoothness.**

_____ a. True

_____ b. False

**2. Smooth operation of the TLB will:**

_____ a. Improve safety

_____ b. Increase efficiency

_____ c. Lengthen machine life

_____ d. All of the above

**3. Controlling the machine with the brakes is most effective on TLB models equipped with automatic, torque converter transmissions.**

_____ a. True

_____ b. False

**4. Excluding the stabilizers, how many functions are controlled by the main backhoe control valves?**

_____ a. 2

_____ b. 3

_____ c. 4

_____ d. 6

**5. If two or more valves are opened at the same time, through which valve will the oil flow?**

_____ a. The valve with the least resistance

_____ b. The valve with the most resistance

_____ c. Through all the valves equally

_____ d. None of the above

**6. Smooth operation can be mastered by a technique called feathering.**

_____ a. True

_____ b. False

**7. Control can only be mastered by making a concentrated effort to be smooth at all times while at the backhoe controls.**

_____ a. True

_____ b. False

**8. What is the fastest way to learn and gain complete control of the backhoe's hydraulics?**

_____ a. Operate the machine at high RPMs

_____ b. Ignore the loader bucket and only use the backhoe

_____ c. Practice and constant striving for smoothness

_____ d. Don't take your eyes off the bucket

**9. The advantages of the two-lever system include less operator fatigue and increased control when using all four functions at once.**

_____ a. True

_____ b. False

**10. The four-lever system gives the operator slightly greater control when propelling or maneuvering the machine with the backhoe itself.**

_____ a. True

_____ b. False

**11. The "floating the bucket" exercise involves following the contour of the ground with the bucket 1 foot off the surface of the ground.**

_____ a. True

_____ b. False

**12. A machine with improperly adjusted or functioning brakes should be reported to a supervisor and taken out of service for repairs.**

_____ a. True

_____ b. False

**13. All TLBs respond the same way to operator input.**

_____ a. True

_____ b. False

_____
_____
_____
_____
_____
_____
_____
_____
_____
_____
_____
_____
_____
_____
_____
_____
_____
_____
_____
_____
_____
_____
_____
_____
_____
_____
_____
_____
_____

**14. The mechanical response of TLBs can vary greatly due to:**

_____ a. Different manufacturers

_____ b. Age of the machine

_____ c. Weight distribution of the machine

_____ d. All of the above

**15. Weight distribution and the center of gravity stays the same from one machine to another.**

_____ a. True

_____ b. False

**16. An older machine should be operated in a more gentle way to avoid overstressing its individual parts.**

_____ a. True

_____ b. False

**17. In what steering configuration can the operator use the brakes to steer and control the machine?**

_____ a. 4wd

_____ b. 2wd

_____ c. Quad-wheel drive

_____ d. All of the above

**18. The machine response in older machines can be degraded by**

_____ a. Broken or missing parts

_____ b. Poor or worn brakes

_____ c. Weaker hydraulic power

_____ d. All of the above

**19. The independent brakes of the two-wheel drive TLB can be used to:**

_____ a. Steer the machine

_____ b. Control the machine

_____ c. Stop the machine

_____ d. All of the above

**20. Proper response and equal adjustment of independent brake systems is critical to safe operation.**

_____ a. True

_____ b. False

**21. When the engine is idling, the hydraulic system**

_____ a. Produces no power

_____ b. Does not produce enough power to move the machine

_____ c. Produces low power and low speed

_____ d. Produces high power and slow speed

**22. The hand throttle is commonly used during all loader operations.**

_____ a. True

_____ b. False

**23. In tight working conditions, or where utilities may be in the area, the operator should lower the RPMs of the engine for slower speed and more precise control over the machine.**

_____ a. True

_____ b. False

**24. Because of the technical skills required for loading and unloading a TLB onto a transporter, only experienced operators should carry out the task.**

_____ a. True

_____ b. False

**25. If you ever find a mechanical problem on any machine that could compromise safety, notify your supervisor immediately, and take necessary action to maintain safety at all times.**

_____ a. True

_____ b. False

# 3. Safety

Over the years the TLB has been continually refined and engineered to provide easier, more productive and safer operation. Many safety devices have been added to ensure safety to operators and workers. However, the machine itself is only part of the picture.

What really makes the TLB safe is the knowledge level, and safety awareness that the operator brings to the job.

## General
### #1 Mounting & Dismounting
Slips and falls while getting on or off are reportedly the most common accident. Mounting the machine is a basic requirement that every operator does many times a day.

This action seems so easy that most people do not recognize it as a potentially hazardous act. However, this simple and easy-appearing act can result in an accident ranging from a bruise, or sprained ankle, to broken bones or even death.

So, deal with getting on and off the machine as you would any other important job…by following a set of safety guidelines.

1) Always use a 3-point contact with the machine – two hands & one foot; or, two feet & one hand.

2) When getting on or off the machine, never carry tools or other objects in your hands.

3) Never jump on or off the machine.

4) Use extreme caution when surfaces are wet or muddy. Your chances of slipping or falling are greatly increased.

5) Always use designated entry and exit points. These are the only safe ways to get on or off the TLB.

6) Immediately report and replace any damaged or missing steps, handrails, or anti-skid material.

7) Clean steps daily if any buildup of mud occurs.

8) Never mount or dismount a moving machine.

9) Always face the machine when getting on or off.

## Safe Clothing
What you wear on the job is an important part of safe operation.

Always wear clothing that is suitable for the job. Loose fitting clothes and jewelry should be avoided because they can catch on equipment and controls.

Safety vests are required when working on any highway, public works, or street job. The vests should also be worn at night, and in poor visibility conditions such as fog, rain, or snow.

It's always important to protect your hearing, particularly if you are operating older equipment. Exposure to loud noise will damage your hearing over a period of time, so you should always use ear plugs or muffs in high noise situations.

## Seat Belt

This safety device is one of the most important of all safety devices, and just as important in the TLB as driving down the street in a car. In the event that you hit an unexpected bump or hole, the seat belt will keep you in your seat and enable you to maintain control.

In the event of a rollover, it will prevent you from being thrown from the machine.

Always use the seat belt when operating the machine. If the seat belt is not equipped with a retractor, place it over the arms of the seat when you remove it. That will make it easier to put on when you get back on the machine.

## Keep Your Machine Clean

This includes all windows, glass and mirrors. Make sure the foot pedals and all hand-operated controls are clean and free of grease.

Keep the floor of the cab area clean and free of obstructions. Items on the floor of the cab can restrict the operator's footing and movements within the cab.

Common items that could be found on the floor of the TLB that do not belong there include: tools, machine parts and supplies, grease gun, chains, thermos, lunch box, or tool box.

Keep rocks, tools, parts, and foreign materials out of the cab because they can stop pedals or controls from being depressed, or could stop them from being released.

## Safety Systems

You may not have thought about safety aspects as a part of the TLB's components and systems.

However, just like the automobile industry, heavy equipment manufacturers have added many safety features.

These safety systems must be maintained in original condition and used by all workers to help ensure safe operation.

**Hand holds** – These should always be kept clean, free of grease and in good repair.

**Steps** – Regularly clean steps of any dirt buildup and grease, to prevent slips and falls. Replace if missing or damaged.

**Safety railings and guards** – These should always be kept in good repair.

**Seat belt** – Always use the seat belt. If not retractor-equipped, when removing the belt, place it up over the sides of the seat. This will prevent the belt from falling down and getting stuck between the seat frame and will keep it handy to put back on.

**Horn** – Check the horn to make sure that it is in working properly.

**Mirrors** – Make sure any mirrors are clean and properly adjusted.

**Back up alarm** – Make certain the back up alarm is in working properly.

**Warning decals** must be clear and intact.

**Roll Over Protective Structure** – The Roll Over Protective Structure, or ROPS, is not only critical in the event of a rollover but can also help to protect the operator from falling objects. ROPS should never be removed from your TLB. A damaged ROPS should be replaced. Never weld or drill a ROPS.

**Loader Arm Service Lock** – This device is provided to ensure safety while performing service to the machine under the loader arms. Always install this device before working under raised loader arms.

**Operators manual** – Make sure the operators manual provided with the machine is on board. Read it, and be familiar with and follow all safety recommendations.

## Neutral Start Systems

By law, all types of heavy equipment must be equipped with a start-up lockout device. **This neutral start system prevents the engine from being started unless the transmission is in neutral.**

Bypassing the neutral start system can result in accidents with the possibility of serious injury or death.

For example, the use of jumper cables to start a machine by connecting directly to the starter bypasses the neutral start system. If the transmission is in gear, the machine will move when the engine starts. A person standing in the machine's path may be run over. Using a screwdriver or other metal object to "bypass start" can produce the same result.

By not starting the machine from the key switch, the operator bypasses the neutral start system that prevents the engine being started while the transmission is in gear. Neutral start systems are important to the safety of your machine. Keep them in good repair, and never bypass or "wire around" them.

☞ *NEVER attempt to:*

• bypass these switches…

• start the machine while standing on the ground…

• or jump start directly to the starter terminals.

## Parking Safety

During the course of a normal working day, it is not uncommon for the operator to mount and dismount the machine while the engine is running. This is because warm-up and cool down periods are required. These warm-up and cool down periods are required to prevent engine damage, especially to turbocharger equipped engines.

Before dismounting the TLB, there are three things that the operator must do.

1) Lower the loader and/or the backhoe to the ground

2) Be sure transmission controls are in neutral.

3) Set the parking brake

## Worker Safety

Even the best operator can only provide part of the active input required in keeping the job safe. It is up to everybody who works around the machine, including laborers, mechanics, foremen, surveyors, soils engineers, technicians, and any other people on the job site, to play their part in keeping the job site safe.

Keep in mind that each operator has a different level of awareness of the work site. Some operators have a highly developed sense of what is going on, and who is approaching the machine at all times. Others do not. As each operator's awareness level varies, you should never assume that the operator is aware of your presence.

Even the best operator can be distracted by any number of things, allowing someone to move unseen into the loader's work area.

Remember that the operator's visual range is often limited, and could be obstructed by the bucket, the cab, or other machine parts. This, plus the noise of the machine in operation, can isolate the operator from what is going on around the machine.

Any and all persons who are working with a TLB, or in the area of the TLB, should think defensively and follow these guidelines.

Always be 100% positive the operator is aware of your presence before entering the work area. One way of doing this is to establish and verify eye contact with the operator.

Even after you have made your presence known to the operator, never let your guard down while you are around the machine.

The author's father always had the same advice for someone new on the jobsite: ***"Treat the machine like it's out to get you!"*** Regardless of the trade or activity you are involved in, **never turn your back to the machine. Always position yourself so that you can see what the TLB is doing at all times.**

If both the operator and worker think safety, and work together, accidents can be avoided.

Here are some important guidelines for the operator to remember when other people are in the work area.

As the backhoe operator in these situations you must:

1) Pay attention and concentrate on what you are doing.

2) Be aware of all persons and activity in your work area.

3) Recognize potentially dangerous situations.

4) Maintain a high level of safety awareness at all times.

5) Never operate the TLB in any situation you feel may be dangerous.

Remember these guidelines from the second your hand touches the machine at the start of the day, and keep them in mind until you shut down at the end of the work day.

## General TLB Safety

No discussion of the operation of any piece of heavy equipment is possible without a strong emphasis on safety. Every move made with the TLB must be done so with safety in mind: safety to you, safety for those around you, safety to property, and safety to the TLB itself. Indeed, safety considerations must be made even before getting on the machine.

According to the State of California Department of Industrial Relations, the leading cause of non-fatal disabling work injuries involving backhoes during a one-year period was simply slipping, falling, or being struck while getting on or off the machine.

It is also quite possible for someone on the job site to never come into direct contact with a TLB, yet be injured due to short-sighted TLB operation. The careful operator must be aware of all possible dangers, at all times, and do everything he can to

reduce the risk of injury or accident. Anything less could cause injury, or even death, to the operator or the workers around him, who are also his responsibility. The operator is always responsible for the safe operation of the TLB.

Every part of this guide, regardless of the technique being discussed, or the information being given, has some aspect of safety underlying it. There are any number of possible hazards to be aware of. Usually, though, the potential for mishap can be effectively addressed if operators make good, safe operation of the TLB their prime consideration at all times.

Many accidents involving construction equipment occur because the operator or helpers fail to follow some very basic rules. When operating equipment, just remember that a little forethought and common sense can prevent some very serious injuries to you or someone else. Take just a moment to consider these basic rules:

***Never take anything for granted*** – Don't assume that everything is all right at the start of the work day just because everything seemed all right at the end of work yesterday. Before beginning operation, thoroughly inspect the equipment to be sure it is in good operating condition.

***Keep the machine clean,*** including all windows, glass and light lenses. Remove any excess oil and grease. Store tools and other necessary items in the tool box.

***Clean mud and grease*** from your shoes before attempting to mount or operate the equipment. Be sure the foot pedals are clean and dry, to reduce the possibility of your boots slipping off the pedals. Also, make sure to keep all hand-operated controls, as well as steps, handholds and the platform, clean and free of grease.

***Clothing*** should be relatively close fitting. Loose jackets, shirt sleeves, rings, and other jewelry should be avoided because of the danger of catching them in moving parts or on controls.

*Always wear required protective equipment* such as hard hats, safety glasses, reflective clothing, safety shoes and ear protection.

*Never start or operate the machine* without protective guards and panels in place.

*Always check height, width, and weight* restrictions for the area and be sure the equipment will not exceed those limitations.

*Be sure that all safety devices* are in place and in good operating condition. Be familiar with the use of all safety devices, including lights, seat belts and reverse warning alarm.

*Plan ahead, and work safely* to avoid accidental damage and injury. If an accident does occur, react quickly with the tools and skills at hand. Know how to use a first aid kit and a fire extinguisher, and where to get assistance.

*Learn beforehand* as much about the working area as possible. Be sure that exact locations of obstructions or hazards are known. Such locations should be precisely marked by the operator to prevent accidents.

Read and heed the operator's manual provided with the machine. It is the best source of information important to the safe operation of the machine.

Each year there are hundreds of fatalities and thousands of serious, lost-time injuries as a result of TLB and other heavy equipment accidents. Most of these could have been prevented, if the operator had only used better judgment and common sense while on the job. Heavy equipment works hard and makes many people's jobs easier, but must be treated with respect...before, during and after the operations.

The condition of the TLB must be checked before starting work. Items to check include the steering, the brakes, the transmission, the hydraulic system and the electrical system. Any defect should be reported at once. Never start work with a defect that could cause an accident.

The safety canopy, or Roll Over Protective Structure (ROPS), was designed to protect the operator from rollovers and also helps to protect in case of falling objects. Make sure the ROPS is maintained in good condition.

Remember to use the seat belt at all times. On a rough grade, the belt can keep the operator in the seat, which will help to maintain better control of the TLB. If the TLB turns over, the seat belt will keep the operator from being thrown. The ROPS is designed to prevent rollover injuries, but the operator must be buckled in during the roll.

Before moving on, it is important to say that there is no substitute for common sense. Simple things like slowing down when unsure of ground conditions, or watching out for other workers because they may not be watching out for themselves, are necessary.

When the operator takes safety for granted, and lets his concentration lapse, trouble begins. Never forget that when you are at the controls of the TLB, the burden of safety is on you.

The most obvious danger presented by TLB operation is the sheer size and bulk of the machine. In addition to the actual machine weight of approximately seven tons, the TLB also generates tremendous hydraulic power. This kind of weight and power can cause crushing injuries. Practically any type of injury is possible, ranging from something as minor as a cut or scrape to the major accidents that can cause permanent disability or even death.

## Backhoe Accidents

According to the Department of Industrial Relations of the State of California, non-fatal disabling work injuries involving backhoes during a one-year period were classified as follows:

| Accident type | # of injuries |
|---|---|
| Fall or strike backhoe while climbing on or off | 16 |
| Struck by backhoe bucket | 14 |
| Struck against backhoe (not classified elsewhere) | 14 |
| Caught in or between backhoe parts | 14 |
| Overexertion involving backhoes | 10 |
| Backhoe overturned | 6 |
| Other | 10 |
| **TOTAL** | **84** |

Accidents can take many forms depending on the conditions and circumstances surrounding each. Here are some examples (all taken from actual accident reports):

■ An equipment operator was working in an excavation when the backhoe's stabilizer lodged in the trench wall. The backhoe overturned, and the operator's back was injured.

■ A construction worker was releasing the latch on a backhoe bucket when the operator inadvertently started the equipment, catching the worker's hand and breaking two bones.

■ A maintenance worker received a hernia when his foot slipped on the wet step of a dew-covered TLB.

■ A worker was shoveling dirt next to a TLB in operation. The bucket overswung the trench and struck the worker, resulting in a broken leg and ankle.

■ An operating engineer was leaning over the edge of a trench between two shoring plates, measuring the depth of the trench. A backhoe hit one of the shoring plates, pushing it into the other, with a scissoring effect on the engineer's neck.

■ A water utility worker was helping a TLB operator change a bucket. While aligning the holes of the pin mechanism, he jammed his thumb and index finger.

■ A grading and paving operator was working on a hillside, trying to remove a stump, when his machine rolled over. His ankle was broken when the roll bar hit it.

■ A worker pulled a back muscle while trying to move a 24-inch bucket.

■ An operator struck his head on the bucket when he slipped while getting off the machine.

## TLB Accidents

California's Department of Industrial Relations also tabulates injuries received while operating front-end loaders, which are relevant to TLB operations. A breakdown of statistics during a one-year period details the types of front-end loader accidents.

| Accident type | # of injuries |
|---|---|
| Fall or strike backhoe while climbing on or off | 16 |
| Struck against loader (not classified elsewhere) | 42 |
| Caught in or between loader parts | 24 |
| Fall or strike against while climbing on or off | 20 |
| Struck by bucket | 16 |
| Operating loader over rough or uneven terrain | 14 |
| Overexertion involving loader (not classified elsewhere) | 20 |
| Loader ran over embankment or overturned | 6 |
| Run over by loader | 2 |
| Other | 10 |
| **TOTAL** | **154** |

Again, some examples from actual accident reports show the types of mishaps that can occur:

■ A laborer was in a trench attaching a shoring pulling device. A second worker, relaying hand signals to the loader operator, failed to halt the lowering of the front bucket. It struck the first employee on the head, causing spasms, stiffness and soreness in his neck and back.

■ An equipment rental operator accidentally drove a front-end loader in a trench, causing the loader to become off-balance and vibrate violently. The operator was bounced around inside the cage, hit his head on the beam, and suffered head injuries.

■ A job foreman hit a rock while operating the loader. His head hit and broke the windshield, resulting in head and neck soreness.

■ An operator who was breaking and removing concrete backed over some rocks, came down hard in his seat, and experienced sharp back pains.

■ An operator had overloaded the front-end bucket on his loader, causing the machine to tip forward. As it did so, the operator grabbed a metal bar on the front of the cage. As the loader returned to a level position, the bucket came back, catching his hand between the bucket and the metal bar. His hand was "severely lacerated," according to reports.

■ A truck driver was unloading a front-end loader from the back of a transport trailer. Because he backed the machine in a curved, rather than straight line to the back of the trailer, it slipped off the trailer and came to rest on its side on the ground. The driver was crushed by the canopy part of the ROPS. He had been thrown from the driver's seat on the loader because he wasn't using his seat belt.

■ An operating engineer was asked to drive a loader to a construction site. He drove the loader in high gear down a 6% grade road. He lost control, hit the shoulder of the road and rolled over. The gas tank exploded into flames and the operator was killed.

■ A survey team was laying out and grading an area prior to concrete work. A loader was being used to level the land. When the loader made a stop, an operating engineer got behind the loader to drive a grade stake into the ground. The loader operator did not notice him, and began backing up. The equipment (which lacked a reverse warning alarm) ran over the engineer, killing him.

## Rollover

During a 15-year period, 229 California workers were killed when the equipment they were operating rolled over or ran off the road. It is useful to examine a breakdown of the types of industries involved in these accidents:

| *Type of worker* | *# of deaths* |
|---|---|
| Construction | 139 |
| Agriculture | 20 |
| Mining | 19 |
| Logging | 18 |
| Government (street maintenance, public utilities) | 15 |
| Equipment rental | 2 |
| Other | 46 |
| **TOTAL** | **229** |

Let's look at a breakdown of the types of rollover accidents recorded in California during a 10-year period:

| *Accident type* | *# of injuries* |
|---|---|
| Operating too close to the edge of a road or embankment | 40 |
| Operating on steep or uneven ground | 20 |
| Equipment defective or malfunctioned | 11 |
| Operating equipment on uncompacted or otherwise unstable ground | 10 |
| Operating equipment at excessive speed | 8 |
| Loading or unloading equipment onto/off of flatbed truck | 6 |
| Equipment struck rock, brush, etc. | 6 |
| Ran equipment up embankment | 5 |
| Operator lost control of equipment while turning | 2 |
| Other, or insufficient information to classify | 21 |
| **TOTAL** | **129** |

Note that in the above table, almost one-third of these accidents (40 out of 129) occurred when the operator moved his equipment too close to the edge of the road or embankment.

Here are some specific accident descriptions reported to the state:

■ A truck driver was using a loader equipped with a rear-mounted drag, pulling some form panels up over a fifteen-foot high bank. The panels had been stripped from a retaining wall and were lying on the slope that had been created when the area was excavated for the retaining wall. The tractor slid backwards and went over the edge of the bank. The rear wheels became wedged between the retaining wall and the dirt bank, and the front of the tractor flipped upward into a vertical position. The operator was pinned between the tractor and the wall. It was later learned that he was not qualified to operate the loader.

■ An operating engineer was running a front-end loader on a rural road about twenty-five feet wide. On the uphill side of the road, a trench was being dug for the installation of a storm drain. The downhill slope from the road was wooded, and sloped about 45 degrees. The operator planned to go for a load of backfill material and proceeded to turn the loader around. As he did so, one of the rear wheels went over the edge of the downhill bank, and he lost control of the machine. The equipment began rolling, and the operator was crushed beneath the machine about thirty feet down the bank. The machine kept rolling until it came to rest about 200 feet below the embankment.

The risk of rollover can be reduced by monitoring how the machine's weight is distributed and transferred while work proceeds. Essentially, the total weight of any piece of heavy equipment is distributed down through the ground at a 45-degree angle in all directions. It is vital, when preparing to operate the TLB, to constantly consider how its weight is going to be supported. Try to visualize the work area as a "platform" on which the TLB will rest. Once this working platform has been established with the stabilizers, wheels, or loader bucket all firmly supported, the operator must constantly think about how the machine's weight distribution will change as the work progresses. The operator must consider not only the machine's weight, but the weight of the material being handled as well.

*Soil Conditions* – The composition, and therefore the stability, of the soil in which the TLB is working can cause a rollover accident. The operator must investigate whether the soil has a high water content, or if it contains mostly sand, or gravel, or some other unstable mixture. Even stable-looking soil could be hazardous…it could conceal an old, covered trench that could lead to a cave-in, rollover, or both.

## Excavations

Excavation work is considered among the most hazardous of all construction operations and the TLB is primarily an excavating machine. Unless precautions such as shoring or sloping the trench walls are taken, cave-ins can occur. If this happens, workers in or near the trench could be injured or buried, and equipment near the trench could topple over into it.

During a 10-year period in California, for example, eighty workers were killed in cave-ins. The reasons for these deaths were given as follows:

| *Reason for cave-in* | *fatalities* |
|---|---|
| No shoring or sloping | .31 |
| Shoring installed/removed in unsafe manner | .15 |
| Inadequate shoring or sloping | .11 |
| Working outside shored area | .9 |
| Shoring was just removed | .2 |
| Weight of adjacent pile or wall | .2 |
| Other (or not stated) | .10 |
| **TOTAL** | .**80** |

Despite laws requiring shoring or sloping, you can see that 57 out of 80 cave-in deaths (about 74 percent) were caused by inadequate shoring or sloping, improperly installed or removed shoring, or no shoring or sloping at all. The law requires that shoring work start at the top of the trench or excavation and work downward, so that workers are protected by the cross-braces already in place. The procedure is reversed for removal. At no time should a worker be inside a trench pulling out a jack above him. Cave-in deaths occur primarily due to suffocation or crushing. Of the eighty workers killed in the period noted above, 47 suffocated when they were buried, while 26 were crushed by falling debris. Six sustained fatal skull fractures, and one worker died of a neck wound caused by a sharp object.

Specific examples of cave-in deaths, and the ways they were caused, include the following:

■ A TLB was excavating a twelve-foot trench for installation of a storm drain. A laborer was standing on the bucket of the backhoe, placing the lower screw-jacks against the uprights, which were spaced about three feet apart. The trench was in an area that had been previously filled. The bottom half of the trench suddenly caved in, knocking the laborer off the bucket and covering him with five feet of dirt and sand.

Another worker was pushed against the opposite wall of the trench by the cave-in, but was uninjured. The first worker suffocated.

■ Two laborers had been told to compact the backfill in a fifteen-foot trench and remove the shoring. One man, who was standing on about seven feet of backfilled soil in the trench, removed a lower jack which was bracing the uprights, and then tried to remove the upper jack. When it was removed, the trench wall collapsed and he was crushed. Another victim of improperly removed shoring.

■ A sewer line project had been completed, but leaks were discovered when the line was tested. The process of re-excavating and patching the pipe began. While this happened, water began accumulating in the bottom of the 10-foot deep trench. Workmen decided to dig a perpendicular trench to provide drainage. A laborer who had been in the excavation looking for leaks stood back in a section of the original trench, as the TLB began to dig the second trench. Almost immediately a section of the wall adjacent to the operation slid in and trapped the worker, who was in a stooped-over position. Because the face of the excavation was very irregular, it would have been difficult to install efficient shoring without dressing down the cut face. In this situation, the sides should have been properly sloped.

## Excavation Safety

Obviously, one of the keys to preventing cave-ins is, again, knowing the ground conditions. Ground that appears stable may not be, due to previous excavations. Or it may be loose, or muddy, or contain sand and gravel. In order to reduce the risk of cave-ins, the Occupational Safety and Health Administration (OSHA) now requires that all trenches deeper than five feet* either be shored or sloped. While shoring is generally not the responsibility of the TLB operator, sloping the trench is done with the TLB.

Another point to consider: when digging an excavation, do not place spoil closer than two feet from the edges, as the weight can cause a cave-in.

The operator must also take care to **never** undermine existing footings, such as piers or walls. Removing the support from under these, or similar heavy structures, could cause them to collapse either onto the TLB and surrounding equipment and workers, or later collapse onto unsuspecting workers at the job site.

In some situations, the TLB operator may be the only person on the job site who is able to evaluate things like existing footings or possibly unstable ground conditions. The operator must learn to watch for telltale signs of a cave-in about to occur, because he or she may be the only person in a position to see them. Soil may begin to fall from the sides of a trench, either up near the edge or down

*Varies by regional regulations*

toward the floor. Cracks may appear in the earth around the trench edges, either parallel with the excavation, or at an angle to it. Any of these signs indicate that movement is taking place in the ground around the trench, and it is the TLB operator's responsibility to act quickly, warning workers in the trench to get out as fast as they can.

If the machine is in a position where it might fall over into the excavation, the operator may have only a few seconds to get the TLB clear of the area, or if that is impossible, to get off the machine and reach safe ground. If unstable ground conditions are present, take care not to cause the TLB to shake or move in a jerky manner, since this may cause a cave-in, especially if the excavation is deep.

## Shoring

As we have noted, the vast majority of trench cave-ins are caused by insufficient or improperly-installed shoring. Remember also that shoring is usually not the responsibility of the TLB operator, although he or she can be called upon to assist the workers who actually install the shoring. A quick overview of the conditions which affect the kind and amount of shoring necessary includes the following points, which the TLB operator should always keep in mind:

**The depth of the trench** – Remember that any trench five feet deep or more must always be shored or sloped. If there is any possibility of soil movement, even shallower trenches should be shored. If there is any doubt, leave nothing to chance: shore or slope the trench.

**Running soils** – The looser or more liquid the soil, the greater the need for precautions against cave-in.

**Changing weather conditions** – Hard-packed soil can become muddy and unstable after rain. Trenches which had been safely shored or sloped in dry weather can become extremely dangerous when the ground is wet. Thawing soil can also become unstable quickly.

**Heavy loads in the area** – Don't park heavy equipment next to a trench. Don't stockpile any material closer than two feet from a trench edge. Also, nearby objects such as buildings, curbs, trees and utility poles will exert stress on trench shoring.

**Vibrations** – If a trench is being dug near a roadway or where other operations create vibrations, the shoring must be strong enough to withstand the added stress.

☞ **NOTE:** The design of any shoring system must be done by a shoring engineer and/or the "competent person" who is trained to recognize and classify soil types.

## Sloping

Unlike shoring, which is usually accomplished by other workers, sloping is a process which the TLB operator is usually responsible for. For this reason, it is important for the operator to thoroughly understand both the procedure as well as the desired results. Sloping an excavation is much more than just digging a hole in the ground. The purpose of the trench is to provide a safe working area for the workers.

As noted earlier, when a trench is to be sloped, the required ratio may be three-quarters of a foot in both directions for every foot in depth. Thus, the sloped area for a 12-foot trench would measure 20 feet across (nine feet on either side plus the actual two-foot trench width). As figures 3-1A, 3-1B and 3-1C clearly illustrate, sloping requires removing a large quantity of material to meet these requirements. Sloping requires the removal of many times the amount of material than would be removed if the trench was simply shored. The rule of thumb to approximate spoil removal is that sloping will require the removal of material about equal to the amount removed by shoring, multiplied by half the depth of the trench.

## Spoil Quantities – Shoring vs. Sloping – using ¾:1 Slopes

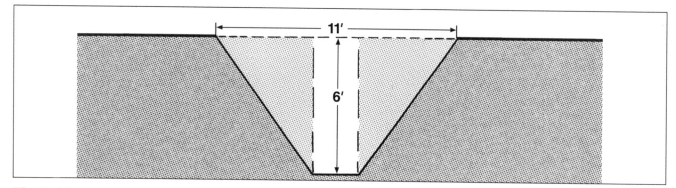

**Fig. 3-1A** *A six-foot-deep trench will require the removal of about three times as much material.*

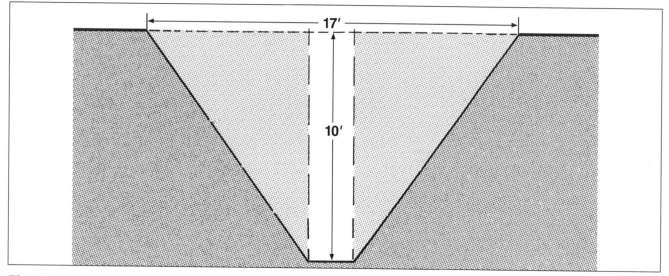

**Fig. 3-1B** *A 10-foot-deep trench will require the removal of about five times as much material.*

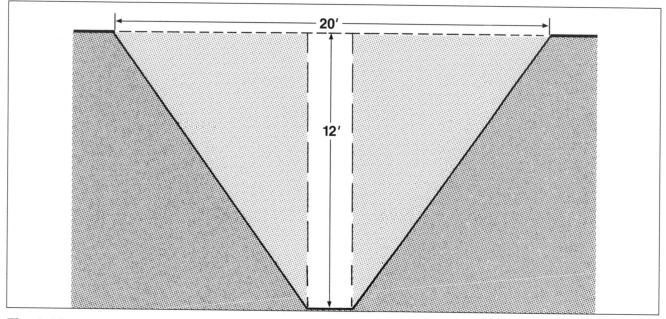

**Fig. 3-1C** *A 12-foot-deep trench will require the removal of about six times as much material.*

**Fig. 3-2** *A sloped trench is dug in steps…*

**Fig. 3-3** *….until the desired slope is accomplished.*

**Fig. 3-4** *The sides are then smoothed by sliding the bucket up and down against the slope.*

**Fig. 3-5** *The accumulated spoil at the top is cleaned away before the final grading is done on the bottom.*

It is obvious that the amount of spoil to be removed in the process of sloping becomes enormous as trench depth increases. This affects TLB work in two ways: 1) Digging time is increased dramatically, 2) Spoil placement quickly becomes a problem and there is often not enough room for stockpiling in the immediate area.

Using a larger bucket will reduce digging time, but the operator must also carefully "dress" or smooth the sides of the slope, which is somewhat time-consuming (see Figs. 3-2 through 3-5). To help the TLB operator stockpile the material, a loader or bulldozer can be used to push spoil back, allowing the digging to continue. If a second machine isn't available, the TLB operator may have to frequently stop digging and move the spoil back from the excavation using the loader.

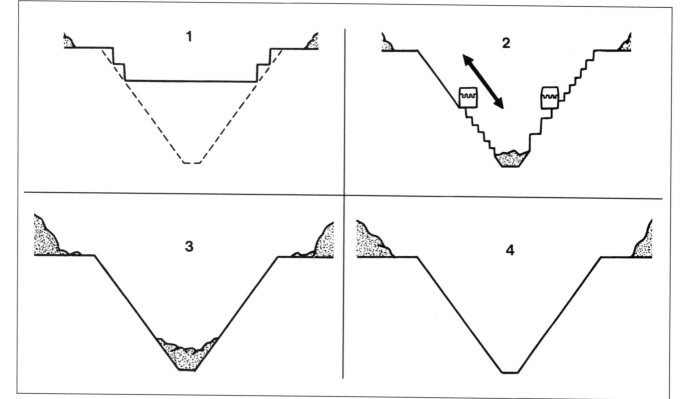

**Fig. 3-6** *SLOPING PROCEDURE: 1) After the correct width is determined, digging proceeds at the outside edge of the excavation. 2) After bulk material removal, slope sides are notched into smaller notches, and then the bucket is used to grade the sides smooth. 3) After the slope has been graded, the "sidewalks" are cleaned and the bottom of the trench is fine-graded. 4) A finished section.*

## Transporting Wheeled Machinery

Here are some suggestions to keep in mind which can help reduce the risk of accidents during heavy equipment transport.

### Prior to loading:

• Be thoroughly familiar with all basic machine controls, levers, pedals, switches, gauges, etc. Test drive the machine to familiarize yourself with the controls, as well as the machine's perform-ance to get the "feel" of how it responds. Unless you are very familiar with the machine's weight dis-tribution and controls do not attempt to load it… get someone else to do it.

• Check the operator's manual to review physical dimensions of the machine. Be sure its width com-plies with state highway laws, and that proper per-mits have been obtained. Check rules regarding use of warning signs, flags, escorts, etc. Make sure that the machine's weight, as specified in the operator's manual, can be supported by the trans-porting vehicle.

• Place chocks or other blocks in front of the trans-porting vehicle's wheels to prevent it from rolling while loading or unloading.

• Make sure there are no slippery surfaces on the bed of the transporter. If the bed is wet or covered with some substance that will reduce traction, dry or clean it.

### During loading:

• Load the machine from firm, level ground. The ramp should be strong, secured and long enough to provide a slope of low angle. There should be sufficient height for proper entrance onto the trans-porting vehicle.

• Make sure that buckets, blades, forks and other mounted equipment are lowered, not obscuring the operator's vision, making the load too top-heavy, or striking surfaces or obstacles while loading.

• Approach the ramp and transporting vehicle in the direction and manner recommended in the operator's manual.

• If possible, use a spotter to help guide you as you load.

### Following loading:

• Lower and secure buckets, booms, forks, and other mounted equipment onto the bed of the transporting vehicle.

• Place the transmission in "park" or low gear. Apply the parking brake.

• Shut off the engine, and remove the key from the ignition.

• Secure chocks ahead of and behind the wheels of the TLB or other equipment being loaded.

• Secure the TLB to the transporting vehicle with chains or cables. Usually, suggested tie-down points are identified in the operator's manual. If none are suggested, common tie-down points include the axle housing, openings in wheels, front axle members, tow hooks and drawbar mounts.

• Check to make sure the tie-downs are not in contact with the machine's equipment hoses, hydraulic cylinders, valves, rods or tires.

## Conclusions

In general, accidents occur when the operator either: 1) fails to recognize a potentially dangerous situation quickly enough to prevent it; or 2) recognizes the danger in time, but fails to investi-gate possible solutions or to consider possible consequences.

In order to prevent these situations from pro-gressing into an accident, operators must be sure of every move they make. Whenever in doubt, they should stop what they are doing. If you are unsure of the safety of any operation you have been asked to perform, you should question it. If a certain maneuver or job seems too dangerous, it would be better for the operator to simply refuse to do it, rather than risk lives and property.

If danger ever develops in the middle of a job, stay calm and think yourself through the situation. The earlier danger is recognized, the easier it can be avoided. Many operators don't recognize danger until it is too late, as we have seen. So think ahead, and come up with a plan. Consider all the possi-bilities. If the TLB becomes stuck, for example, don't sit there and spin the wheels; get off, walk around the machine, and think: Where is the weight? How is it distributed? How should it be distributed? Come up with a well thought-out plan to get from where you are to where you want to be.

Look out for workers and other people on the job site. Make sure no one wanders into the swing range of the machine, and if they do, tell them to move to a safe distance.

If you suspect there are hidden dangers, such as unstable ground conditions, speak up. An electrician, or a plumber, or a property owner probably doesn't know as much about safe TLB operation as you. Don't be afraid to voice an opinion on what procedures should be followed.

Use your head, consider all possibilities, observe common sense, and be safe every minute the TLB is in operation. A safe operator is the best defense against needless TLB accidents.

## Questions – Chapter 3 **Safety**

*Notes:* _____

_____

_____

_____

_____

_____

_____

_____

_____

_____

_____

_____

_____

_____

_____

_____

_____

_____

_____

_____

_____

_____

_____

_____

_____

_____

**1. What is the number one cause of accidents with the TLB?**

_____ a. Backing over fellow workers

_____ b. Rollovers

_____ c. Getting on and off the machine

_____ d. Getting caught between the machine's moving parts

**2. You turn the TLB off at the end of a working day and everything is okay. It is all right to start the machine up the next day and start working.**

_____ a. True

_____ b. False

**3. What safety devices should you check?**

_____ a. Reverse warning alarm

_____ b. Seat belt

_____ c. Guards

_____ d. All of the above

**4. When must you wear your seat belt?**

_____ a. Over rough ground

_____ b. When "roading the machine" or going fast

_____ c. All of the time

_____ d. Going up or down hill

**5. When loading a machine onto a truck or trailer, the ground conditions should be:**

_____ a. Firm and level

_____ b. Sloped

_____ c. Soft and sandy

_____ d. Compacted

**6. When loading the machine, make sure buckets, blades, forks and other mounted equipment are:**

_____ a. Raised

_____ b. Lowered

_____ c. Disconnected

_____ d. Not loaded with the machine

**7. Following loading you must:**

_____ a. Lower and secure buckets, booms, all other equipment

_____ b. Shut off the engine and remove the key

_____ c. Place transmission in park or low and apply brake

_____ d. All of the above

**8. When securing the TLB to the transporting vehicle with cables or chains, be sure that they are not in contact with the machine's hydraulic hoses, hydraulic cylinders, valves, rods or tires.**

_____ a. True

_____ b. False

**9. One of the designated exit points on all TLBs is at the rear of the machine at the stabilizers.**

_____ a. True

_____ b. False

**10. Safety systems on the TLB must be maintained in original condition. Which of the following are considered to be safety systems?**

_____ a. Hand holds, steps and railings

_____ b. Seat belt, horn and mirrors

_____ c. Reverse warning alarm

_____ d. ROPS

_____ e. Loader arm service lock

_____ f. All of the above

**11. The loader arm service lock should always be installed when operating the backhoe.**

_____ a. True

_____ b. False

**12. The neutral start safety system is designed to prevent:**

_____ a. Children from starting the machine

_____ b. The machine from being started while the backhoe is off the ground

_____ c. The machine from starting while the transmission is in gear

_____ d. The machine from starting unless the seat belt is in use

_____
_____
_____
_____
_____
_____
_____
_____
_____
_____
_____
_____
_____
_____
_____
_____
_____
_____
_____
_____
_____
_____
_____
_____
_____
_____
_____
_____

**13. The rollover protective structure (ROPS) was designed to protect the operator from rollover accidents.**

_____ a. True

_____ b. False

**14. When operating a machine with a ROPS it is not necessary to use the seatbelt.**

_____ a. True

_____ b. False

**15. About one third of all rollover accidents occurred when:**

_____ a. Operator lost control when turning

_____ b. The machine was moved too close to the edge of a road or downslope

_____ c. When loading or unloading from a transport vehicle

_____ d. While operating at excessive speed

**16. The risk of rollover can be reduced by monitoring how the machine's weight is distributed as the work proceeds.**

_____ a. True

_____ b. False

**17. Cave-in deaths occur primarily due to suffocation or crushing.**

_____ a. True

_____ b. False

**18. Ground conditions that appear to be stable may not be, due to previous excavations.**

_____ a. True

_____ b. False

**19. According to OSHA, trenches deeper than six feet must be shored or sloped.**

_____ a. True

_____ b. False

**20. Shoring is usually the responsibility of the backhoe operator.**

_____ a. True

_____ b. False

**21. Sloping a trench is usually the responsibility of the TLB operator.**

_____ a. True

_____ b. False

**22. Sloping requires the removal of many times the amount of material than would be removed if the trench was simply shored.**

_____ a. True

_____ b. False

**23. Always watch out for workers, or other people on the job site    .**

_____ a. True

_____ b. False

**24. If you suspect there are hidden dangers, such as unstable ground conditions, you should:**

_____ a. Continue operating as normal

_____ b. Notify your supervisor immediately

_____ c. Lower the machine's RPM and continue digging

_____ d. Use more caution when moving the machine

**25. Safety should be the operator's number one concern at all times.**

_____ a. True

_____ b. False

# 4. Maintenance

Maintenance responsibilities are areas of operation that can be different, depending on the company that the operator works for. Different companies will require varying levels of operator responsibility in the maintenance of the machine.

When you start working in the trade, you may not be responsible for all machine maintenance duties. Even though you may not end up responsible for all the duties required for proper machine maintenance, you will need an in-depth knowledge of all the machine's systems and components.

The best way to learn the specific details of maintenance is to study the operator's manual. The manual should be carefully read from cover to cover. For the average person to get a working knowledge of these machines, the entire manual will need to be covered several times.

## Operation and Maintenance Manual

A typical manual provided by the manufacturer will include the diverse information that is required to operate the machine in a safe and professional manner. The following is typical of the subjects covered in the operation and maintenance manual supplied by the manufacturer.

- Safety
- Machine Specifications
- Operational Controls and Procedures
- Maintenance Section
- Maintenance Intervals

The operation and maintenance manual provides the most in-depth and specific information for each machine model. It contains information on the machine that is not available anywhere else. It is such an important document that some manufacturers attach one to the machine with a steel cable.

### *Know the machine that you are operating!*

The TLB, like any piece of heavy equipment, requires maintenance on a periodic basis. Some machine components require checking every day. The operator's manual provides maintenance schedules that are broken down into specific timeframes.

The manufacturer has divided maintenance procedures into groups. These maintenance procedures are performed on the machine at specific intervals.

A typical manual will divide service intervals as follows:

### When Required

- Every 10 Service Hours or Daily
- Every 50 Service Hours or Weekly
- Every 100 Service Hours or Every Two Weeks
- Every 250 Service Hours or Monthly
- Every 500 Service Hours or Every 3 Months
- Every 1000 Service Hours or Every 6 Months
- Every 2000 Service Hours or Every 1 Year
- Every 3000 Service Hours or Every 2 Years

The modern TLB is a complex piece of machinery. Although it is a complex machine, we can understand it more easily if we look at its components and systems one by one.

## Machine Components & Systems

- Sealed Components
- Engine
- Cooling System
- Transmission
- Differentials
- Final Drives
- Hydraulic System
- Brakes
- Safety Systems

**Sealed Components –** With the exception of the Safety Systems, all of the TLB's components are sealed compartments.

To gain a better understanding of the machine, we have to take a look at the structure of these sealed compartments.

Although all of these sealed compartments have different functions, they have many things in common.

**Outer Casing –** The outer casing of any component serves as a structural support and frame-work for the gears, bearings and shafts that make up the component. In addition to providing the structure, **the outer casing keeps the lubricating fluids in and dirt and contamination out.**

**Input and Output Shafts** are required to transfer the power in and out of components such as the engine, final drive and hydraulic pump. **Seals** are located around the shafts. **Bearings** support the shafts and prevent damage to the seals. **Lubricant** prevents metal to metal contact and wear.

One of the most important things to remember is that these compartments must remain sealed and the fluid level maintained to get the full life out of the component.

**Engine –** The engine has several systems that provide the required elements for it to produce controllable power on a long term basis. These include: fuel delivery and control, a pressurized lubrication system, a cooling system, and electrical components. Also located around the engine are auxiliary components that provide other needs, such as the power steering pump, alternator, fuel pump, water pump, and air conditioning compressor.

**Cooling System –** The cooling system includes the radiator, water pump, hoses, and a thermostat.

**Transmission –** The transmission is a self-contained unit that receives power directly from the end of the crankshaft and delivers torque to the differentials as directed by the operator.

**Differential –** The differential splits the power and delivers it to each of the wheels.

**Hydraulic System –** The typical hydraulic system for one of these machines consists of a pump, a reservoir, various valves, hydraulic cylinders, and many hoses and pipes to connect all of the parts.

**Brakes –** Braking systems on the TLB vary from machine to machine, because of the many different designs in today's marketplace.

# Engine

Now, let's take a look at the most complex of all the systems, the engine.

Of all the sealed systems the engine deserves special attention. This is because the engine is far more complex than the other sealed components, such as the transmission or differential. Large amounts of fuel and air pass through the engine. This, combined with the fact that combustion is taking place, means many types of contamination are possible.

## Oil

There is only one way to service oil and that is with extreme care. Whether you are checking and refilling the oil level, or changing oil and filters, you must keep the dirt out!

**Keep it clean** – Dirt and the contamination it causes is your engine's biggest enemy. It only takes a small amount of dirt to destroy an engine. Experiments have shown as little as 2 ounces can destroy an engine. That 2 ounces of dirt could enter the engine within six days, or ten years, the result will be the same, a ruined engine.

For example, dirt naturally tends to collect around the fill cap and dipstick guide. It is because of this natural accumulation of dirt around these service points that the simple task of checking and adding oil can be the easiest way for dirt to enter the sealed compartment!

☞**Remember**, the oil filler neck is the largest opening for contamination to enter the engine compartment.

Many people involved in maintenance don't realize how easy it is for dirt to enter the engine while checking or adding to the oil.

Be aware of this danger, and perform this task with extreme care.

**Before removing the fill plug** – Check and clean the oil fill area. Inspect the oil fill plug and remove any accumulated dirt with a rag. Also take notice of and remove any dirt that may be present above the oil fill area.

**Remove fill plug** – Carefully remove the fill plug and clean off any dirt with a clean rag. There is often an area here that cannot be cleaned until the plug is removed. Next, check the oil fill neck and very carefully remove any remaining dirt from this area with a clean rag. A clean rag is then used to clean the inside of the fill pipe. Be sure to carry out this procedure carefully every time you add oil to the engine.

**Periodic oil changes** – In addition to ensuring absolute cleanliness within the engine compartment, changing the oil and oil filter regularly is vital. As a general rule the engine oil and filter should be changed every 200 hours. However, every machine has a different schedule recommended by its manufacturer, so once again you should refer to your machine's manual.

Your manual will also tell you the grade/specification of oil for your TLB. Always be sure that the oil you use has the proper rating.

## Air

Engines use an incredible amount of air as they work. In addition to this huge demand for air, the TLB often works in extremely dusty conditions. TLBs are designed to handle these conditions, and most are equipped with a three stage air filter system. This system consists of the pre-cleaner, primary filter and secondary filter.

As the air is drawn into the air intake, it first encounters the **Pre-Cleaner**.

The pre-cleaner spins the air in a round chamber, removing the majority of the dirt particles.

The **Primary Filter** then removes the majority of the larger dust particles.

The **Secondary Filter** traps the finest remaining particles and is the final and ultimate protection for the engine.

**Servicing the air intake system** – The pre-cleaner should be monitored visually, and emptied before the dirt reaches the sight line.

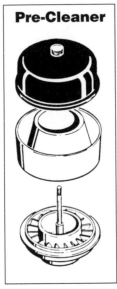

**Pre-Cleaner**

**Fig. 4-1**

The air filters should be serviced as per the manufacturer's instructions. Keep in mind that extremely dusty conditions will require more frequent filter changes.

The primary filter should be blown out with water or air, according to your manual's instructions, and replaced at specific intervals. Never attempt to clear the dust by bouncing the filter, as this practice can distort the metal, damage the seal, and work the dirt further into the filter element.

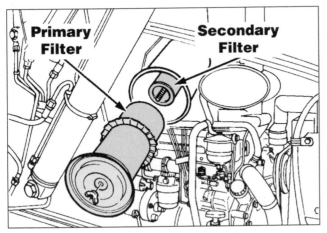

**Primary Filter**

**Secondary Filter**

**Fig. 4-2** *Typical primary and secondary filters*

The secondary filter is the engine's last defense from airborne contamination. Due to its great importance, it should always be replaced with a new filter and **never** cleaned and reused.

Also, to be sure that the air reaching the engine is properly filtered, make sure the complete air intake system, including air cleaner, hoses, clamps and manifold gaskets are completely tight.

## Fuel

Dirty fuel can plug up filters in just a few hours and is the greatest cause of fuel-injection system failure. Using the best quality fuel and keeping the filters clean will extend the life of diesel fuel-injection components. It is also critical to keep contamination out of your fuel supply. Here are some easy ways to keep your fuel supply clean.

Always top off the tank of fuel at the end of the day to eliminate condensation inside the tank. Air that cools inside a fuel tank overnight will cause condensation and significant amounts of water to accumulate. By eliminating the airspace in the tank, during falling temperatures condensation is also eliminated. Periodically open the petcock at the sediment bowl in the fuel tank, if your machine is equipped with such a device.

The fuel tank water separators, sediment bowl fuel filters and screens are critical for protection from contamination, and should be serviced regularly.

## Daily Maintenance

Daily maintenance is a basic responsibility of any person that operates one of these machines. Greasing, fluid levels, and walk-around inspection are the basics of daily maintenance.

- Fluid Levels
- Pre-Operation Inspection
- Greasing

Depending on the structure and size of your outfit, servicing and maintenance may be done by mechanics or operators. However, every operator must understand the requirements of daily maintenance. Daily inspection and servicing of the TLB is the backbone of TLB maintenance.

Daily inspection is not only critical to the life of the machine, but also for the safety of the operator and the other people on the job site. As with every other aspect of TLB maintenance, the daily maintenance is carried out in an organized and thorough way.

This is the best time that problems can be spotted before causing greater problems as the work day progresses.

***Fluid Levels*** – Monitoring and checking fluid levels is one of the most basic yet vital daily maintenance checks.

Always check: the engine oil, water level in the cooling system, and hydraulic fluid levels before operating.

Again, refer to your owner's manual for the correct fluid levels and follow your company's guidelines for daily servicing.

***Pre-Operation Procedures*** – Another important step before you start the day's work is the pre-operation inspection. This is usually done at the same time as your daily maintenance procedures.

This walk around inspection provides an opportunity to check for problems. As you walk around the TLB you should be on the lookout for anything unusual or improper such as:

• Leaks

• Cracks in the frame or any other part of the machine

• Loose bolts or fasteners

• Ground engaging tools for missing parts or excessive wear

• Tire pressure: Check that it is to manufacturer's recommendations. If not, premature wear or damage can occur.

***Always correct any problems that you find before beginning work.***

## Greasing

Following a thorough greasing plan is a critical part of your overall maintenance program. Greasing habits have a direct bearing on your TLB's working life, maintenance costs and resale value.

Unfortunately, greasing is probably one of the least liked jobs in routine maintenance. For someone

who has little or no experience with grease guns, it can be a messy, awkward, and frustrating job.

On the other hand, a person who knows the ins and outs of the task, and what tools and supplies are needed, can get the job done quickly and easily. The following recommendations have been developed to raise the level of knowledge and skills required for everyday greasing procedures.

***Greasing Intervals*** – The first thing that you need to do is check the owner's manual for the recommended greasing intervals for the various grease points on your machine. Keep in mind that the

**Fig. 4-3** *Thorough and regular greasing is a critical part of your overall maintenance program.*

**Fig. 4-4** *Don't over-grease the machine.*

joints that contact the backhoe and loader bucket need the most frequent greasing. This is because the bucket is constantly in contact with dirt as the TLB is working, and dirt will naturally absorb grease.

**Clean Rags –** One of the most important things needed for proper greasing is plenty of clean rags. The rags will be used to keep your hands and grease gun clean and free of grease at all times. Also, any dirt on the zerk fittings should be cleaned off with a rag before connecting the gun. This will prevent dirt from being injected into the joint.

**Changing Grease Cartridges –** Now, let's take a look at the grease gun itself and how to load it.

1) The first step in changing a cartridge is to remove the pump and handle assembly.

2) Then, pull back the plunger and release it, which will push out the empty cartridge.

3) The plunger should now be pulled back into the loading position and into the holding notch.

4) The new cartridge is inserted and its metal cap removed.

5) Replace the pump and handle assembly until the threads are engaged at least one-and-a-half turns.

6) Then replace the plunger to force out air pockets. This will eliminate the most common problem with greasing. If the air pocket is not

cleared the gun will not prime and you may have problems with pumping the grease.

7) Finish by screwing in the body of the gun and then wipe any excess grease off the gun immediately.

The grease gun should now provide trouble-free operation.

**Fittings –** If the fitting has any visible dirt, wipe the fitting off before you insert the grease gun.

Some grease points are recessed to provide protection for the fitting, and often become packed with dirt.

To clean these grease points, use a tool such as an old screwdriver to clear the dirt out of the hole, and then clean off the fitting with a rag.

Sometimes you will find dented or damaged grease points that will not take the grease. These should be replaced immediately.

You should establish a routine for greasing your machine and modify it as necessary for safety and efficiency.

Always start at one given point on the TLB and work around the machine in an orderly sequence.

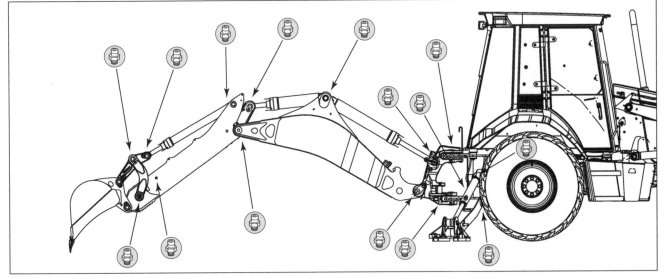

**Fig. 4-5** *Typical grease points for the backhoe.*

***Greasing Tips*** – When greasing the wear parts on the TLB, some helpful suggestions include the following:

• Make it a habit of greasing the machine lightly and frequently, as opposed to a heavy greasing less often.

This is the best protection against wear, and it also prevents dirt from collecting in and clogging the grease flow passages (Fig. 4-3).

• Do not over-grease the machine (Fig. 4-4). Pumping grease through the joints and onto the machine only wastes grease, collects dirt, and quickly makes the whole machine dirty.

• If the fitting will not take grease, move that particular hydraulic function to relieve any possible stress that might be preventing the grease from flowing through the joint.

## Warm-Up and Cool-down

Because of the nature of diesel engines, they require a period of warming up in the morning (or before being used under load), as well as a brief cool-down before shutting the engine off. Along with keeping the oil and other fluid levels maintained, this is an important factor in prolonging machine life. Each manufacturer has its own recommended warm-up procedure; some recommend idling the engine, while others suggest running at half-throttle. A good rule to follow, when in doubt, is to run the engine just slightly above idle for at least five minutes.

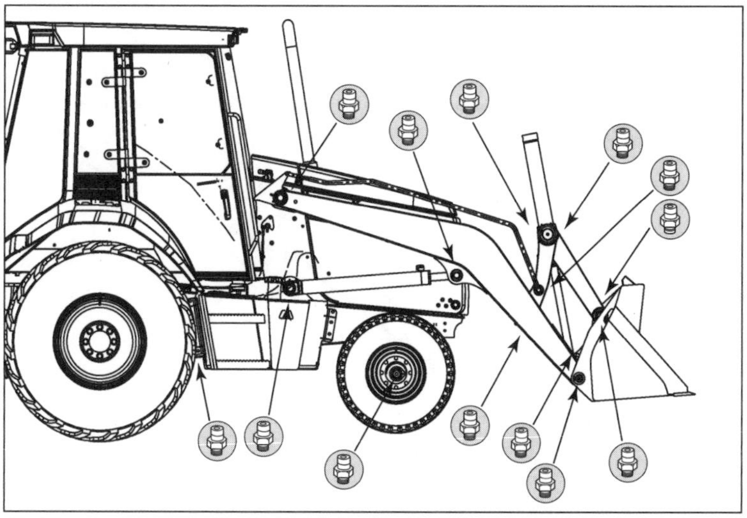

The warm-up period is necessary to bring the engine and hydraulic system up to running temperature; therefore, cold weather starts require somewhat longer warm-up time. The warm-up also turns the gears in the hydraulic pump, warming the fluid and circulating it through the system. Once the machine has warmed up, the operator should check to make sure the various hydraulic functions perform smoothly.

While the engine is warming up, the operator should get in the habit of looking over the machine, quickly checking such points as tire pressure, hoses and connections (look for leaks or signs of wearing), and the bucket pins and clips, to make sure they are properly seated. This is also a good time to get in the habit of greasing the machine regularly.

While working, the operator should also be alert for changes in the operation of the TLB's hydraulic system. If the pump makes an unusual noise or whine, or if slow or jerky operation of the hydraulic functions is noted, it probably means the fluid level has fallen too low, allowing air to work into the system. If this happens, the operator should stop the machine immediately.

Operating the machine with insufficient hydraulic fluid could damage the pump and the system itself.

## Machine Life

When one looks at the TLB itself and considers the tremendous stress and force associated with its operation and the number of hinge joints that the hydraulic power is transmitted through, it becomes clear why preventing wear in these joints is an important aspect of extending the TLB's machine life.

The two most important factors which contribute to unusual wear are:

1. Unnecessary stresses, strains or shocks to the structural bearing surfaces. To prevent such stress and strain, the TLB must be operated in as smooth and flowing a style as possible.

**Fig. 4-6** *Typical grease points for loader and drive shaft.*

2. Failing to grease the bearing surfaces on a regular basis. Without this lubrication there is nothing to keep these surfaces from wearing quite rapidly. Once they become worn, the resulting looseness will cause the surfaces to hammer against each other, causing even more wear. It should also be noted that the hinge joints do not have any seals to keep grease in or dirt out, so they must be greased frequently.

## Bucket Changing Tips

☞ **NOTE:** The procedures described here apply only to the basic (old style) 2-pin bucket attachment systems. They do not apply to quick-change or other designs.

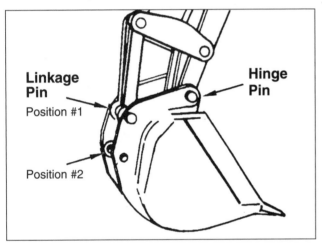

**Fig. 4-7**

Changing over from one bucket to another is a fairly straightforward task, but as the saying goes, there are a lot more ways to do it wrong than to do it right.

The secret of easy bucket changing is to align the holes of the bucket and the boom perfectly

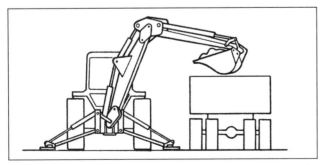

**Fig. 4-8** *Linkage pin in position #1 allows the most curl for loading trucks*

(Fig. 4-10). This will allow the pins to be pushed into place, rather than hammered (Fig. 4-11). Whenever possible, avoid hammering the bucket pins. Hammering distorts the pins and will result in "mushroomed" or generally enlarged ends, which make the process more difficult.

Eliminating the need for hammering is not always possible. New machines, for example, have very tight tolerances and are generally the most difficult to change. In this case, a large drift pin (preferably made of a softer material than the bucket pin) can be used with a hammer to force the pin out. After several hundred hours of machine use, the pins will wear slightly, becoming easier to install.

There are two "natural" positions which are critical to the bucket changing process (Fig. 4-12). Notice the position of the bucket when it is lying on flat ground. When attempting to remove the bucket hinge pin, it is important to place it in the same position as if it was resting on the ground in the "natural position" before it was on the machine.

Notice the position of the bucket when it is hanging with only the hinge pin attached. This is the correct position to use when attempting to remove the linkage pin (see Fig. 4-12).

It is important to take note of these two positions and use them when removing the pins. The buckets will naturally "find" these positions when the operator removes the pins.

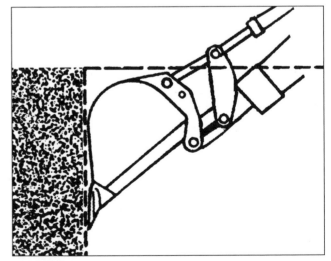

**Fig. 4-9** *Linkage pin in position #2 allows maximum bucket rollout.*

**Fig. 4-10** *Align the holes of bucket and boom perfectly.*

**Fig. 4-11** *Perfect hole alignment eliminates the need for hammering the pin into place.*

Other useful tips to keep in mind:

• When a hammer must be used, a four to six-pound hammer works best.

• Always have the proper tools and supplies on hand necessary for bucket changing.

• Keeping the pins well-greased will greatly ease removing and installing them.

• Keep rags handy to handle the pins and clean your hands after the change is completed.

• When replacing the boom pin, after the pin has started working its way into the bucket the boom can be swung by hand slightly while exerting pressure on the pin.

This motion will rock the bucket slightly, allowing the pin to align itself with the holes in the boom and the bucket.

• Keep the pins ground to a taper to ease the replacement process.

• Safety glasses should always be worn when hammering pins into place to protect against flying debris.

### Correct pin removal/replacement procedure.

Always select a smooth, flat, open area to change buckets, and do the actual changing with the boom positioned straight with the machine. This allows easy adjustment of the machine to line up the holes  (Figs. 4-13, 4-14). Then, the following procedure should be used:

1. Position the bucket in the "natural" hanging position. Remove the linkage pin. Retract bucket linkage.

2. Position the bucket on the ground in the "natural" lying position. Make sure the bucket is not

**Fig. 4-12** *The bucket on the bottom shows the natural lying position, and the top bucket shows the natural hanging position.*

hanging from the hinge pin, and also that there is no down pressure from the boom. Remove the hinge pin.

3. Align the boom with the desired bucket. Install the hinge pin.

4. Raise the boom and lower the bucket linkage to the desired position. Install the linkage pin.

Note: This is the **only** acceptable sequence to follow during the standard bucket changing process. Any other sequence could cause severe damage to the linkage, or the bucket.

**Bucket Teeth** – As the bucket teeth wear, digging resistance will increase. When hard ground is encountered, digging efficiency may suffer. As the teeth continue to wear, they will become thin and will eventually fall off if not replaced. The operator should replace them before this happens; if teeth fall off and digging is continued, the tooth shank will become worn and will eventually be unable to hold a tooth properly. Do not dig with teeth missing from the bucket.

**Poor maintenance habits** will begin a domino effect that will result in:

- Low fluid levels
- Dirt in oil
- Oil contamination
- Increased wear
- Infrequent greasing
- Increased wear
- Unexpected breakdowns
- Increased downtime
- Major component failure
- Repair costs
- Rental costs
- Lowered equipment value

**Fig. 4-13** *Incorrect alignment makes the holes very difficult to line up properly.*

• Shorter machine life

• Early replacement

This is an example of a series of events that can have a devastating effect on the profitability of the company.

However, machine damage can be avoided. As you have just seen, following a maintenance program is not hard. Taking the time to do the job properly will pay off for the owner and the operator of the machine.

The owner will get a highly productive machine with the longest life and lowest operating costs.

The operator will have a safer, more reliable machine that's easier to operate.

**Fig. 4-14** *Correct alignment – always position the boom straight with the machine when changing buckets.*

## Questions – Chapter 4 **Maintenance**

*Notes:* _____

_____
_____
_____
_____
_____
_____
_____
_____
_____
_____
_____
_____
_____
_____
_____
_____
_____
_____
_____
_____
_____
_____
_____
_____
_____
_____
_____
_____
_____

**1. What are the most important factors which contribute to unusual wear to the TLB's mechanical joints?**

_____ a. Unnecessary stresses, strains or shocks to the structure and bearing surfaces

_____ b. Failing to grease the bearing surfaces on a regular basis

_____ c. Dirt entering pin and bushing areas of mechanical joints

_____ d. All of the above

**2. The best schedule for greasing the machine is:**

_____ a. Every other day

_____ b. Every week

_____ c. Every other week

_____ d. Lightly and frequently

**3. Weakening of hydraulic hoses will occur over a period of time due to what factors?**

_____ a. Weathering of the rubber coating

_____ b. Hitting or rubbing against objects

_____ c. Rubbing against machine parts while working

_____ d. All of the above

**4. To ensure proper installation and long hose life, what main factors should you check when installing hydraulic hoses? (choose two)**

_____ a. The hose must follow its natural flex

_____ b. You must use hose clamps

_____ c. Must be the correct length

_____ d. Must look like the old hose

**5. When changing buckets, and the bucket and the boom are properly aligned, the pins can be pushed into place, rather than hammered.**

_____ a. True

_____ b. False

**6. There are two "natural positions" which are critical to the bucket changing process. These are: (choose two)**

_____ a. Extended

_____ b. Curled up all the way

_____ c. Lying

_____ d. Hanging

**7. When removing the bucket from the backhoe, the proper order of pin removal is:**

_____ a. Remove the hinge pin first and then the linkage pin

_____ b. Remove the linkage pin first and then the hinge pin

**8. When putting a bucket on the backhoe, the proper order of pin replacement is:**

_____ a. Replace the hinge pin first and then the linkage pin

_____ b. Replace the linkage pin first and then the hinge pin

**9. What is the best source of information for your particular machine?**

_____ a. The operator's manual that was supplied with the TLB

_____ b. The overhaul manual at the dealership

_____ c. This book

_____ d. Your supervisor

**10. Which components require their fluid levels to be checked daily?**

_____ a. The engine

_____ b. The transmission

_____ c. The hydraulic system

_____ d. All of the above

**11. What should you do if you notice a sudden change in the fluid level of any component?**

_____ a. Investigate it immediately

_____ b. Wait unit the shift is over and check it out

_____ c. Nothing, it is probably okay

_____ d. All of the above

_____
_____
_____
_____
_____
_____
_____
_____
_____
_____
_____
_____
_____
_____
_____
_____
_____
_____
_____
_____
_____
_____
_____
_____
_____
_____
_____
_____
_____
_____

**12. The most common cause of a sudden drop in fluid level is a leak.**

_____ a. True

_____ b. False

**13. The design of the pre-cleaner for most air filter systems is:**

_____ a. Oil bath

_____ b. Foam element

_____ c. Centrifugal

_____ d. Paper element

**14. To clean a dirty primary filter you should:**

_____ a. Bounce it off the ground

_____ b. Strike it against a hard flat surface

_____ c. Blow it out with compressed air

_____ d. Kick it several times

**15. A dirty secondary filter should be cleaned by blowing it out with compressed air.**

_____ a. True

_____ b. False

**16. Filling the fuel tank at the end of the work shift will eliminate condensation from forming in the tank.**

_____ a. True

_____ b. False

**17. The best source of maintenance information for any machine is the operator's manual.**

_____ a. True

_____ b. False

**18. On a sealed component, such as an engine, transmission, or differential, the outer casing provides the structure of the component and keeps lubricating fluids in and the dirt and contamination out.**

_____ a. True

_____ b. False

**19. The differential unit on a TLB**

_____ a. Equalizes the power between the transmission and hydraulics

_____ b. Regulates the electrical power in the machine

_____ c. Controls the weight distribution of the machine

_____ d. Divides and delivers power to the drive wheels

**20. The oil and filter on a TLB engine should be changed every 500 hours or 3 months.**

_____ a. True

_____ b. False

**21. Most TLBs are equipped with a _____ stage air filter system.**

_____ a. 1

_____ b. 2

_____ c. 3

_____ d. 4

**22. Secondary air filters are lifetime components and should be cleaned and reused.**

_____ a. True

_____ b. False

**23. Daily maintenance of the TLB includes:**

_____ a. Greasing the machine

_____ b. Checking the fluid levels

_____ c. The pre-operation inspection

_____ d. All of the above

# 5. Utilities

**Ruptured Pipeline** – Culver City, CA, 6/76
In June of 1976, a construction crew hit and ruptured a petroleum pipeline. The resulting explosion killed nine people and an entire city block was burned to the ground, causing millions of dollars worth of damage.

**Gas-Distribution/Power** – Trenton, NJ, 3/98
Gas escaping from a broken 2-inch main was ignited by electrical sparks from a damaged power cable. Both lines were damaged at the same time by a crew working on a housing development. Flames shooting 30 feet into the air slightly damaged siding on a new home, but no one was injured. Gas workers shut off the gas within an hour.

**Ammonia** – Matoon, IL, 3/98
A power company backhoe damaged an ammonia pipeline. Two roads had to be closed for two days while a hazmat team from St. Louis was called in. The team checked water and air in the area and determined that only a low level of ammonia had leaked out.

• • •

When digging, one potential hazard that is critical to the planning and execution of the job is the presence of underground utility lines. These include sewer pipes, gas lines, phone lines, electrical cables, and so forth. The knowledge and skill required to avoid breaking utility lines is very important for the operator to understand and practice. This knowledge is needed to prevent devastating accidents involving natural gas or high voltage power lines. In addition, they can keep a simple two-hour backhoe job from becoming a costly, time-consuming repair project.

During the last 20 years, underground installation of utilities has increased dramatically. In the past, all electrical-based utilities such as power, telephone and cable TV were traditionally above ground installations, strung on power poles. However, in the past two decades, building codes have changed, requiring that these electrical-based utilities are now buried underground, away from wind, weather, trees, ice, snow, and water.

These electrical-based utilities now join the water, sewer and gas installations underground. As a result, the amount of underground utilities is at an all time high and more are being installed every day. As a backhoe operator, you will need to know the procedures to handle digging around utilities.

In order to understand the wide ranging concepts of utilities and how they affect the TLB operator, we need to examine three major areas.

*1. One Call System* – Know, use and comply with all the requirements of the One Call System.

*2. The Limitations of the One Call System* – The limitations of the One Call System and what to expect after you have fully complied.

*3. How to Proceed with the Job* – When it is time to "sit in the seat" and start digging.

## 1. One Call System

In this chapter we will learn that the One Call System is the <u>best</u> <u>defense</u> <u>against</u> <u>accidents,</u> <u>the</u> <u>standard</u> <u>procedure,</u> <u>and</u> <u>the</u> <u>law</u> for all digging procedures. However, we will also learn that the One Call System <u>is</u> <u>not</u> <u>perfect,</u> that it <u>has</u> <u>many</u> <u>limitations,</u> and it <u>will</u> <u>not</u> <u>protect</u> <u>all</u> <u>digging</u> <u>operations.</u> The purpose of this chapter is to help backhoe operators "pick up" where the One Call System leaves off to help ensure a safe and accident-free work site.

*History of the One Call System* – During the building boom of the past thirty years literally thousands of miles of pipes, conduits, cables and utilities have been laid underground. This has led to an ever increasing and complex maze of underground utilities for the contractor and the backhoe operator to deal with.

With the spread of such underground utilities and the possible consequences to contractors in the event of an accident, it became apparent to owners of underground utilities that a system was needed to provide contractors with information on all the underground utilities on the job site with just one call.

In Rochester, New York, in September of 1974, this idea became reality with the creation of the One Call Notification Center. The One Call System provides a service center that notifies its members (utility companies) of an impending excavation at or near their underground installations. This allows them to mark the existing utilities, with color coded paint markings indicating their location.

## How does the One Call System work?

☞ *Note:* The One Call System is an international system that is divided into regional areas. These areas are usually divided by states, and some larger states are also divided to create a more manageable system. These regional centers have the ability to set their own rules and regulations for the region. While most of the rules and regulations are uniform in nature, they sometimes vary in requirements, and details. In the following material, the symbol "**" indicates that this item may vary in different regions.

☞ Always be familiar with the One Call regulations in the region that you are working in.

### Before You Dig

You are required by law to contact the One Call System a minimum of 48 hours in advance ** of any digging operation. When you contact the One Call System, your call will be answered by a trained representative who will ask you for some information about your job.

You will be asked for:

• Your name • The job location • Phone number • Contractor • Starting date • The type of work you will be doing

Once these very simple questions have been answered, the representative will assign you a **One Call Number**. This number is usually good for **fourteen calendar days**\**. If you find that you are going to need more time, simply telephone One Call for an extension.

Once all of the relevant information concerning your future excavation is logged into the One Call computer, they will quickly inform all their members who have underground utilities in the area.

The members will then dispatch a field locator to your job site to clearly mark out the position of their underground facilities prior to your excavation. You can further clarify the job by marking out the excavation with white paint. In some states this process is a legal requirement ** .

The markings will follow the uniform color code as laid down by the APWA Utility Location and Coordination Council. Your workers and operators should be aware of the code and what each color signifies.

*Red:* Electric power lines, cables, conduit and lighting cables

*Yellow:* Gas, oil, steam, petroleum, chemicals, or gaseous materials

*Orange:* Communications, alarm or signal lines, cable TV, or conduit

*Blue:* Water, irrigation, and slurry lines

*Green:* Sewers and drain lines

*White:* Proposed excavation

*Pink:* Temporary survey marking

*Purple:* Reclaimed water

The One Call System members will mark the location of their installations using these standard colors. It is the contractor's responsibility to expose these utilities using hand tools. In most states this hand digging is required by law.

## The Tolerance Zone

The tolerance zone refers to the line that has been marked in paint, and also includes 24 inches ** to both sides of the pipe. In some regions, the tolerance zone is 18 inches on both sides of the pipe, and in others, 36 inches to both sides.

This is **a hand-dig-only zone**, legally defined as 24 inches ** to either side of a marked facility. **Always observe proper hand-dig procedures in this zone.** If the utilities are not exposed with hand tools, it is just as dangerous as digging without having the lines prelocated!

☞ *IMPORTANT:* **Even when digging with a pick or a shovel, great care must be used** to avoid damage. Two of the most dangerous utilities (gas and power), can be damaged and broken even when only using hand tools. It is not uncommon for plastic gas lines and high voltage electrical cables to be cut or broken with a pick or shovel.

*Who is required to use the One Call System?*
**Anybody who is planning to dig** should use the system. Underground utilities are not confined to major city streets. They are present in rural areas and often run through private land. Using the One Call System is just as important to the homeowner, who is planning to put in a pool, as to the contractor planning a major excavation.

Other trades who are required to use One Call include plumbers, electricians, landscapers, and swimming pool builders. In fact, if your job involves any kind of digging, the One Call System needs to be notified 48 ** hours in advance. Failure to do so that results in damage to utilities could leave the contractor, the property owner, or even the operator liable for the cost of repair.

## Points to remember:

*Dial before you dig* – In most states it is the law. No matter what size job you are planning, call before you excavate. The law provides penalties for those who do not comply.

*Call at least two days before you start digging* – You may call up to ten working days prior to excavation**, but don't wait until the last minute!

*The contractor is responsible for digging.* If damage to underground utilities results from digging, the contractor may be charged for the full cost of repair, loss of services and other legal implications.

*You only make one call.* That's all it takes to have all of the underground utilities on your site located and marked before you dig.

*It costs you nothing.* There's no charge to call the toll-free 800 number ** in your state.

*Calling saves time.* The One Call System helps to speed your job up by providing notice to all utility owners in the job site area.

**ACCIDENT LOG – Gas Distribution**
**Southington, CT** - A 4-inch high pressure gas main was severed by backhoe being used by a highway department crew installing a storm drain. Nine people were evacuated from the neighborhood while the line was repaired. The evacuation was achieved by firefighters minutes after the break. The gas was turned off within 20 minutes. A report from the scene indicated the line may have been mismarked.

*Everyone should call.* Not just professionals. Calling is just as important for property owners as it is for plumbers, electricians, contractors, landscapers, swimming pool builders, or anyone who is planning to dig.

☞ *Standard digging procedures as per One Call System requirements:*

> 1. Notify the One Call System
> 2. The utilities are marked by the utility company representatives
> 3. The marked utilities are exposed by hand
> 4. Digging carefully proceeds with the backhoe

\*\* Laws and requirements vary from state to state. Check with your local One Call center for the exact information for your area. If you do not know the number for your local One Call center, use the national number **1 888-258-0808**.

## 2. The Limitations of the One Call System

Let's assume that you have complied with all of the One Call requirements, a One Call representative has checked and marked the area, the marked utilities have been located and exposed by hand, and you are ready to begin digging.

*Is it safe to assume that all the utilities in the work area have been located and marked?*

*Is it safe to assume that there are no other utilities in the work area?*

The answer to both of these questions is **NO!**

The One Call System works well for what it was designed for. However, it does not solve all of the utility problems that are encountered in underground trenching and excavation.

☞ *Remember:* When the opinion is offered that "all of the utilities have been marked and located," nine times out of ten, **ALL** of the utilities have **not** been marked and located.

## Public Property vs. Private Property

As a backhoe operator you need to know what to expect when you get to the job. The location of the job site and who owns the property will have an impact on the utilities that you will encounter and how the encounter will occur.

*Public property –* The greatest concentration of utilities are located on public property and right-of-ways. These areas include streets, highways, roads and other areas that have been designated for present or future utilities.

It is in these areas that the One Call System provides most of their service. Other than a few exceptions, such as residential homes, One Call does not locate utility lines on private property.

*Private Property –* Any private property such as (but not limited to) rural land, farms, mobile home parks, factories, airports, industrial and manufacturing plants of any kind may be considered private property.

When working on private property, the quality of the information, as well as the amount of information, goes down dramatically.

The owners of private property usually do not keep detailed records of utility installations. They also do not have the equipment and expertise to accurately locate existing utilities.

## The Good, the Bad, and the Ugly
### THE GOOD
#### *Public property –*
- The One Call System provides good information on existing utility installations in the area.

#### *Private property –*
- Usually (but not always) there are fewer utility installations to deal with on private property.

### THE BAD
#### *Public property –*
- Usually there are many different types of utility installations in public property.

- Many utility lines in a small area can make digging difficult.

### *Private property –*

- The utility installations are usually beyond the jurisdiction of the utility companies.

- Many of the existing utilities will not be marked or located.

- Property owners usually have information that is not precise enough to be helpful, or no information is available at all.

- Quite often, someone will make a statement such as, "There are no utilities in this area," only to be proven wrong soon after the digging begins.

### *THE UGLY*

### *Private or public property –*

The following are examples of things that can happen, concerning utility lines, at any time on public or private property.

- The line was not marked.

- The line was marked in the wrong place and never located.

- Mistaken identity. The line is marked and located only to find out later that there was an abandoned line that was mistaken for the existing utility.

- An existing line is unknown to any job site authorities.

- An existing line is not shown on the plans.

- The line is marked indicating a depth of three feet. The actual depth is 7 feet.

- "I forgot that the pipe was there."

- A pipe was located, but it was the wrong pipe.

- One Call paint markings had become obliterated before work began in that area.

☞ *Note:* These are just **a few examples of the wide ranging problems** that can be encountered at any time when the backhoe is engaged in digging operations. In addition, the Accident Logs throughout this chapter are real world events that show the "ugly" as it happens in the field.

## 3. How to Proceed with the Job

In the old days (before the One Call System), operators were constantly digging "blind," trying to detect the slightest change in resistance at the bucket and hoping to do the job without breaking any utilities. Day in and day out, they operated with great attention and caution to prevent damaging or breaking existing utilities.

The operators would, after a time, develop a "sense" for underground pipes. They would often be able to tell a lot about an underground object simply from the way the bucket made contact with it. The experienced operator would know if the object was a rock, a chunk of concrete, or a pipe. If it was a pipe, the expert operator would sometimes be able to tell what type of pipe it was, as well as the direction in which it was laid. These skills were developed through years of experience, and they demanded the highest degree of concentration, as the operator carefully proceeded with the digging.

It is these high level skills, developed by operators of the past, that continue to be of great value today. After complying with all of the One Call requirements, **it is only these high level skills that stand between the operator and the unknown – and unseen – danger of existing utility installations.**

☞ *Note:* The following information in this chapter should be used by the operator **only after all the One Call requirements have been complied with.**

When looking over the job site, always inquire about possible locations, depths, and types of utilities that may be present. It may often be impossible to get exact location information. Even if the utilities are marked, the markers may not be in the right locations, so there can be many surprises as the job progresses. The operator should learn to take notice of the telltale signs of underground utilities.

**ACCIDENT LOG – Power**

**Danbury Township, OH** – 5/7/98 – A construction crew installing a new water system struck an underground power cable, causing a power outage. Arcing from the damaged cable caused a small fire, but no other damage.

Learn to spot such things as the location of gas meters, water boxes, sewer cleanouts, above-ground conduits, electrical vaults and pull boxes, and electrical signs or lights with underground feed. Long, narrow depressions could be the sign of an old trench. When working in paved areas, trench or pothole patches could indicate underground lines as well.

An old saying reminds us that "Nothing escapes the master's eye," and this is especially true when looking for telltale signs of underground utilities. By being an observant operator, and learning to spot these telltale signs, trouble with utilities can sometimes be avoided.

## The "Four Stages of Alert"

There are generally four sets of conditions, or stages of alert, which may exist on any job site with regard to utilities. Knowing how to respond and proceed under any of these four stages is vital to handling utilities successfully.

*Stage 1* exists when the operator is working in an area where no utilities are expected to be encountered. This would include open areas, fields, rural sites, such as farmlands, or new construction areas. When this is the case, the operator can usually proceed ahead at full digging speed. The operators can work as quickly as their skills and safety will allow, but they will also be able to stop instantly, if the bucket makes contact with anything unusual. At that point, the operator should use an investigative procedure (described later in the chapter) to determine the nature of the object.

*Stage 2* is where information about utilities is limited, or otherwise incomplete, and the operator simply cannot tell if there are any present. The area will probably have some utilities, but there are no obvious signs of them. This could include most urban locations and many open areas, such as parking lots, large lawns, etc. in or near any sizable human population. At any rate, Stage 2 is observed when it is believed there are no utilities present. Here, the operator can proceed at nearly full speed, but he or she must be much more careful than in Stage 1. Any bucket contact should be investigated with hand shovels to determine what the object is.

*Stage 3* exists when it is likely that there are utilities in the area, but none are known to exist. This would include any time the TLB is operating within the boundaries of "city property," including the street, the sidewalk, or even further in some cases. In this situation, the operator must exercise great care. He or she should throttle the machine down and proceed very slowly and carefully. This is one more instance when the operator's skills come into play, and great care must be used at all times to avoid breaking an existing utility.

*Stage 4* is when the operator knows there are utilities in the area. Even though One Call has completed their marking and those utilities have been exposed by hand, there are reasons to believe that other utility lines may be present. In this case, it is important to understand that officials of utility companies often make mistakes about the exact location of their lines. They will usually try to determine a line's location and its depth, but they may be wrong on both counts. Obviously, extreme care must be used in Stage 4 situations. The machine should be throttled down to about one-half, and the operator should proceed slowly and very carefully taking only a few inches with each pass. When the bucket teeth come in contact with something, go back slightly and raise the bucket over the obstruction. At that point, a worker should go into the trench to identify the obstruction.

In some situations, a laborer can work ahead of the machine, exploring the width of the trench. This can be done with a shovel, digging across the trench in the expected pipe area, removing 6 to 8 inches at a time, or a probe could be used if the soil is soft.

## Keys to Pipe Detection

There are three factors which determine whether an operator can successfully find a pipe through bucket contact and avoid breaking it:

*1. Bucket Movement* – Watch the bucket carefully for changes in speed caused by resistance from obstructions. When the bucket first contacts an object, the bucket speed will change, slowing down as it resists. At that exact instant, the operator must react quickly, stopping the bucket. The operator can then relieve pressure on the object by backing off in the opposite direction.

**2. Control –** The operator must be able to move the bucket slowly while maintaining total control at the same time. This can be achieved by following the same practice exercises explained in Chapter 2, "Floating the Bucket" and the "Water Dipping" exercise. Here, however, the object is to go as slowly as possible. Performing the Water Dipping exercise very slowly will teach total control of all TLB functions in combination, while practicing the "Floating" exercise will simulate the exact motion used when digging in Stage 4 alert situations.

**3. Total Concentration –** This is the key that combines bucket movement and control into a workable method. The operator should exercise the greatest control over the machine he or she is capable of and concentrate both on the bucket and the ground in the immediate area of the bucket. The operator should watch for signs of ground movement near the edge of the trench that would indicate a possible pipe, or a change in soil content indicating an old trench. Stay alert to any possible sign of previous excavations. If any are discovered while the trench is shallow, it is best to use hand labor to explore deeper, before using the backhoe in that area.

## Variables That Determine Pipe Breakage

There are a number of variables that determine whether or not a pipe will be broken in the course of backhoe operations. These can include:

**Soil Conditions –** If soil is hard or rocky, detecting or "feeling" the pipe may be difficult or impossible. Detecting pipes in soft or sandy ground is much easier.

**Depth of Pipe –** If a pipe is fairly close to the surface (two feet or less), contacting it will sometimes cause earth movement in the immediate area, or on the sides of the trench. When this happens, stop and investigate. This warning sign becomes less useful at greater depths, since ground move-

ment is less likely to occur, unless the soil is very soft or loose.

**Type of Pipe –** Steel pipes (three inches and larger) and concrete storm drains are the only types of pipe which are fairly easy to locate with little risk of breakage. Cast iron, copper, clay, transit and large-diameter plastic pipes are possible to locate by feeling them with the bucket, depending on the operator's skill and other variables. However, it is more likely that bucket contact with these types of pipes will result in damage.

**Diameter of Pipe –** Small-diameter pipes (three inches or less), and wires are almost impossible to feel except when ground conditions are very soft and movement is noted along the side of the trench as discussed earlier. In general, these types of lines need to be located and exposed by hand to prevent breakage.

**The angle of the pipe when encountered –** Ideally, the best way to locate a pipe with the least chance of breakage is when the pipe crosses the trench perpendicular to the machine. Contacting the pipe in a perpendicular manner will equalize the bucket force at all points touching the pipe, and the chances of breaking it will be reduced. Of course, it usually doesn't happen that way; the pipe will often lie at an angle to the trench. Even finding the pipe to be exactly parallel to the trench (i.e., running directly under the machine) is not as bad as hitting the pipe at an angle. Depending on the severity of the angle, contacting the pipe this way concentrates the backhoe's power at only one point on the pipe. This greatly increases the risk of breakage and should be avoided whenever possible.

---

**ACCIDENT LOG – Gas Distribution**

**Hebron, CT** – Gas service to 72 homes and businesses was cut off when a public works crew working on a drainage project damaged a gas main. A township official said the gas main was four feet deep rather than five feet specified on blueprints provided by the gas company. Apparently the crew was digging with a backhoe when they hit the top of the gas main. This would seem to indicate they were digging inside of the safety buffer specified by state law.

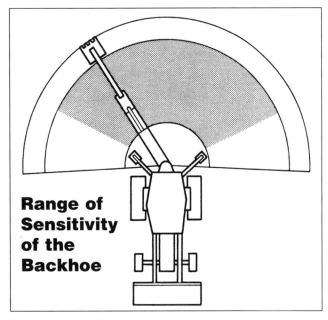

**Fig. 5-1** *The shaded area depicts the range of sensitivity of the backhoe, within which unknown utilities are easiest to detect. Outside of this range utilities are much more difficult to detect during digging.*

***Age and condition of the pipe*** – It is often impossible to determine how long some pipes have been buried and the amount of deterioration that has taken place over time. Most types of concrete, clay and plastic pipes generally do not deteriorate as rapidly as other types. A rusted water or gas line, on the other hand, can start to leak sim-

ply by disturbing the soil around it. To avoid breakage or leaking in these cases, extreme care must be used to locate the lines and dig around them by hand.

☞ ***Remember:*** When digging with the backhoe, many types of utilities are not possible to detect without breaking them. Extensive use of hand labor is the best method to avoid damage to utilities.

## Investigating Possible Utility Lines

This is the procedure commonly used when the operator encounters an unknown bucket obstruction. First, he or she must remove the bucket from the trench without breaking whatever it might be and then determine what the object is. If it is a pipe, go on to the following procedure. If the object is a rock, a root, or debris from an old excavation, digging may continue as before.

***Digging Around Pipes*** – Once a pipe has been located and identified, the operator must monitor its exact location until the excavation is completed to the point where it is out of the machine's working range. The best way of monitoring the pipe's position is to be able to see it at all times. If the pipe is plastic, copper, or clay tile, or if the line in question is electrical wiring or telephone cables, hand labor should be used to remove the dirt within two feet of the pipe to prevent major repair problems.

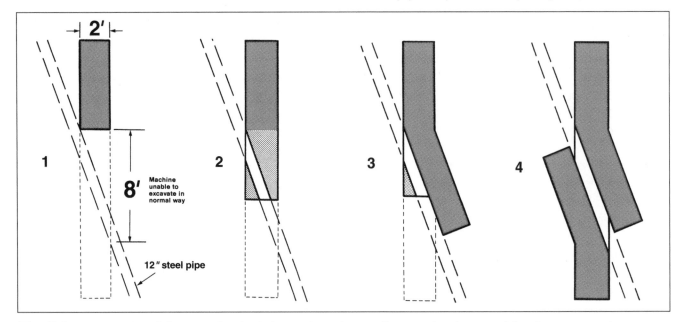

**Fig. 5-2** *In this series of diagrams the shaded area shows how to dig around a pipe once it has been exposed.*

**Fig. 5-3** *Often hand labor will need to be used, once the bucket has encountered an unmarked pipe, to carefully expose it.*

As digging continues it is common for the pipe to become covered with loose dirt. When this happens, the backhoe operator will not be able to see the pipe. In this situation, the pipe can easily be broken because the operator can not see it. Any time a located pipe is not visible to the operator, it should be immediately cleaned off. This cleaning may need to be done several times until the backhoe moves on, and the pipe is no longer in the work area.

## Digging Around Utilities

Learning to operate around utilities is an important element of the operator's control skills. Even experienced operators occasionally break a pipe because, as noted earlier, it is often impossible to detect unknown pipes. But learning to distinguish a pipe from a rock or other buried object is another acquired talent that comes only from experience and skill. As these skills are gained by the operator, the chance of delays and repairs caused by utility accidents will be lessened.

***When a Pipe is Broken*** – If a pipe happens to be broken (as it sooner or later will) during the course of TLB operation, the operator will know it fairly quickly. If it is a water line, the water will make its presence known. The operator will be able to smell, see and hear the gas escaping from a rup-

tured gas line. If any kind of electrical or telephone cable is severed, the exposed wires will be visible, jutting from the sides or floor of the trench.

***When a pipe or other line is broken, stay calm and think about what to do.*** Your response should depend on what type of line has been broken.

If a water pipe has been broken, move the TLB away from the flood plain. If it is a water service to

*(text continues on page 100)*

**Fig. 5-4** *Example of how the bucket carefully works around a pipe once it is exposed, to avoid breakage.*

---

**ACCIDENT LOG – Water**

**Owosso, MI** – 5/15/98 – A backhoe being used to dig a settlement basin next to an abandoned water treatment plant struck a 14-inch main that had carried water from the plant when it was still in operation. Reports indicated no one knew the line was still in use, and an estimated 80,000 gallons of water gushed into the excavation. Quick thinking by the equipment operator enabled him to get his machine out of the hole quickly, before it filled with water. The main had reportedly been capped inside the building when the plant shut down.

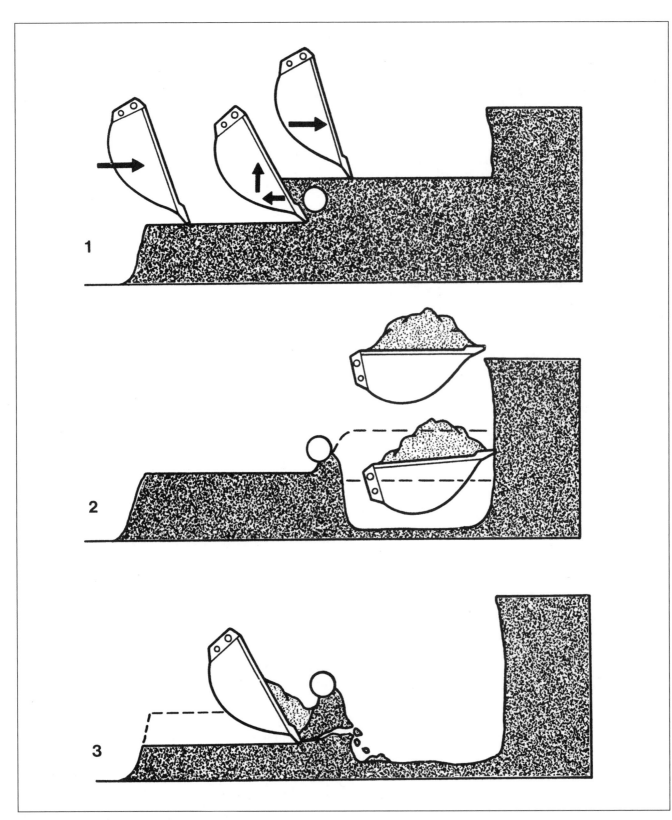

**Fig. 5-5** *DIGGING AROUND UTILITIES:* *1) During the digging process, when contact is made with an unknown object, pressure is relieved and the bucket is backed off and then raised over the object. The obstruction is checked out by hand, and if it is a pipe, it will be exposed so that the operator can see it from his operating position. 2) Here, material on the near side of the pipe is carefully removed. 3) Then, by carefully pushing material under the pipe, it is then freed of the surrounding material.*

**Fig. 5-6** *5-6 (above) and 5-7 (below) show a water pipe near the surface that was inadvertently broken during a concrete breaking and removal job. When such a break occurs quick action is necessary, such as shutting the water off at the main, before repairs can begin (Fig. 5-8, next page).*

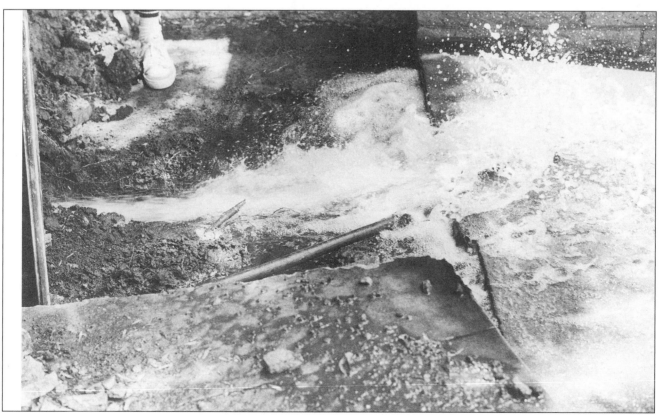

**Fig. 5-7**

**Fig. 5-8** *Beginning repair work after a break in a water pipe.*

Here are some **helpful tips** to remember to prevent utility line damage.

• **Always comply with all One Call System requirements** before starting any digging project.

• **Plan to use plenty of hand labor** to investigate any unusual or unexpected obstructions.

• **Always have hand tools available** during all digging operations. Some of the most useful tools are: a round point shovel, a spade or "sharpshooter," a pick, a flat shovel and a push broom for clean-up.

• When the bucket is digging nearby or around existing utilities, **maintain visual contact with the pipe at all times**. This may require repeated use of hand labor to remove dirt that is obstructing the operator's view of the pipe.

a residence, there is usually a shutoff valve at the street. It is advisable to locate these shutoff valves prior to digging, so quick action can be taken if a break occurs. These may include water control boxes, or gas shutoff valves.

If it is a gas line, the most important thing to do is to **PROTECT YOURSELF!** That could mean different things, depending on the type of line that is broken. If it is a high pressure gas line for example, your first action should be to turn off the machine, get out of the area immediately, and call 911.

If it is a low pressure line, carefully and quickly getting the machine out of the area may be the best move. This is because the gas could collect around the machine, and prevent access to the repair area. **Never attempt to start the machine if gas is present** because the resulting spark at the starter motor could ignite the gas.

• Always report damage to existing lines. Even the slightest scrape or nick to a gas line could cause corrosion and a future tragedy.

During day-to-day operations, all backhoe operators should be conscious of, and use great care to prevent accidental breakage of existing utilities. In many situations, the concentration and effort of the operator is the final line of defense against devastating accidents.

☞ *NOTE* – See Appendix A on page 275 for important information on natural gas installations.

**ACCIDENT LOG – Telephone+Fiber**

**Ellensburg, WA** –5/19/98 – A road construction crew cut a fiber optic telephone cable, causing a loss of 911 and long distance service in several communities. The 911 outage lasted four hours in three of the communities. Well over 4,000 people were affected. A report from the area indicates the local One-Call Center had received a locate request for the site...after the accident had occurred.

## Questions – Chapter 5 **Utilities**

**1. In what year was the first One Call System introduced, and in what city?**

_____ a. 1922, in Chicago, Illinois

_____ b. 1952, in New York City

_____ c. 1974, in Rochester, New York

_____ d. 1972, Sacramento, California

**2. What must be done to the work area before calling the One Call?**

_____ a. Mark out the work area in white paint for concrete or with flags or stakes for dirt areas

_____ b. Smooth out the work site

_____ c. Notify residents that work is going on

_____ d. Nothing, Dig Alert takes care of everything

**3. Orange paint markings by a One Call representative indicates what type of installation?**

_____ a. Electric power lines, cables, conduit and lighting cables.

_____ b. Gas, oil, steam, petroleum, or gaseous materials.

_____ c. Communications,alarm or signal lines, cable TV, or conduit.

_____ d. Water, irrigation, and slurry lines.

**4. In most states, a One Call permit is valid for how long?**

_____ a. 14 days

_____ b. 1 month

_____ c. 1 week

_____ d. 2 days

**5. Existing pipes positioned at an angle to the trench are easy to detect without damaging them.**

_____ a. True

_____ b. False

_Notes:_ _____

_____
_____
_____
_____
_____
_____
_____
_____
_____
_____
_____
_____
_____
_____
_____
_____
_____
_____
_____
_____
_____
_____
_____
_____
_____
_____
_____
_____
_____
_____
_____

**6. Who is legally responsible to call the One Call System?**

_____ a. Contractors

_____ b. State and Highway

_____ c. Anyone about to dig

_____ d. Homeowners

**7. Most types of pipes are possible to locate through contact when digging with the backhoe.**

_____ a. True

_____ b. False

**8. One Call representatives have marked the utilities on the work site. The proposed trenching will cross a telephone line, an electrical main, a water main and a gas main. Prior to digging, the law in most states requires:**

_____ a. All utilities must be shut off

_____ b. Metal detectors must be used

_____ c. The existing utilities must be exposed by hand

_____ d. The trench must be dug by hand

**9. The high-level skills developed by operators in the past are not relevant to modern day backhoe operators.**

_____ a. True

_____ b. False

**10. The One Call System and the utility companies have marked your site. You have exposed the marked utilities by hand and are now ready to begin digging.**

**It is now safe to assume that all the underground utilities have been located.**

_____ a. True

_____ b. False

**11. When working on private property the One Call System will provide locations for all of the existing utilities.**

_____ a.True

_____ b. False

**12. When investigating a new job site before digging, there can be telltale signs that will help operators to spot potential underground hazards. Mark any of the following that could alert you to unmarked underground utilities.**

_____ a. Long narrow depressions in the ground

_____ b. Water boxes

_____ c. Sewer clean outs

_____ d. Gas meters

_____ e. Electrical vaults and pull boxes

**13. A highly-skilled and experienced operator uses which of the following techniques to detect an unmarked pipe through bucket contact and avoid breaking it:**

_____ a. Bucket movement

_____ b. Control

_____ c. Total concentration

_____ d. All of the above

**14. When digging in hard soil, underground pipes are easier to detect.**

_____ a. True

_____ b. False

**15. White paint markings indicate what type of installation?**

_____ a. Proposed excavation.

_____ b. Water, irrigation, and slurry lines.

_____ c. Temporary survey marking.

_____ d. Sewers and drain lines.

**16. A Stage 1 situation is where there are no utilities in the area, such as farmland and some construction sites.**

_____ a. True

_____ b. False

**17. A Stage 2 situation is where information about utilities is limited or incomplete, but there are some utilities believed to be present.**

_____ a. True

_____ b. False

_____
_____
_____
_____
_____
_____
_____
_____
_____
_____
_____
_____
_____
_____
_____
_____
_____
_____
_____
_____
_____
_____
_____
_____
_____
_____
_____
_____
_____

**18. If a gas line is broken during digging procedures, or if the smell of gas is detected**

_____ a. Move the machine out of the area immediately

_____ b. Call 911 immediately

_____ c. Both of the above

_____ d. Neither of the above

**19. Stage 3 exists when it is possible that utilities exist that have not been located and marked by One Call representatives.**

_____ a. True

_____ b. False

**20. Red paint markings by a One Call representative indicate what type of installation?**

_____ a. Electric power lines, cables, conduit and lighting cables.

_____ b. Gas, oil, steam, petroleum, or gaseous materials.

_____ c. Communications,alarm or signal lines, cable TV, or conduit.

_____ d. Water, irrigation, and slurry lines.

**21. In a Stage 4 digging situation, the operator should:**

_____ a. Proceed as normal

_____ b. Use half throttle and proceed as normal

_____ c. Use half throttle and proceed slowly and carefully

_____ d. Position the throttle just above an idle and proceed

**22. Services provided by the One Call System covers job sites throughout the United States.**

_____ a. True

_____ b. False

**23. The One Call System notifies all contractors in the area of the proposed excavations in the area.**

_____ a. True

_____ b. False

**24. Yellow paint markings by a One Call representative indicate what type of installation?**

_____ a. Electric power lines, cables, conduit and lighting cables.

_____ b. Gas, oil, steam, petroleum, or gaseous materials.

_____ c. Communications, alarm or signal lines, cable TV, or conduit.

_____ d. Water, irrigation, and slurry lines.

**25. The One Call System must be contacted a minimum of _____ prior to starting digging operations.**

_____ a. 12 hours

_____ b. 48 hours

_____ c. 24 hours

_____ d. 72 hours

**26. Blue paint markings by a one call representative indicates what type of installation?**

_____ a. Electric power lines, cables, conduit and lighting cables.

_____ b. Gas, oil, steam, petroleum, or gaseous materials.

_____ c. Communications, alarm or signal lines, cable TV, or conduit.

_____ d. Water, irrigation, and slurry lines.

**27. The greatest concentration of underground utilities is located on public property.**

_____ a. True

_____ b. False

**28. Pink paint markings by a one call representative indicate what type of installation?**

_____ a. Proposed excavation.

_____ b. Water, irrigation, and slurry lines.

_____ c. Temporary survey marking.

_____ d. Sewers and drain lines.

# 6. Planning the Job

The TLB is one of the most versatile and widely used pieces of heavy equipment in the world. This is because it is actually two machines in one, a backhoe and a loader, as well as a base machine that can handle a wide variety of attachments.

As a TLB operator, you will be faced with a wide variety of tasks. There will always be new situations that you have never faced before. In addition, a "job" may last for weeks, and will include dozens of "tasks" that are done one after another.

In order to complete these varied job tasks in a safe and efficient manner, you will need to learn about and practice the technical and practical aspects of planning the job.

The underlying basis of job planning is a very basic concept. Job planning skills are developed by taking a moment to think ahead to plan and perform your work safely, and to make your later work easier.

☞ *Remember*

*Think about the job…*
*before performing the work…*
*to make your later work easier.*

When the TLB operators first arrive on the job site, they need to make a mental inventory of the tasks expected of them. They should walk the job site, developing a job scenario in which they visualize: 1) the types of tasks they will need to perform, and 2) the order in which they will proceed, to complete the entire job as efficiently as possible.

The operator should consult the person in charge of the job site to determine the scope of the work involved.

- Will it involve excavation for footings, utility lines, sewers, basements or septic tanks?

- Will material have to be stockpiled, transferred, removed or loaded onto trucks?

- Will land have to be cleared or graded?

- Will roads need to be built?

- Will the job require demolition?

These are some of the common tasks TLB operators will find themselves confronted with. Coming up with a logical, efficient job plan will make it easier to move from task to task.

Important points to consider, when consulting the person in charge, include: utility locations and possible problems arising from them. Placement of spoil, bucket requirements, and bucket changes may need to be planned in advance. Discuss anything that may be relevant to the work expected of the TLB, and do not start to dig until each sequence of the excavation has been planned. This will avoid digging the machine into unmaneuverable situations and causing delays.

In addition to determining the digging sequence, the operator should also be mindful of coordinating the TLB's work with the other trades on the job site. The operator will also have to plan locations for stockpiling and how to transfer the material to the stockpile area when necessary. As the TLB's work nears completion, the operator should think about the following phase of construction and plan the wrap-up of the work accordingly.

On some jobs, where shuttle operations will require large quantities of material to be moved about, it may be necessary to build or grade access roads, or build ramps over curbs, footings, trenches, etc. (See chapters on **Grading and Compaction** and **Loader Technique**.)

## Placement of Spoil

The main consideration in placement of spoil on the job is, of course, what will eventually be done with the material. If it is to be used for back-filling, it should be placed in an area that will facilitate back-filling when the time comes. Or, if it is to be trucked out, put the spoil in an area that is accessible to the loader and the truck itself, to facilitate loading.

## Layout

Be wary when the person in charge says, "Well, start out over here, and dig me a ditch over to there." Trenching is rarely such an inexact process. Yet, when people try to explain what should be done, they are often unclear. Misunderstanding someone's instructions can create problems throughout the entire job. The best way to avoid this kind of misunderstanding is to clearly mark the proposed excavation. Occasionally, those in

**Fig. 6-1** *Precise layout lines on the sides of the excavation are an integral aspect of correctly planning any precision digging job.*

charge of a job may avoid clearly marking the excavation. This might be due to simple laziness, or more likely, they may not know exactly where they want the operator to dig. But it's not up to the TLB operator to decide where to put a trench. That information can only come from the person in charge, and they must communicate it to the operator as exactly as possible.

## Precision Job Layout

In some types of excavations (particularly footings), a precise layout is the most important element in completing the job with professional results. Because of the high cost of concrete and labor, it is very important to get the footings cut to the exact specifications, and in the exact locations, the first time.

Whenever the operator is called on to achieve this kind of precise work, he or she must have a thorough understanding of the job and its dimensions. Discuss the job with those in charge until all aspects of the excavation are clear and each step is understood completely. Go over the plans and make sure of the layout.

To be structurally sound, walls must be built directly on the footing to the approved plan. Since the wall will occupy a fixed, exact location, the footing must also be in the exact location. When marking the area to be dug using a string or other straight edge, along with lime or some other white powder, care must be taken to keep the marks clean, straight and narrow. Applying the marking material from a few inches above the ground will assure a precise layout.

Marking both sides of the footing is essential if the footing to be dug is wider than the bucket being used. It's also a good rule to mark both sides whenever precise excavation is required.

Sometimes, excavations for plumbing or electrical lines will also require precise layouts. In plumbing, these layouts will usually be called for when planning groundfloor lavatories, floor spills, or any place where pipes will come up through the concrete in an exact spot. The same requirements apply for placement of electrical conduits.

## Job-Planning Tips

As a review of the material included in this chapter, as well as a suggested procedure to follow when inspecting the job site prior to beginning work, the TLB operator should keep the following tips in mind when planning the job:

• Always select the shortest and safest route through the job site.

• Check the terrain and soil conditions that may reduce traction or require changes in the direction of travel.

• Be aware of the following obstacles and plan your work to avoid damage to them: trees, buildings, pavement, equipment, embankments, personnel, and utilities (either underground or overhead).

• Consider the nature of the work expected of the TLB, the amount of earth to be moved, and the time available to perform the work.

• Place temporary reference markers such as tall stakes with colored ribbons or paint to indicate obstacles to be avoided. These obstacles could include items such as: grade stakes, utility pipes or wires, thin concrete, objects that could cause tire damage, etc. Discuss the nature of the work with other personnel involved in the job as necessary

***In conclusion*** – No operator likes to do a job a second time because of poor planning. As we've seen, poor planning can be very costly when precise excavation is required, in addition to causing needless delays. When planning a job, expert operators are the ones who have all their moves planned out well in advance, so that as one part of the work is completed, they will know what the next step is, and be able to move right into it without error and delay.

## Questions – Chapter 6 **Planning the Job**

*Notes:* _____

_____

_____

_____

_____

_____

_____

_____

_____

_____

_____

_____

_____

_____

_____

_____

_____

_____

_____

_____

_____

_____

_____

_____

_____

_____

_____

_____

_____

_____

**1. The operator should walk the job site to consider:**

_____ a. The types of tasks he will have to perform

_____ b. The order in which he will proceed

_____ c. How to complete the entire job as efficiently as possible

_____ d. All of the above

**2. The best operators plan out the job sequence well in advance.**

_____ a. True

_____ b. False

**3. Some of the important things to discuss with the person in charge include:**

_____ a. Utility locations

_____ b. Placement of spoil

_____ c. Bucket size requirements

_____ d. All of the above

**4. In order to avoid digging the machine into an unmaneuverable situation the operator should:**

_____ a. Dig the smaller size trenches first

_____ b. Plan the location for stockpiling

_____ c. Plan the sequence of the digging

_____ d. Dig the shallow trenches first

**5. Shuttle operations are often required to move large quantities of material from one place to another.**

_____ a. True

_____ b. False

**6. The placement and stockpiling of spoil is determined by what will eventually be done with the material.**

_____ a. True

_____ b. False

**7. The best way to avoid misunderstandings about the work to be done is to have the area clearly marked.**

_____ a. True

_____ b. False

**8. Precision layout is most often required when digging footings.**

_____ a. True

_____ b. False

**9. Precise layouts are also required in which of the following situations?**

_____ a. When planning ground floor lavatories

_____ b. Floor spills

_____ c. Any place where pipes or electrical conduits will come up through the concrete in an exact spot

_____ d. All of the above

**10. Marking both sides of the footing is essential if the footing to be dug is wider than the bucket being used.**

_____ a. True

_____ b. False

**11. In addition to determining the digging sequence, the operator should also be mindful of:**

_____ a. Coordinating the TLB's work with the other trades on the job site

_____ b. Planning locations for stockpiling

_____ c. Planning and preparing a shuttle route to the stockpile area

_____ d. All of the above

**12. When sizing up a job, the operator should consider:**

_____ a. The nature of the work expected of the TLB

_____ b. The amount of earth to be moved

_____ c. The time available to perform the work

_____ d. All of the above

_____

_____

_____

_____

_____

**13. Place temporary reference markers to indicate obstacles to be avoided. Use markers such as tall stakes with colored ribbons or paint, that are easily visible from the cab of the machine.**

_____ a. True

_____ b. False

_____

_____

_____

_____

_____

_____

_____

_____

_____

_____

_____

_____

_____

_____

_____

_____

_____

_____

_____

_____

_____

_____

_____

# 7. Set-up

## Introduction

Set-up of the TLB is a basic fundamental, one which applies to every job the backhoe will perform. Correctly positioning, or setting up the machine prior to digging, must be understood to operate the backhoe efficiently and professionally.

Proper set-up consists, basically, of lining up the machine with the trench, at the optimum digging distance. The main elements of a correct set-up are: 1) the center line of the hoe, which must be positioned correctly to cut the trench exactly to the layout lines; 2) positioning of the entire machine in such a way that easy stockpiling of spoil in the desired area is possible; 3) making sure the machine is level, in order to produce a plumb trench.

When making plans for stockpiling, the operator must consider areas that will permit easy access to the machine or other equipment, such as trucks, in order to make back-filling or spoil removal easier. Positioning of the machine in relation to the stockpile is done by placing the "arc of the swing" in the correct position. This is done by angling the machine itself in one direction or another, relative to the excavation (Fig. 7-1).

## The Tripod Set-Up

The backhoe can only be operated efficiently when it is positioned on a solid base. The weight of the machine should not be supported by the tires. Instead, the machine is best supported by a **tripod set-up**, consisting of the **front loader bucket** and the **two stabilizers** (Fig. 7-2). There are numerous advantages to using this method, while problems created by it are few.

***Advantages.*** For whatever reason, many operators choose not to lower the front loader bucket during operation. Quite simply, efficiency is lost in this manner. When the weight of the tractor and loader is supported by the front tires, the machine will bounce slightly. The operator will, in turn, bounce slightly also, and this motion is transferred directly into the controls (usually causing the machine to shake even more). The backhoe cannot be operated to its maximum potential in this manner. However, this can be easily corrected by using the tripod setup.

The loss of control produced by the extra motion also costs the operator a degree of safety. This alone is good reason to use the tripod method.

Another point to consider is the tendency of the backhoe to be constantly pulled backward during

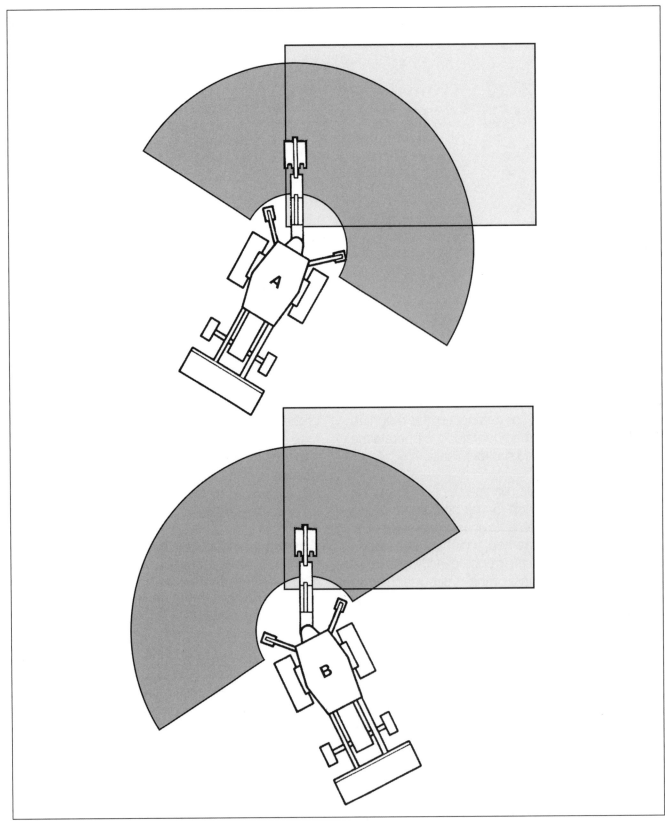

**Fig. 7-1** *SET-UP A – In this example, the desired depth of the excavation is six feet deep. Keep in mind that the spoil must be kept back away from the excavation. In this position, the operator will rapidly run out of space for spoil placement. SET-UP B – In order to increase the spoil placement area, the arc of the swing is adjusted by re-positioning the machine at a different angle to the excavation.*

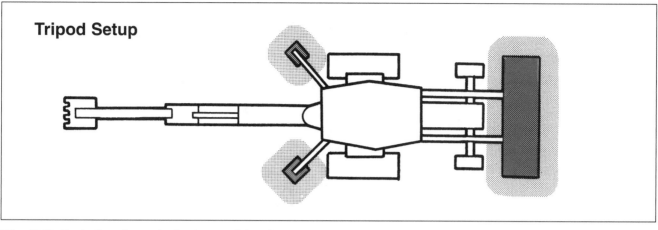

**Tripod Setup**

**Fig. 7-2** *Illustration shows the basic use of the tripod set-up using the loader bucket and two stabilizers to provide a working platform for the backhoe.*

operation due to the tremendous forces generated by the hydraulic system. The tripod set-up, however, puts more weight on the stabilizers. This has two positive effects: 1) With the front bucket off the ground, the hydraulic digging force tends to lift the stabilizers off the ground, freeing the machine to roll on the front tires. The tripod set-up puts more weight on the stabilizers, keeping them firmly on the ground. 2) The extra weight also increases traction, which further prevents backhoe slippage. **In this position, the operator can summon the greatest machine resistance against being pulled backward due to the digging forces.** This concept should be understood and practiced and used to the operator's advantage whenever possible.

One other advantage of the tripod set-up is that with the loader bucket firmly lowered on flat ground, the TLB is stabilized. Any time the loader bucket is off the ground, stability is decreased.

***Problems.*** The tripod set-up is not without some drawbacks. When operating on concrete or a delicate surface such as tile, masonry or stonework, direct front bucket contact is undesirable. In these situations, it may be necessary to place wooden planks or plywood between the contact areas, or have the front bucket raised while working.

When operating on hillsides or anywhere the area under the front bucket is not level, the machine will be forced in the direction perpendicular to the

surface (Fig. 7-3). To avoid this, lower the bucket only until it makes enough contact to stabilize the machine.

Using the tripod set-up may sometimes cause problems when there is insufficient area to rest the front bucket. These situations present themselves rather infrequently, however, and can be remedied by rais-

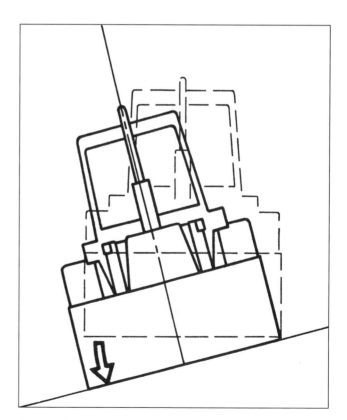

**Fig. 7-3** *When the bucket is lowered on sloped ground, the machine will be forced in the direction perpendicular to the slope.*

ing the loader bucket up until it no longer presents a space problem.

## The Pivot Method

When using the tripod set-up, the TLB may be pivoted 25 degrees in either direction, using the lowered front loader bucket as the pivot point as the machine maneuvers to one side or the other (Fig. 7-5).

Repeating the pivot procedure over and over would result in the machine making a circle, with the loader bucket/pivot remaining in the same place. While the need for this maneuver might not arise very frequently, understanding the pivot concept is important because it is used often in different situations.

This pivot method is used most often when aligning the machine to the excavation, when connecting two trenches, or when crossing trenches. In fact, crossing trenches without using the front loader bucket as a stabilizer pivot is not recommended, as it would be unsafe. Whenever the front loader is firmly down on flat ground, the machine is stabilized and tipping or rollover is controlled while the machine moves sideways for a new set-up.

There are many job situations where the pivot method is useful. Here we will examine one common situation, and some of the possible set-up procedures. Often, the operator will be asked to dig a trench between two buildings. To accomplish this task, the trench must be started at the ends first, and dug until the two trenches meet at a **planned** mid-point and a single trench is produced. If the trench is shallow enough, and the area stable enough to support the weight of the TLB, there are three possible set-ups to choose from.

***Set-up #1.*** As seen in Fig. 7-6, the machine is driven to the desired position and the stabilizers lowered. Fig. 7-7 shows the bucket lowered to a

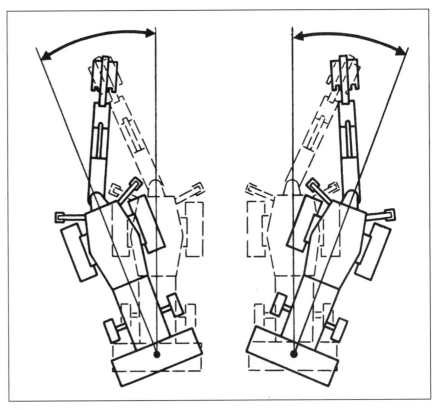

**Fig. 7-5** *The pivot method*

**Fig. 7-6** *Setup 1 – This setup procedure could be used...*

stable area at an angle that will actually increase the stability of the machine as the pivot is performed. After the pivot is completed (Fig. 7-8), the stabilizers are lowered onto stable areas and the swing pin is positioned directly over the center of the trench.

***Set-up #2.*** Using the loader bucket as a stabilizer is useful in many ways (Fig. 7-9). The TLB was driven into the position shown here, with the loader bucket supporting its weight. Again, the stabilizers were lowered and the bucket positioned at an angle advantageous for the pivot. Fig. 7-10 shows the position directly after the pivot has been made. By comparing these two pictures, the movement of the machine becomes clear. Of course, such maneuvers are only attempted on very stable ground.

***Set-up #3.*** The loader bucket is again used to support the weight of the machine as it is slipped to the opposite side of the trench. The stabilizers are lowered, and the operator takes his position at the backhoe controls (Fig. 7-11). Because this particular pivot is too much to make in one "jump," the machine is moved to the point where the sta-

bilizer is nearest the trench and still on stable ground (Fig. 7-12). The bucket is then re-positioned and the second "jump" is made (Fig. 7-13). Again, notice the position of the stabilizers and the swing pin. In this particular case, the operator needed to end up on the other side of the trench, so this method worked very well (Fig. 7-14). It should also be noted that the "arc of the swing" is positioned differently in each of these set-ups (Figs. 7-8, 10 and 13).

## Precision Set-up

Precision set-up is called for most often when the backhoe must dig footings (see ***Footings***). It simply involves aligning the machine exactly with the excavation. As seen in Fig. 7-15, the backhoe is extended to the farthest point desired, and the operator adjusts the swing so the bucket touches the layout line at the desired point. (Once the swing is in the correct position, it is not moved until an alignment check is completed.) Then the bucket is lifted up and pulled in to the closest part of the layout (Fig. 7-16). If the bucket contacts the layout at the desired point, the backhoe is perfectly aligned to excavate that particular section of the job.

**Fig. 7-7**...*if you want to keep the machine on the same side of the trench...*

**Fig. 7-8** ...*after the trench is completed.*

117

**Fig. 7-9** *Setup 2 – This setup can be used to allow the machine to exit on either side of the trench, and should only be used in shallow and very stable ground conditions.*

**Fig. 7-10** *An example of these conditions would be an 18 inch deep trench, 24 inches wide, dug in an asphalt parking lot.*

If the backhoe does not line up correctly, it can be pivoted slightly to the side, with the procedure repeated until the machine aligns perfectly with the excavation. With practice, this technique becomes a habit and is performed quickly. After the machine is set up properly, the operator must be **constantly aware of the machine's alignment**. The **bucket** can be knocked out of alignment by some type of obstruction such as a rock, pipe, a piece of concrete or even a root. In addition, the **machine** can be pulled out of alignment by the hydraulic digging forces, as we have noted. This usually occurs in hard or rocky soil conditions.

The best way to avoid the machine being pulled out of alignment is to position the machine straight with the excavation. This means that if the machine is pulled backward by the digging forces, it will still be aligned with the trench (Fig. 7-17). Any other set-up will cause the back-hoe to be pulled out of alignment by the digging forces.

In deep or large excavations, the operator must pay particular attention to the sides of the trench, leveling the machine to keep it plumb, as plumb sides are important to precision digging.

**Fig. 7-11** *Setup 3 – This version of setup...*

**Fig. 7-12** *...could be used when the work in area has been completed,*

**Fig. 7-15** *When precision digging is required, the backhoe must be aligned perfectly with the excavation. To check for proper alignment, extend the backhoe out, and place the bucket exactly in the desired digging position.*

**Fig. 7-16** *Then, (without touching the swing control) raise the bucket, pull it in close to the machine, and then lower it to the ground. If the bucket tooth does not line up exactly, then the back of the machine needs to be moved sideways using the pivot method. Make the adjustment, then start the procedure again, and repeat the procedure until the machine is aligned with the trench as in 7-15 and 7-16.*

**Fig. 7-13** *…and the machine needs to cross over the trench…*

**Fig. 7-14** *…to exit the area.*

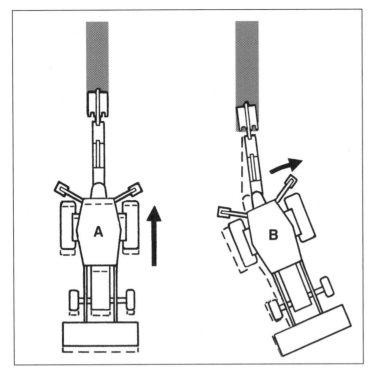

**Fig. 7-17** *A) Shows the best backhoe setup position for maximum resistance from being pulled backwards due to digging forces. B) Shows machine being pulled out of alignment by digging forces.*

## Set-Up Techniques

In order to examine different set-up procedures, we will depict three different examples of how to set up the TLB to dig a common pier footing. The procedure that the operator will choose on the job will depend on the working area available and the desired spoil placement area. The excavation in all examples is the same – twelve feet square and four feet deep.

*Fig. 7-18* illustrates the first approach to accurately digging this kind of excavation. Because the sides are the most important element of pier excavating, the set-up must aid in the precise cutting of the sides that will follow. To save time and make the job easier, two sides of the excavation will be dug from a single set-up, setup #1. The machine is pivoted to the side slightly, and is perfectly aligned with the other side. When following this procedure for pier excavation, the sides are always dug first, and the center area is cleared afterward. After the bulk of the dirt is removed, the bottom of the footing is fine-graded and cleaned carefully, without over-digging. Spoil is then pulled into one corner of the excavation and removed. When completed, the TLB is moved to the other side of the excavation, set-up #2. The same procedure – digging

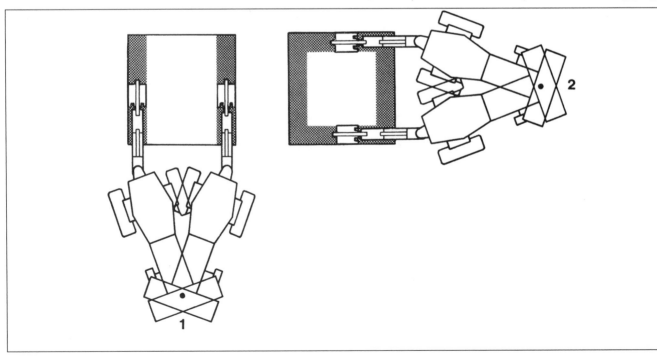

**Fig. 7-18**

the sides first, and **then** digging the center out – is repeated.

The second approach to setting up for this type of excavation is illustrated in **Fig. 7-19**. The operator moves the machine to the first set-up position and

digs the first two sides. The TLB is then moved to set-up #2, where the other two sides are excavated. At that point, the perimeter of the footing is completed, and the center is then dug to the desired depth or elevation, and cleaned.

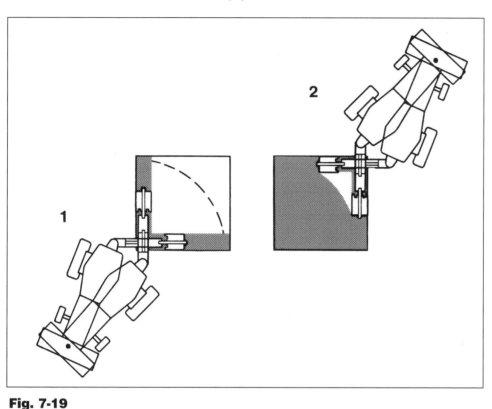

**Fig. 7-19**

The third example is illustrated in **Fig. 7-20**. This procedure requires three separate set-ups, but works well when very precise results are desired. The operator starts in the first position, from which side "A" of the footing is dug to the desired depth. The machine is then moved to the second set-up position, from which sides "B" and "C" are dug. At this point, three sides of the excavation are dug to the correct depth.

As the operator begins to clean the center, the three completed sides give him good visual aid in cutting

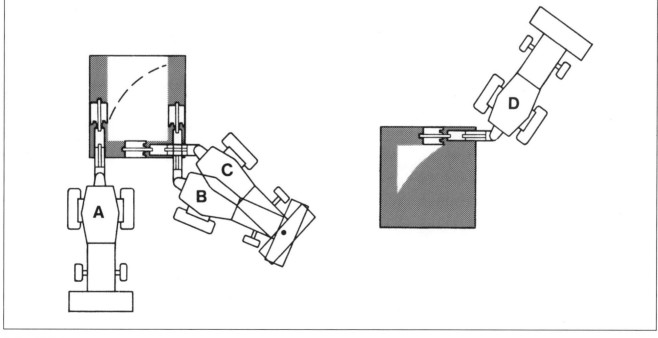

**Fig. 7-20**

and cleaning the center. When work is completed, the machine is then moved to the third set-up position. The operator then cuts the final side "D" and cleans the remaining spoil from the excavation.

## Conclusion

In this chapter, we've tried to explain the two major components of backhoe set-up, namely the tripod set-up and the pivot method. The two procedures are interrelated and both enhance the operator's control of the backhoe. Whether the job is a precise excavation, as for a footing, or just a simple trench, proper set-up is essential to getting the work done correctly and efficiently. Like other aspects of TLB operation, set-ups, once they are practiced, become second nature to the operator. When care is used in pivoting the machine, the operator will discover many ways the backhoe can be used to perform a number of jobs, under many circumstances, such as the unusual set-up seen in **Fig. 7-21**.

**Fig. 7-21**

## Questions – Chapter 7 **Set-up**

**1. The main elements of a correct set up are:**

_____ a. The center line of the hoe must be positioned correctly to cut the trench exactly to the lay out lines

_____ b. Positioning of the entire machine in such a way that stockpiling of spoil in the desired area is possible

_____ c. Making sure the machine is level in order to produce a plumb trench

_____ d. All of the above

**2. The backhoe can only be operated efficiently and safely when it is positioned on a solid base. When it is positioned on the solid base the weight of the machine is supported by the tires.**

_____ a. True

_____ b. False

**3. The tripod set-up is a working platform for the backhoe and consists of the front loader bucket and the two stabilizers.**

_____ a. True

_____ b. False

**4. If the operator uses the backhoe with the loader bucket off the ground, the machine will bounce slightly on the front tires. What will the effect of this bouncing be?**

_____ a. Loss of efficiency

_____ b. Loss of safety

_____ c. Loss of resistance to being pulled backward due to digging forces

_____ d. All of the above

**5. When the tripod set up is used and the loader bucket is firmly lowered on flat ground, what is the effect on the backhoe?**

_____ a. The machine is stabilized

_____ b. The machine does not shake and bounce

_____ c. The operator does not shake and bounce

_____ d. All of the above

Notes: _____

_____

_____

_____

_____

_____

_____

_____

_____

_____

_____

_____

_____

_____

_____

_____

_____

_____

_____

_____

_____

_____

_____

_____

_____

_____

_____

_____

_____
_____
_____
_____
_____
_____
_____
_____
_____
_____
_____
_____
_____
_____
_____
_____
_____
_____
_____
_____
_____
_____
_____
_____
_____
_____
_____
_____
_____
_____

**6. The tripod set up has drawbacks when the machine is operated on:**

_____ a. Concrete or a delicate surface such as tile, masonry or stonework

_____ b. A hillside or anywhere the area under the front loader bucket is not level

_____ c. When there is insufficient area to rest the bucket

_____ d. All of the above

**7. When is the pivot method used?**

_____ a. When aligning the machine to the excavation

_____ b. When connecting two trenches

_____ c. When crossing trenches

_____ d. All of the above

**8. When the front loader is firmly down on flat ground, the machine is stabilized and tipping is controlled while the rear of the machine moves sideways.**

_____ a. True

_____ b. False

**9. A precision set-up is aligned and confirmed by:**

_____ a. Extending out the backhoe and touching the bucket to the layout line

_____ b. Placing the bucket on the layout line close to the machine.

_____ c. Both of the above

_____ d. None of the above

**10. After the machine is set up properly, the operator must be constantly aware of the machine's alignment with the trench.**

_____ a. True

_____ b. False

**11. The bucket can be knocked out of alignment by obstructions such as:**

_____ a. Rocks or roots

_____ b. Pipes

_____ c. Pieces of concrete

_____ d. All of the above

**12. In some situations, the backhoe can be pulled out of alignment by hydraulic digging forces.**

_____ a. True

_____ b. False

**13. When using a tripod set-up, a TLB can be pivoted how many degrees in either direction?**

_____ a. 10 degrees

_____ b. 25 degrees

_____ c. 90 degrees

_____ d. 360 degrees

**14. When digging pier footings, there is only one procedure that can accomplish the desired results.**

_____ a. True

_____ b. False

# 8. Footings

## Precision, Skill, Concentration

The digging and excavating of footings is a common operation that requires a high degree of precision and skill and is one of the most difficult skills to fully develop. In the process of excavating footings, the backhoe operator actually builds a form for the concrete as the dirt is removed. These concrete forms must be dug in an exact location and to the dimensions in the job plan. If they are dug too large, more concrete will be required; if they are dug too small, the reinforcing steel will not fit. When this occurs, the contractor faces increased costs or risks failing an inspection by building inspectors.

In this chapter, we'll examine precision layout and digging techniques that will enable you to excavate footings correctly **the first time**. This is extremely important because you only have one chance to get it right.

## Footing Types

*Trench-type footings.* These are generally the easiest types of footing to dig, as they usually have only two requirements: 1) proper set-up of the machine, to ensure correct location of the trench; and 2) achieving the correct depth of the trench, including a smooth, flat bottom.

Before starting to excavate, consider all aspects of the job ahead of you. Plan the layout as thoroughly as possible, to get a good mental picture of the excavation sequence.

Important points to consider include the amount of spoil that will be created by digging, and where it will be placed. The operator must also plan a step-by-step order in which to proceed with digging, so that all the footings may be dug easily and an exit route provided for the TLB.

When excavating trench footings, it is best to dig each section of the trench as long as possible, going down quickly to within about one foot of the desired elevation. Then, the operator should use long, level passes with the bucket, taking out about two inches at a time, checking elevation at both ends when necessary, until the desired grade is reached. Another good idea, when the operator gets to within about six inches of the desired grade, is to clean the sides of the trench with the bottom of the bucket, creating a clean trench area and a safer working environment (Fig. 8-1).

Sometimes it may be necessary to start the footing at both ends, working toward a meeting point. Plan ahead where the two trenches will meet, so there will be enough room to use the pivot method if necessary (see **Set-up**).

**Pier-type footings.** These are the footings usually called for when large, multi-story structures are being constructed. They are basically large concrete platforms, either square or rectangular in shape, that will eventually support the weight of the entire structure.

Requirements for pier-type footings include straight, smooth sides that are plumb, and in exactly the right location, as well as a smooth, level bottom at the correct elevation. The best approach to digging pier footings is to dig out the sides first, making sure they are straight and correct, and then simply removing the earth remaining in the "center" of the footing (Figs. 8-2, 8-3, 8-4, 8-5).

For example, let's consider a typical pier footing, to be dug twelve feet square and four feet deep.

Excavating a footing of this size will require removing 21.3 cubic yards of material. Since the standard 24-inch backhoe bucket has a capacity of about one-quarter cubic yard, it will require a minimum of 85 full buckets to remove the required amount.

Of course, just removing spoil from the area is not enough to finish with a professionally excavated pier footing. Before removing the dirt, think about the requirements: 1) straight smooth sides that are plumb and in exactly the right location, and 2) a smooth level bottom at the correct elevation.

## Layout

As we have already noted, an accurate layout is essential to digging a footing to the correct dimensions and in the right location. Since dimensions and locations are so important to the excavation of footings, it follows that an accurate layout is indispensable when footings are to be dug.

**Fig. 8-1** *Here the operator cleans the side of the trench, which will prevent materials from falling back into the trench, as well as ease the work of the laborer.*

Layouts for footings must be clearly marked with narrow, precise markings of lime, or any material that can be clearly seen (Fig. 8-8). Layout lines should be extended past the limits of the excavation, so the location is still visible after digging has begun. When digging trench footings, be sure to mark **both** sides of the trench, especially when the footing width is wider than the bucket.

It should also be noted that a clean area for a layout is a **must** for jobs involving any amount of precision. Cleaning the layout area ahead of time will ease the operator's task by simplifying precise layouts and making maneuvering of the TLB easier. (See Figs. 8-6, 8-7 and 8-8.)

## Precision Digging

Footings require the most precise digging the TLB operator is capable of. And yet, this type of digging is difficult only when the operator does not understand, or is not aware of, the basic requirements of precision digging. They are: 1) digging to the exact perimeter in the right location, and 2) digging to the desired elevation.

To meet these requirements, the operator must have an **exact** layout; some means of checking elevations at any time during excavation; and a laborer to assist the operator during excavation. These factors, combined with a knowledgeable operator, usually result in clean, precise footings (Figs. 8-9, 8-10).

## Elevation Importance and Checking Methods

The depth, or elevation, of the footing is one of the two requirements for expert results. The main idea is to dig to the depth required, but not any deeper. Some jobs are more exacting than others, and it is sometimes very difficult to dig exactly to a certain elevation and produce a perfectly flat, level bottom. It is a skill that requires total operator concentration, great bucket control and a deliberate style of cutting and correcting as the work progresses. Being able to periodically check the elevation while digging is also important, and there are several methods that are widely used.

The most common grade-checking procedure involves a builder's level, which is capable of pin-

**Fig. 8-2** *The first step to accurate excavation of pier-type footings is to dig out the "side" first.*

**Fig. 8-3.** *Once one side is complete, move to the opposite side and repeat the procedure.*

**Fig. 8-4** *After all four sides are dug out, the operator then removes remaining material in the "center" of the footing making sure that the bottom reaches the desired elevation.*

**Fig. 8-5** *Photo shows the results of a correctly-dug footing.*

**Fig. 8-6** *Area of the desired layout*

**Fig. 8-7** *Area has been cleaned of debris and smoothed for the layout*

**Fig. 8-8** *The finished layout*

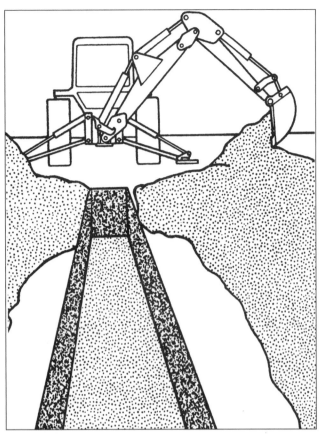

**Fig. 8-9** *A correctly dug pier footing will have straight sides, and a smooth, flat bottom...*

pointing a level plane at any point on the job site. Once the instrument is set up and leveled, the grade is then checked, and the operator knows how far he has to dig to reach the bottom of the excavation (Fig. 8-11).

A "story pole" is often used with the level, but a simple tape measure will suffice when the reference plane is within reach of the person checking the grade. When the job is especially exacting, it is absolutely necessary to check the grade as digging proceeds, at both ends of the ditch.

Measuring the **depth** from either side of the trench is usually unacceptable, because it is not an accurate grade check. However, this method is all right for other types of excavations, such as plumbing or utility lines, and reduces the need for constant references to elevation.

## Laborer Involvement

When digging precise footings, it is advisable to use a laborer to assist the TLB operator in checking elevations and in other tasks. One common practice is to have the laborer clean the excavation of loose spoil, to provide a more solid base for the

**Fig. 8-10** *...and the top of the excavation will be cleaned of spoil.*

concrete to be poured on. The sides of the footing are also cleaned to prevent dirt from falling in later, making it safer for the men who will be working in the excavation after the backhoe's work is done (Fig. 8-12).

When the operator and the laborer work together as a team, digging efficiency is increased. The laborer aids the operator by cleaning the grade and providing a visual grade-checking function. As he pushes loose dirt toward the machine, cleaning the bottom of the excavation, the laborer indicates to the operator how much more to cut,

and warns the operator against over-digging. The operator then removes the spoil, making the laborer's job easier.

Having a team of an experienced TLB operator and laborer makes digging footings more efficient, and greatly reduces the chance for error and delay. This teamwork greatly enhances the likelihood that the footings will be dug correctly the first time, which is of prime importance.

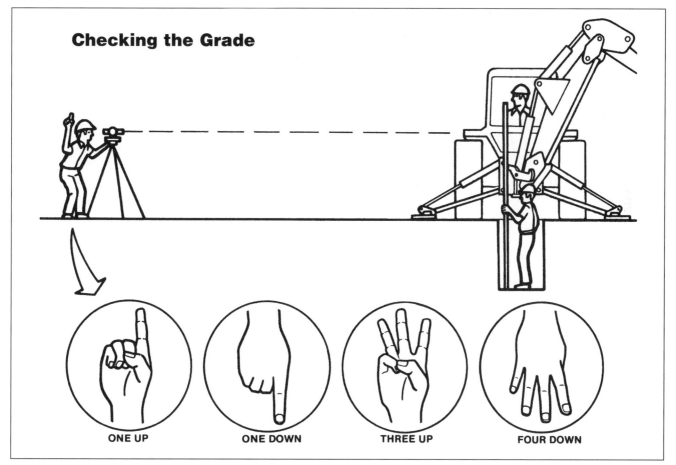

## Checking the Grade

ONE UP   ONE DOWN   THREE UP   FOUR DOWN

**Fig. 8-11** *When checking grade with a transit, laser, or other devices, it will become necessary to use hand signals because of high noise levels or distance between the grade checker and the operator. There are two required elements that the operator needs to know to proceed. These are the distance (up or down) to the correct elevation, and which direction, either up or down, **to get to the desired grade.***

*This method can instantly transmit this information without disrupting the flow of work. Also be sure that both grade checker and operator understand that all signals indicate what needs to be done to get to the desired grade, and **not what the existing is** from the desired grade.*

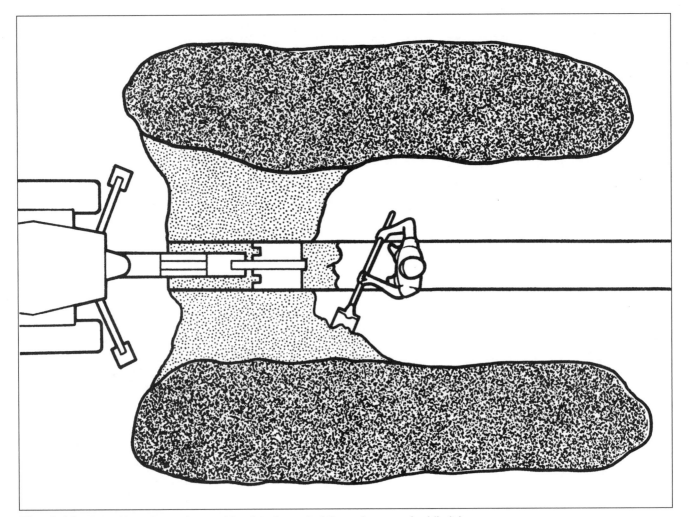

**Fig. 8-12** *The laborer faces the machine (staying out of the swing range) while it is working...cleaning the spoil from the sides and pushing the spoil forward in the trench for the machine to remove.*

**NOTE:** Sequence 8-13 through 8-20 shows the order in which to proceed when excavating footings, and not the correct procedure itself. In an actual job situation, a laborer would help clean the footing and assist the operator in checking the grade as digging progresses. If no laborer is available, the operator should proceed in the same manner depicted here, digging as best he can and cleaning the work area of spoil.

**Fig. 8-13** *At this point the operator has dug two sides of the footing and has piled the spoil outside the excavation area.*

**Fig. 8-14** *As the operator moves to the next set-up, the machine is angled to allow spoil placement outside the excavation area.*

**Fig. 8-15** *As the trenches are dug, they are graded as cleanly as possible on the bottom.*

**Fig. 8-16** *The inside as well as the outside of the work area is cleaned of spoil to provide a usable working area.*

**Fig. 8-17** *After cleaning the completed area, the digging is resumed.*

**Fig. 8-18** *Beginning the surface cut.*

**Fig. 8-19** *The footing is completed, and the spoil removed.*

## Questions – Chapter 8 **Footings**

**1. Digging footings is one of the easiest tasks for an operator to perform.**

_____ a. True

_____ b. False

**2. When digging footings, an operator is creating a concrete form by the dirt that is removed.**

_____ a. True

_____ b. False

**3. The requirements for trench-type footings are:**

_____ a. Correct location

_____ b. Correct depth

_____ c. Correct width

_____ d. All of the above

**4. When planning a footing job, the most important consideration is:**

_____ a. The amount of spoil that will be created

_____ b. Where the spoil will be placed

_____ c. The order in which to proceed with digging

_____ d. All of the above

**5. When the footing is getting close to the desired elevation, the operator should use long level passes with the bucket and check the elevations at both ends.**

_____ a. True

_____ b. False

**6. Cleaning the outer sides of the trench with the bottom of the bucket creates a clean trench area and a safer working environment.**

_____ a. True

_____ b. False

_Notes:_ _____

_____

_____

_____

_____

_____

_____

_____

_____

_____

_____

_____

_____

_____

_____

_____

_____

_____

_____

_____

_____

_____

_____

_____

_____

_____

_____

_____

_____

_____

_____
_____
_____
_____
_____
_____
_____
_____
_____
_____
_____
_____
_____
_____
_____
_____
_____
_____
_____
_____
_____
_____
_____
_____
_____
_____
_____
_____
_____
_____

**7. Requirements for pier-type footings include:**

_____ a. Proper location

_____ b. Straight, smooth sides

_____ c. Level bottom at the correct elevation

_____ d. All of the above

**8. The best approach to digging pier footings is to dig out the center first and then finish by cutting the sides.**

_____ a. True

_____ b. False

**9. Layout lines should be extended past the limits of the excavation so that the location is still visible after digging has begun.**

_____ a. True

_____ b. False

**10. Cleaning and smoothing the layout area before doing the layout will:**

_____ a. Simplify precise layouts

_____ b. Make the operator's task easier

_____ c. Make maneuvering the backhoe easier

_____ d. All of the above

**11. Measuring the depth of the footing from the side is the best method because it is the easiest and most accurate grade check.**

_____ a. True

_____ b. False

**12. When digging footings, the operator and a laborer should work together for the best results.**

_____ a. True

_____ b. False

**13. If footings are dug too large:**

_____ a. The reinforcing steel will not fit

_____ b. Less concrete will be required

_____ c. More concrete will be required

_____ d. It helps to make the building stronger

**14. If the footings are dug too small, the reinforcing steel will not fit.**

_____ a. True

_____ b. False

**15. Before starting to excavate any type of footings:**

_____ a. Consider all aspects of the job ahead of you

_____ b. Plan the layout as thoroughly as possible

_____ c. Get a good mental picture of the excavation sequence

_____ d. All of the above

**16. When excavating a trench footing, it is best to dig each section of the trench as short as possible.**

_____ a. True

_____ b. False

**17. Sometimes it may be necessary to start a footing at both ends and work toward the center to a pre-planned meeting point.**

_____ a. True

_____ b. False

# 9. Job Site Cleanliness and Cleanup

## Introduction

*The message of this chapter is "**NEATNESS COUNTS!**"*

**WHAT –** A smooth work area is a key to safety and production when using the backhoe or the loader. You, the operator, and no one else on the jobsite has the ability to begin and maintain a job in a smooth, polished, and professional manner.

**WHEN –** When using the backhoe a smooth area provides for a proper layout for the digging, and makes it easier to move the machine from one setup to another.

When using the loader a smooth working area helps to make the job easier and safer for the operator, and is critical when raising the loader bucket for truck loading or any other purpose.

When operating a loader backhoe there is absolutely no job, task, or procedure... that is aided, enhanced or helped in any way... by a rough, bumpy or uneven jobsite!

☞ *Keep the work area smooth and clean to make your job easier!*

**WHY –** As we discussed in chapter 6, **Planning the Job**, the operator should take every opportunity to make the work easier. Keeping the jobsite smooth is another example of how you can "make your later work easier."

Here is an example.

You have the job of moving about 100 cubic yards of rocky spoil from the inside of a building area to a stockpile in the parking area. The existing shuttle route is rough, bumpy, and uneven.

What effect will "jobsite cleanliness" have on the process of moving this material? The results of a rough, bumpy and uneven shuttle route are as follows:

1) The machine gets beat up.

2) The operator gets beat up (and of these two, only the operator can do anything about it).

3) The movement of material will be very slow.

4) Rocks and spoil will spill from the bucket and create even more bumps.

5) The safety of the site will be compromised.

In the short term (immediately) by having less control over the machine.

In the long term (before the end of the work shift) by operator fatigue, which causes a loss of awareness and an increased chance of an accident.

Using the same jobsite situation, if the operator makes a few grading passes to knock down the bumps, fill the low spots, and to smooth the shuttle path, the results will be completely different. Here are some examples of how a smooth working area can enhance the completion of the job.

1) The job can be performed in a safe manner.

2) The operator and the machine can move more quickly and therefore be more productive.

3) The movement of the machine and the operator will be smooth and controlled, and therefore easier on the operator.

4) The operator can begin, perform and complete the entire job in a safe, professional manner.

Beginning operators should note that these work principles are the basis for professional operation and they should be "practiced" whenever possible when you are in the seat.

*HOW* – Keep the work area polished. Traveling from one point to another can also include knocking down a few bumps or filling in some low places. A few back-drags throughout the shift will usually keep the shuttle route polished and smooth.

☞ When back dragging with the loader, you will get the best results when the loader control is in the float position, and the loader bucket is barely tipped up from the level position.

## Shuttle Operations

When an area is to be utilized for any repeated shuttling back and forth of material or machine, it should be graded smooth before starting to transport material. After several trips are completed, any soft or uncompacted areas will be compacted, and should be back-dragged to fill any depressions or smooth out rough areas. As work progresses, the operator should continue to

back-drag the rough areas, keeping the shuttle area smooth and polished.

Some operators may overlook this technique and dismiss it as a waste of time. On the contrary, it is time well spent, because efficiency is increased in many ways.

Even when shuttle operations aren't involved, a clean working area is important to performing nearly any TLB job. In some situations, the benefits may not be readily apparent; in the long run, however, more often than not, a clean area will simplify the work greatly.

On nearly all job sites for commercial and high-rise construction projects, spoil is stockpiled outside the immediate building area in a designated stockpiling area. In the case of plumbing or electrical excavations, which require back-filling, material is shuttled or trucked in from the stockpiling area later, when it is required.

As spoil is being removed from, and returned to, the excavation area, the main consideration is to maintain a clean, smooth shuttle road from the work area to the stockpiling area.

## Spoil Removal

To remove spoil from the trench area, first drag it back away from the trench (Fig. 9-1). This prevents any spoil from falling back in, and at the same time it cleans the area next to the trench. If there is enough room, it should be pulled back about 10 feet. This will provide room for side-spill from the

**Fig. 9-1** *Dragging spoil back and away from the trench.*

bucket without material falling back into the trench during cleanup.

If the TLB operator makes a habit of smoothing his working area, soon the entire job site will be cleaner and more productive for all trades on the job. If the operator's loader skills and finish grading skills are sharp, they can make the job site look polished to the eye *(Fig. 9-2)*. In the long run, the ability to produce these kinds of results will make one's services as a TLB operator more valuable.

## Importance of Excavation Cleanliness

TLB operators and their functions are not independent of the other workers and roles on the job site. As the backhoe creates trenches and other excavations, these areas will become the working location for other construction trades, such as electricians, plumbers, laborers, ironworkers and concrete finishers. As the backhoe digs excavations for any of these purposes, the methods and procedures followed by the operator will determine the productivity and safety of the work area for all trades on the job that will follow. While the TLB operators must keep in mind the fact that they are digging a trench, it is often matched in importance by how they have prepared the work area for the other trades that will also work on the job.

## Cleanup

The cleanup methods described here are used for clearing and cleaning an area of spoil piles or stockpiles. These materials could include dirt, gravel, sand, concrete, etc.

Cleanup is sometimes used in the beginning of a job to clear the area of debris, or smooth the area to allow clear and precise layouts for footing excavations. Cleanup is also used toward the end of the job, or periodically, to "clean and polish" the work area.

Cleanup is commonly required at the end of most jobs. It may involve back-filling the trench, moving or stockpiling materials, or loading spoil onto trucks. In the case of paved areas, cleanup may require the removal of excess material so the area is clean enough for sweeping. How to best complete these tasks usually depends on the type of surface the TLB is working on.

**Fig. 9-2**

**Fig. 9-3** *As the loader moves forward from this position the bucket will cut the high places as desired.*

**Fig. 9-4** *Back-dragging will fill the low areas.*

***Sod or lawn surfaces* –** When working on sod, the main goal is to do as little damage to the surface as possible. If the topsoil is wet, it may be too soft to support the machine's weight without some damage. In such conditions, a half-full loader bucket could sink the front wheels, making movement impossible and creating quite a mess. If conditions are ever this unstable, it may be necessary to use the backhoe for back-filling. In this situation, it is advisable to distribute the machine's weight through the stabilizers and the tires. This provides a larger area of weight distribution, and less chance of the machine creating ruts or holes in the lawn.

When cleaning up in sod areas, the loader bucket should be flat, with a slight downward pressure applied. With the bucket flat, it will not dig into the sod; and with a little practice, it will be possible to clean off large, flat areas right down to the grass, without digging in. Areas that are not flat are somewhat more difficult and should be finished by hand after the bulk of the spoil is removed.

Another aspect to keep in mind is to apply power to the rear wheels carefully, to avoid spinning them. It may even be necessary to take smaller "bites" of the spoil pile to prevent spinning the wheels unnecessarily.

***Dirt Surfaces* –** Cleanup of dirt surfaces is less complicated than cleaning sod areas, and usually consists of cleaning off the surface to the original grade, or simply leveling and grading the area. Like sod cleanup, the bucket should be flat on the ground during actual cleaning. If a cut is desired, the bucket should be tipped slightly down, and more weight applied by lowering the loader more. To prevent overcutting, the bucket should be re-set in the flat position.

The simplest and best method of cleaning up in dirt areas is to cut down the high areas on the bucket's forward passes (Fig. 9-3), and filling the low areas while back-dragging (Fig. 9-4). This method wastes no motion, and the job site should quickly take on a "polished" look.

***Paved Surfaces* –** The object of cleaning paved surfaces is to scrape the area clean and either consolidate the material or load it out on trucks. This task is most often called for when trenches have been dug in a street, parking lot, or similar paved area. In these situations, the operator should be careful not to push material back into the trench, and to limit the spread of the dirt on the paved surface. To accomplish this, the cleanup procedure, depicted in Fig. 9-5A, B and C, works quite well.

As the cleanup procedure nears completion, the remaining material may be next to the excavation (Fig. 9-6). By positioning the TLB, as seen in Fig. 9-7, and applying the right brake while making a series of sweeping passes, the edge of the excavation is cleaned safely without pushing the spoil back into the excavation. This motion is continued until cleanup is completed (see Fig. 9-8).

***Pile cleanup* –** Another common cleanup task is the removal of a stockpile or spoil from an area. When a back-up is available (some object to push the load against to help push it into the bucket), the job is much easier. In many cases, however, there is no available back-up, so the following pile cleanup method can be used.

When filling the loader bucket from a large pile of dirt, the bucket will fill easily and quickly. As the pile becomes smaller, the back-up (the pile itself) becomes smaller, and filling the bucket becomes more difficult. When the pile is reduced to only two or three cubic yards of material, the most the operator can expect to load into the bucket is less than half of the remaining amount. At this time, the pile can be "groomed" by the operator in such a way that he or she can continue to take advantage of it as a back-up. Figs. 9-9 through 9-12 illustrate how the operator can "groom" the pile to provide a constant backup to facilitate loading.

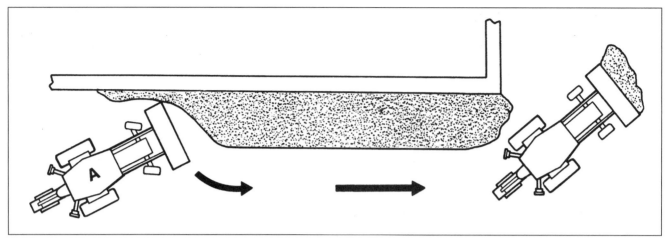

**9-5A.** *On the first pass the bucket is filled and the edge of the pile is cleaned. The material is then stockpiled in the desired area.*

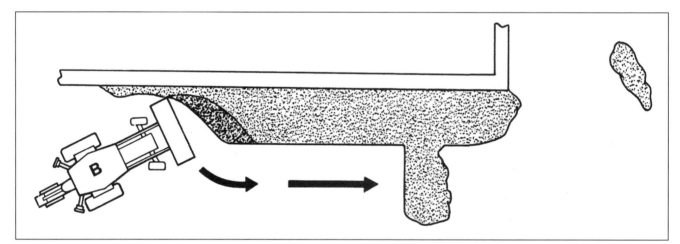

**9-5B.** *On the remaining passes the machine is initially positioned at a slight angle. This will prevent the tires from running over the edge of the pile causing the machine to tilt. Instead of pushing one bucket at a time, the fill length of the cleanup section, every other bucket can be pushed part-way.*

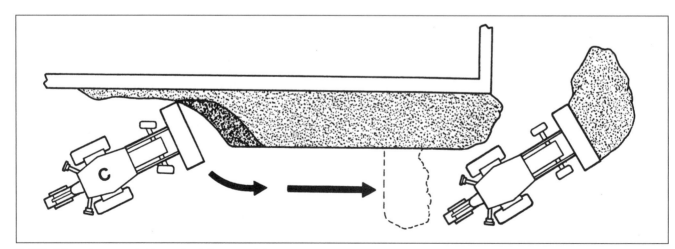

**9-5C.** *Then the material is pushed the rest of the way on the next pass.*

☞ *Here are some tips that will help to make the cleanup process easier*

- Never widen the footprint of the existing dirt pile.

- Always push toward the center of the footprint, rather than pushing material out of the footprint.

- Avoid pushing the pile to the extent that it begins to move.

- Once the pile (back-up) begins to move, the amount of material in the bucket will not increase.

- As loading continues, the amount of material on each bucket load will become smaller and smaller until only about one-third of a yard of material remains.

At that point, the remaining material can be loaded by hand, and the area cleaned by hand with a flat shovel if desired.

**Fig. 9-6** *The material next to the edge may be left for the final cleanup.*

**9-7.** *By positioning the machine in this manner the edge can be cleaned while keeping most of the machine's weight away from the excavation.*

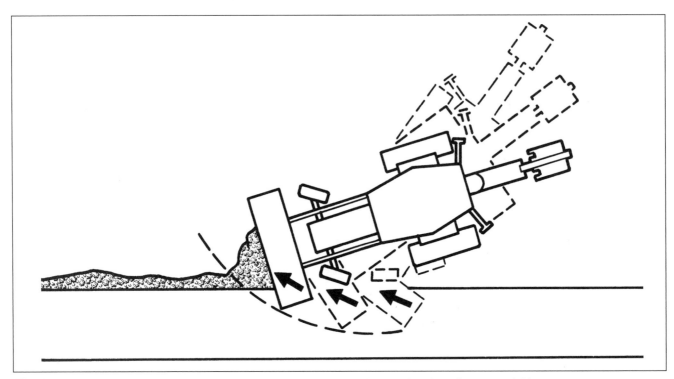

**Fig. 9-8** *By making several sweeping passes while applying the right brake, the edge can quickly be cleaned without pushing material back into the trench.*

**Fig. 9-9** *As the pile becomes smaller it will no longer serve as an effective back-up...*

**Fig. 9-10** *By pulling the corners back...*

**Fig. 9-11** *…the center of the remaining pile will serve as a back-up.*

**Fig. 9-12** *This procedure is repeated several times until the pile is cleaned up.*

## Questions – Chapter 9  **Job Site Cleanliness and Cleanup**

**1. A smooth well graded work area is the key to safety and productivity when using the loader.**

_____ a. True

_____ b. False

**2. When an area is to be used for shuttle operations of material back and forth it should be graded smooth before starting to transport material.**

_____ a. True

_____ b. False

**3. A smooth work area can help to prevent:**

_____ a. Loss of control when traveling around the job-site

_____ b. Loose material from spilling from the bucket

_____ c. Operator fatigue

_____ d. All of the above

**4. When shuttle operations are not involved, a clean working area is not required.**

_____ a. True

_____ b. False

**5. In general building construction, spoil from excavations is often stockpiled outside of the building area.**

_____ a. True

_____ b. False

**6. The TLB and its function are independent of other workers and trades on the jobsite.**

_____ a. True

_____ b. False

**7. Trenches and excavations dug by the backhoe often become the work area for workers in other construction trades.**

_____ a. True

_____ b. False

_Notes:_ _____

**8. Methods and procedures followed by the operator can determine the productivity and safety of the work area for the other trades on the job.**

_____ a. True

_____ b. False

**9. When working on sod (grass surface) the main goal is to do as little damage as possible to the surface.**

_____ a. True

_____ b. False

**10. When cleaning up in sod areas the loader bucket should be:**

_____ a. Flat

_____ b. Tipped down slightly

_____ c. Off the ground

_____ d. None of the above

**11. The best method of cleaning up dirt areas is to cut the high areas on the bucket's forward passes and fill the low areas while back-dragging.**

_____ a. True

_____ b. False

**12. As the pile becomes smaller the back up:**

_____ a. Becomes larger

_____ b. Becomes smaller

_____ c. Stays the same size

_____ d. Is no longer important

**13. When back-dragging with the loader, you will get the best results when:**

_____ a. You are using first gear

_____ b. When the loader control is in the float position

_____ c. When the loader has down-pressure on the bucket

_____ d. When the bucket is off the ground

**14. At the end of asphalt cleanup procedures, it is a common procedure to:**

_____ a. Use a flat shovel to clean the remaining material that the machine is unable to pick up

_____ b. Clean the area with a push broom

_____ c. Both of the above

_____ d. Neither of the above

**15. A bumpy and uneven jobsite can compromise operator safety. This can affect the operator immediately by:**

_____ a. Having less control over the machine

_____ b. Loss of traction

_____ c. Less power to the rear wheels

_____ d. The machine is less productive

**16. A bumpy and uneven jobsite can compromise operator safety. This can affect the operator before the end of the day by:**

_____ a. Slowing down the operation

_____ b. Causing operator fatigue

_____ c. Using the same shuttle route repeatedly

_____ d. All of the above

**17. When filling a loader bucket the further you push the pile the more material you get in the bucket**

_____ a. True

_____ b. False

# 10. Grading and Compaction

## Introduction

In this chapter we will discuss both rough grading and finish grading techniques as well as the principles and methods of soil compaction. Although the TLB is not designed specifically for grading, it can be used efficiently as a grading machine in some situations. Grading, simply, consists of cutting down the high places and filling in the low places.

## Required Skills

To be effective at grading, the TLB operator must develop and practice two abilities. First, he must possess expert loader skills. This includes the ability to cut, grade and maneuver the machine in such a way that certain cuts and other moves can be "attacked" from optimum angles. Second, the operator must be familiar with the grading process and how to complete a job. To get the most out of the TLB's capabilities when performing these tasks, the operator must pay attention to these skills and develop them through practice whenever possible.

## Grading Techniques

As we mentioned, grading is simply a matter of cutting the high places and filling the low ones to produce the desired grade. By visualizing the entire grading job as it will look when it is finished,

and at the same time looking at the job as it is, the cut-and-fill areas will become clear to the operator. As he travels the job site during the grading process, "bucketing" material from the cut areas to the fill areas, he should continually study the cut and fill sections. He should also make constant mental comparisons between the desired finished grade and the actual grade. As this evaluating process is repeated from several different vantage points on the job site, the required movement of material will become very clear. This process is repeated as the grading job progresses, until the required grade is achieved.

By following this procedure, cutting can usually be done to the exact elevation the first time, requiring only a light pass at the end to level the area. Filling, on the other hand, often requires compaction of the earth, and then refilling and leveling to the desired grade.

## Loader Grading Techniques

Rough grading with the loader is usually possible only in areas that are relatively flat, because of the TLB's greatly reduced stability and maneuverability on slopes. Attempting to use the loader for any type of slope work is not advisable, since the results will usually be unsatisfactory, and the procedure is generally unsafe.

It should also be noted that the grading process may include a general cleanup of the job site. The operator may be required to separate debris like rocks, roots, broken concrete or asphalt, waste construction materials, etc. The materials, once separated, are then usually stockpiled for loading onto trucks, or dumped into trash bins on the site.

The range of jobs the operator may be required to perform can be broken into three categories: 1) cutting an area and either loading the material onto trucks or stockpiling it for later loading; 2) cutting from one area and filling another area elsewhere on the site; 3) filling an area with material from a stockpile, or with material that has been trucked in. The common element running through all these types of tasks is that grading materials on the job site will often need to be adjusted (stockpiled, moved about, etc.) to achieve the desired grade.

In contrast to the frequent teamwork called for by the TLB operator with other workers, grading is a job where the operator is usually "on his own." After receiving and discussing job instructions with the person in charge, it is then a matter of the TLB operator alone "at the controls." It is his job to plan and execute the necessary movement of material to achieve the desired grade. It is also his job to come up with a well thought-out plan of exactly how the work will proceed, step by step.

Controlling the TLB to produce exactly the desired results is the operator's responsibility alone.

During both the planning and execution phases of this type of job, the operator should do his best to avoid wasted motions. He should move directly from one phase to the next: cutting, transporting material, compacting, and then filling. He should also correct the grade as the job progresses, and keep the cut and fill areas, as well as any access roads, polished and free of obstructions. Accomplished operators will blend these tasks together into a procedure that will always have a goal, or purpose, or at least ease completion in some way.

One example of this efficiency effort is to keep the loader bucket full, whenever possible, to improve the TLB's compaction capabilities. This can be done by driving over the fill areas while bucketing material from the cut areas.

As work proceeds, with one area being cut and then another being filled in, the visual results won't become apparent until the bulk of the material has been transported into or out of the area, whichever the case may be. Only when the polishing or finish-grading has begun, and corrections made, will the desired results appear. At that point, what may have appeared as a disorganized mess will finally begin to make sense.

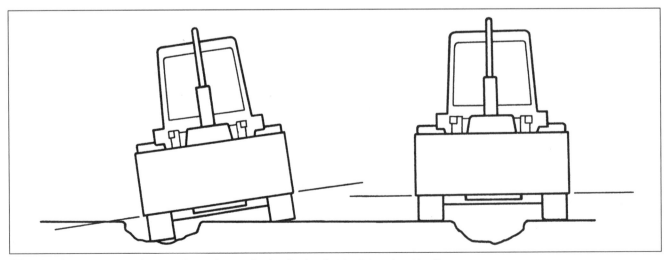

**Fig. 10-1** *The angle of the cutting edge on the loader bucket is determined by the area where the rear tires are contacting the ground.*

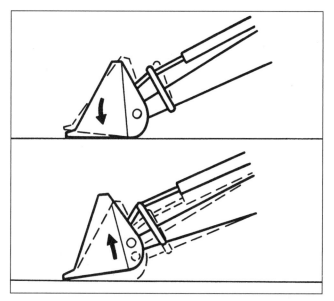

**Fig. 10-2** *Bucket Level Check – This procedure can be used to check the accuracy of the bucket level indicators. On machines without an indicator, it can be used to determine the level position of the bucket. The machine must be positioned on a flat surface. 1) Lower the loader lift so it is in the "float" position. Starting with the bucket rolled slightly from the level position, the bucket is rolled down slowly. 2) At the instant the bucket is level, the loader lift arms will begin to raise.*

## Cutting

***Starting the cut.*** The first step for the operator is to envision the desired cut in his mind. Take notice of the desired grade and the degree of slope, if any, and compare it mentally to the existing grade and/or slope. The key to the cutting process is that the attitude or angle of the bucket cutting edge is determined by the angle of the area where the rear wheels are making contact (Fig. 10-1). Because the cutting edge angle cannot be adjusted, the operator must instead make necessary adjustments in the work area, so that the bucket will make the cut at the desired angle or level.

Once the machine is at the desired angle or level of the cut, the cutting process can then easily continue at that grade. There are several methods that can be used to provide a suitable starting place for the loader to complete the cut. For three examples of how this can be accomplished, see Figs. 10-3, 10-4, and 10-5.

Once the cut is started, and the TLB is supported by an area with the desired angle of grade, then the cutting process can be carried out effectively.

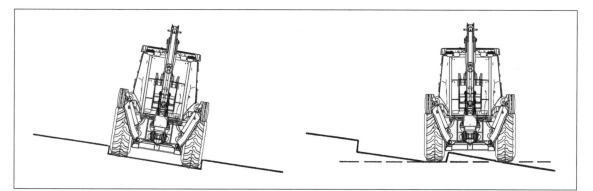

**Fig. 10-3** *Using this technique, the first cut is made to allow the wheels on the upper side to be lowered into the "notch." Later cutting passes will be performed with the correct bucket attitude.*

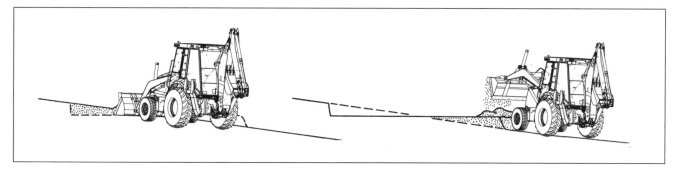

**Fig. 10-4** *Using this method, the machine will "attack" the slope at a 45 degree angle. By taking small cuts, and potting material into the immediate fill area, the area is slowly leveled for the machine to work from. Once the TLB is level, the cutting procedure will progress much more easily.*

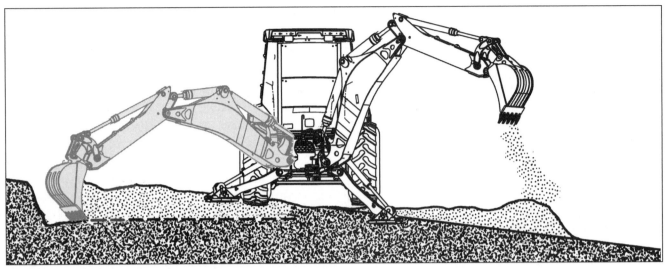

**Fig. 10-5** *This is also a very useful technique. The backhoe is used to cut, as well as deposit material into the fill area.*

As material is removed from the cut area, it is then either deposited in the fill area, or stockpiled. The cut area should be kept graded and polished so that the cut continues as desired. If a particular cutting pass is either too deep or not deep enough, the mistake can be corrected on the next several passes.

If soil in the cut area is of medium hardness, or soft, cutting will be easier than when hard soil conditions exist. The bucket can penetrate soft soil easier, and the operator will have greater control over the depth of the cut. When soil is hard, however, the cutting edge won't penetrate as easily. To overcome this resistance, and better control the bucket and the cutting depth, a series of scraping passes can be made. The scraping is done in a definite pattern so the operator can control the depth of the cut more easily (Fig. 10-6A). This pattern will produce a shallow "trough" (Fig. 10-6B) from which the operator can continue cutting by starting in the center, and then working outward in both directions. If increased cutting penetration is needed, the operator may position the TLB at a slight angle in the trough. With the machine in this position (Fig. 10-7), the corner of the bucket will receive more weight and power.

Another way to enhance the degree of control when cutting in hard areas is to increase the weight on the cutting edge of the bucket. This can be accomplished by filling the loader bucket about one-quarter to one-third full prior to attempting the cut. This added weight will enable the bucket to penetrate harder material, and the operator will also have better control over the depth of the cut.

## Filling

In any filling or backfilling operation, the actual filling as well as the compaction, and at least the rough grading, should be done as the job progresses. To link these procedures together into a workable job plan (one that is smoothly, easily, and professionally performed), the fill material must be dispersed in such a way that after compaction, the correct grade will have been achieved.

The closer the operator can come to the right grade the first time, the easier the finish grading will be. On jobs that take an entire day or more, the operator can constantly correct and polish the cut-and-fill areas, and carry out the compacting and grading requirements at the same time, as he travels around the job site. By keeping this in mind, the operator will actually save time in the long run and ease the work performed by others on the job site.

To better understand the filling procedure, let's break it into two parts: dispersing the material and compaction.

***1. Dispersing the material in the fill area*** – Depending on the depth of the fill area, the fill

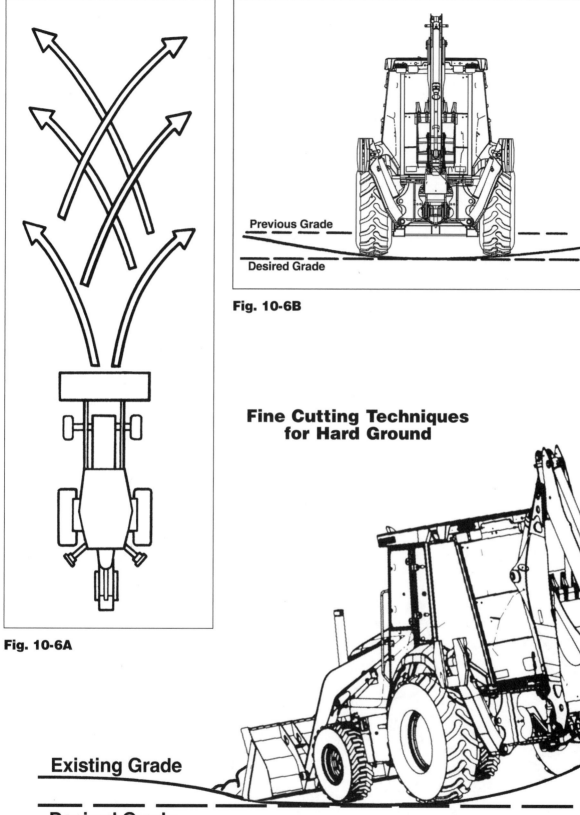

Fig. 10-6A

**Previous Grade**

**Desired Grade**

**Existing Grade**

Fig. 10-6B

## Fine Cutting Techniques for Hard Ground

**Existing Grade**

**Desired Grade**

Fig. 10-7

material must be dispersed at a level higher than the desired finished grade, to allow for compaction. The extra amount required is usually about one-third of the fill depth. So a fill area three feet deep will require about one foot of extra material; if the area is six feet deep, about two extra feet of material will be required, etc.

As the depth of the fill area increases (six feet or more), extra care must be taken as the TLB works near the edge. For increased safety, and to aid in the compaction of the fill, material can be dumped into a pile on top of the fill, and then carefully pushed over. On fills of ten feet or more, extreme caution is advised due to the possibility of a slide caused by poorly compacted material in the middle or lower areas of the pile. As an extra safety measure on deep fill jobs, material should be dispersed in an arc to ensure stable ground for machine support (Fig. 10-8).

It should also be understood that the same principles discussed here apply to the back-filling of trenches and excavations.

***Dispersion techniques.*** Here we will explain the techniques involved in the actual fill procedure, for the entire range of fill area depths recommended for the TLB. The fill area we will examine is the other half of the cutting job described earlier. And the filling process is performed at the same time the cut is done – that is, at the same time cutting is started, the spoil from the cut is transported and the fill is also started.

There are basically two methods of accurately dispersing material: in front of the bucket (going forward), and behind the bucket (going backward). The former approach – dispersing material in front of the bucket – is the most usable of the two, and can be used for all depths of fill.

For shallow fills, the bucket can be dumped quickly, spilling the material in front of the bucket. Then, by moving forward slowly and carefully, following the desired grade with the lower edge of the bucket, the material is dispersed to the correct depth (Fig. 10-9). As the fill deepens, the material is again dumped on the surface of the fill

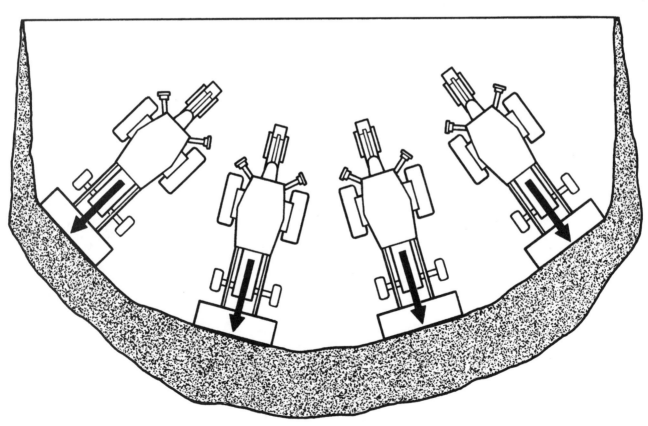

**Fig. 10-8** *By approaching and forming the fill slope in this manner, the TLB will always be positioned on solid ground.*

and pushed forward, piling it high enough to allow for compaction.

Another effective method for shallower and more precise fills is to disperse the material behind the bucket, while traveling backward. Figs. 10-10 through 10-13 illustrate how this is done. Notice that the angle at which the bucket contacts the ground is different in each photo. When a shallow fill is desired, the bucket is positioned to pull the material back and disperse it very gradually. As the amount of material remaining behind the bucket is reduced, the bucket is rolled to allow for even dispersion.

***2. Compaction*** – The second phase of the filling procedure is stabilizing the fill material, which is accomplished by compacting it, using the weight of the TLB (Fig. 10-14).

The fill area should be compacted as the fill procedure goes on, and the grade corrected as the work continues. The grading and compaction in this type of situation can usually be accomplished with little delay before returning to the cut area for more material. The operator can effectively compact the fill when the bucket is full. The TLB

depicted in the photos, with a loader bucket capacity of one cubic yard, will carry 1,700 to 3,250 pounds when full. The weight of the material will vary depending on its water content. In fact, 2,000 pounds of dry soil can weigh up to 3,000 pounds when wet.

Using a full loader bucket and compacting the area with the TLB's front tires will result in the highest degree of compaction capable of the TLB, in the absence of specialized compaction attachments.

## Finish Grading

Finish grading (or fine grading) involves essentially the same principles as rough grading, except that it requires much more precision. Instead of moving the cut-and-fill material in bulk to accomplish the task, finish grading requires the cutting and filling of as little as one to four inches of material. If the rough grading was done correctly, very little additional cutting or filling should be needed – perhaps only a few inches in some spots. Of course, on any finish grading project, the entire area should be smoothed with the loader to produce a clean, even-textured surface – free of dips, bumps and even tire marks.

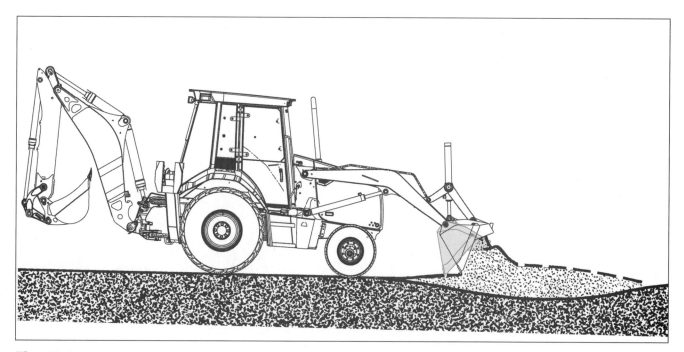

**Fig. 10-9** *When using this method, the bucket is dumped quickly, and the fill depth is adjusted to the correct level by raising or lowering the bucket. In order to achieve accurate results, the TLB must move forward slowly so the operator can make necessary bucket adjustments.*

**Fig. 10-10** *The fill material is dumped, and the bucket is moved past the pile. This photo shows the operator applying down pressure to the bucket to prevent it from sliding over the pile. Once the pile begins to move, the loader control is placed in the "float" position.*

**Fig. 10-11** *As the machine backs up, the bucket is slowly rolled out, more quickly if a deep fill is desired, or less quickly for a shallow fill.*

**Fig. 10-12** *Continue rolling the bucket as the machine travels...*

**Fig. 10-13** *...and the result will be a fill area that will always be tapered into the existing grade, with a smooth working area maintained*

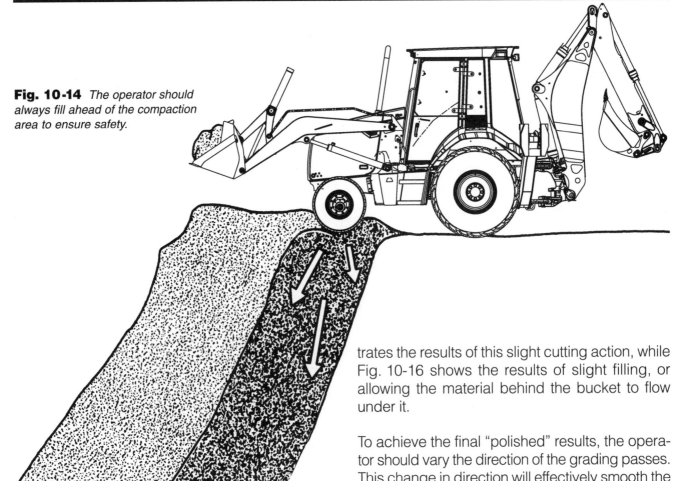

**Fig. 10-14** *The operator should always fill ahead of the compaction area to ensure safety.*

***Finish grading technique.*** Because of the different ground conditions that will be encountered, it is difficult to explain any one finish grading technique that can be used in all cases. However, the method which produces the best finish grading results is to position the loader bucket flat. By using the bucket at a flat or very nearly flat angle, the cut-and-fill can be adjusted to a very fine degree.

At the start of a finish grading job, the site may contain ruts, bumps or any variety of surface irregularities. As work gets underway, the operator will first eliminate the larger bumps, and then continue smoothing and polishing, using special grading patterns which will produce a perfectly smooth area.

When fine grading is required, back-dragging will produce the best results. This is best accomplished with the loader in the float position, and the loader bucket tipped to produce a slight cut. This slight cutting action will continue to fine grade the area as back-dragging continues. Fig. 10-15 illustrates the results of this slight cutting action, while Fig. 10-16 shows the results of slight filling, or allowing the material behind the bucket to flow under it.

To achieve the final "polished" results, the operator should vary the direction of the grading passes. This change in direction will effectively smooth the area and leave it with an evenly textured surface (Fig. 10-17).

When ground conditions are about average, with normal soil hardness, the procedures shown in Figs. 10-18 and 10-19 represent the most useful finish grading method:

***Fig. 10-18:*** The loader bucket is loaded about half full, to provide extra weight as well as a "reserve" of fill material. The TLB is first backed up to the far end of the grading area. The loader bucket is then lowered to the ground in the flat position. The operator begins to slowly move forward. With the bucket perfectly flat on the ground, it will not make a cut, nor will it add any fill to the area. To make a cut when desired, the operator may tip the bucket **down** slightly, and for a fill, he will tip it **up** slightly. In areas where no cut or fill is required, the bucket is returned to the flat position. When the machine has traveled to the farthest area where grading is required, the bucket is raised just high enough to clear the material that has been accumulated, and then moved past it.

**Fig. 10-15** *Back-dragging with the buckets slightly tipped up will produce a cutting action. The cutting abilities of this technique can be increased by adding weight with down pressure, or by adding material to the bucket.*

**Fig. 10-16** *When a fill is desired, the bucket is tipped down slightly. The fill material behind the bucket will flow evenly under it.*

**Fig. 10-17** *After back-dragging the entire area in one direction, the direction of the passes can be changed 60 to 90 degrees to put the finishing touches on the area. Finish grading using this particular grading pattern will produce excellent results.*

***Fig. 10-19:*** Then, this material is then **back-dragged**; first, with the loader lowered all the way, and the bucket tipped up (or back) slightly. This action will trap the accumulated pile behind the bucket. A large pile will offer great resistance, and will require extra weight and a slight cutting action with the bucket. After the pile begins to move, the extra weight of the loader is removed by placing the control in the "float" position.

## Backhoe Grading Techniques

Although the grading capabilities of the backhoe are very limited, it can often be used in situations where the loader cannot, or where the loader operation would be unsafe. These situations may arise in a variety of circumstances, such as job sites with poor access; a working area too small for effective loader use; ground conditions too soft to support the TLB's weight or provide necessary traction for effective loader use; or where slopes or differing elevations do not permit loader use.

One example of how the backhoe may be effectively used for grading work is when the operator must "scratch out" a driveway. This common procedure is necessary whenever a dirt or gravel driveway is to be replaced with concrete. Dirt will usually have to be removed three to five inches below the existing grade. Fig. 10-20 illustrates the procedure.

In other situations, the swing can be used for grading small areas that are either flat or sloped. When using the swing of the hoe to grade, it is important to utilize the backhoe's hydraulics to provide the necessary force, and not the momentum of swinging, to push heavier loads.

The point here is that the swing motion of the hoe can move the bucket faster than it should be for this type of operation, and this should be avoided. The hazard presented by swinging too fast is that a hidden obstruction could suddenly stop the bucket, and severe damage to the structural mem-

**Fig. 10-18** *When fine grading an area, the ideal method is to cut off the high spots on the forward pass...*

**Fig. 10-19** *...and use the accumulated material to fill the low areas on the backward pass.*

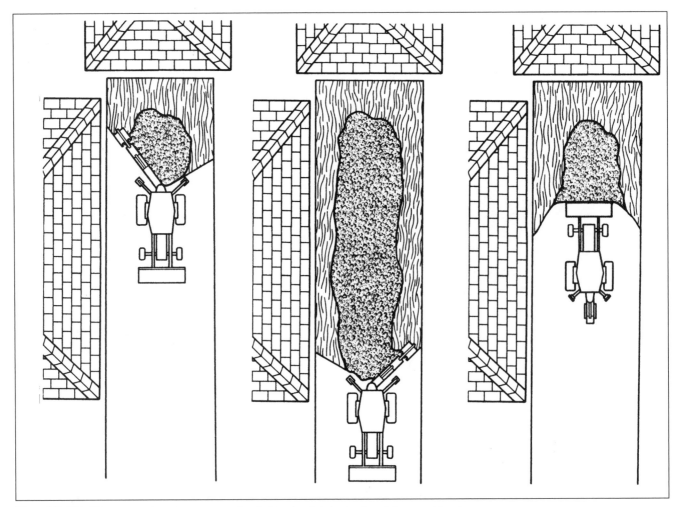

**Fig. 10-20** *This procedure is started at the farthest point desired and the machine is moved forward as work progresses. Hard material is "scratched" and loosened with the bucket teeth. Loosened material is pulled to the center to ease cleanup. The loader is then used to remove the material to a stockpile or for loading onto trucks.*

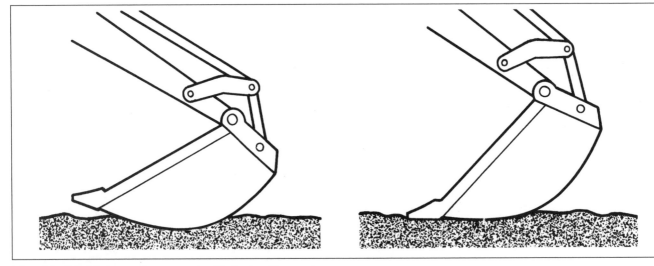

**Fig. 10-21** *When grading an area with the backhoe swing, the bucket should be positioned to produce flat results.*

bers of the hoe could result. Never swing the hoe deliberately into a solid object, such as a wall or stump, or anything that could suddenly stop the boom and crowd assembly. Instead, the swing should be operated slowly and carefully during this type of procedure.

The stabilizers can often be used to tilt the machine slightly in one direction or the other to adjust the grading results. To produce the optimum results, the bucket must be manipulated in such a way that it will produce a flat area, rather than a rounded one, as it contacts the ground (Fig.10-21).

## Compaction

***Principles of compaction.*** Depending on many factors – local weather, water tables, and the presence or absence of rock, sand or gravel – soil may be in any consistency when first encountered. It may be dry or wet, hard or soft, or any condition in between; it may fall apart easily, or be quite difficult to break up. In any case, however, once the soil has been dug up and worked around the job site by the TLB or other earthmoving equipment, it will be fairly loose. For this reason, filling or backfilling will often require compaction of the material.

The compacting procedure could involve anything from light wheel-rolling to the use of specialized compaction equipment or attachments. In some areas, strict testing of soil density is required prior to and during construction, to minimize the risk of future subsidence or other ground movement. In these situations, soil engineers will work with the TLB operator, testing the percentage of compaction as work progresses. During these operations, several principles of compaction must be followed to achieve the desired results. Essentially, compaction is accomplished by applying great weight or impacts on the area to be compacted. These compaction forces compress the soil downward and outward at an angle, as shown in Fig.10-22.

For the actual compaction of the soil to occur, two things must happen: excess air and water must be forced out of the soil and out of the fill area, and the individual particles of soil must be compressed together very tightly.

***Excess air and water removal.*** To achieve the right soil density through compaction, soil must be placed in layers thin enough to permit the expulsion of air and water. Some soils, depending on their content, may be placed in thicker layers, or "lifts," than others. This is because some soil types allow greater movement of air and water than others. For example, sandy soil allows air and water to pass through fairly easily, so it can be layered in thicker lifts than clay, which does not easily allow air and water to flow through.

To achieve the highest degree of compaction, soil is often placed in lifts of about twelve inches. When compaction is not a critical factor, lifts may be increased in thickness to eighteen or twenty-four inches, to speed the filling procedure.

***Compression.*** Viewed on a very small scale, compaction serves to compress individual soil particles together. When soil is dry, this compression is resisted due to friction between the particles. However, this friction can be effectively

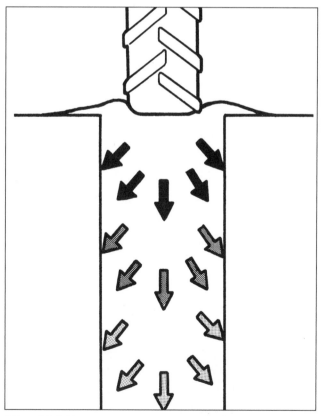

**Fig. 10-22** *As the machine drives over the area, the forces not only radiate straight down, but also at an angle into the sides of the excavation. Compaction is greatest near the surface, and forces are reduced as depth increases.*

reduced by providing lubrication to the soil, in the form of water. Compaction cannot be done effectively with dry soil. Once the soil becomes wet, the individual particles will come together more closely, and the area will begin to sink.

On the other hand, the soil shouldn't be over-saturated. Too much water can make the soil muddy or mucky, and compaction will be impossible. Also, too much water can actually prevent compression when the excess water cannot escape into the surrounding soil.

In order to achieve the optimum water content, soil should be moistened evenly, with enough water to dampen it, but not so much that it will become muddy or mucky. Since water content is critical, it is a good idea to have a worker moisten the soil as it is filled or back-filled into the trench. When soil is very dry, it will be necessary to push or dump it into the fill area very slowly, to ensure even and complete moistening.

***Jetting.*** This is another useful method of using water as a compaction tool. It involves the injection of great amounts of water into the area to be compacted, using a water hose equipped with a solid pipe on the end (Fig. 10-23). By injecting water in this manner, it will actually perform most of the "work" of compaction, the way it usually occurs in nature. This technique is more useful in sandy or gravelly soils than clay or other soils that do not allow the water to escape easily. It can also be effective when applying quick road patches, as it provides stability to the area.

Figs. 10-24, 10-25 and 10-26 depict how jetting can be applied most effectively under several different soil conditions.

## Wheel Rolling

Although wheel rolling may seem to consist simply of running over an area with the TLB's wheels, it must be done very methodically. Filling and back-filling are common TLB procedures, and in many cases, compaction will also be required, as we have noted. Wheel rolling is the most common technique for accomplishing the necessary compaction.

In order to achieve the highest degree of compaction possible, the loader bucket should be filled with heavy material. With the bucket loaded, the operator then rolls the front wheels over the entire fill area. This procedure is then repeated two, three, or even four times, until the area is completely stabilized. It is important to note that when the loader bucket is loaded, the front wheels will achieve a greater degree of compaction than the rear wheels, even though more of the machine's weight is concentrated over the rear wheels.

It should also be pointed out that the operator must always exercise great caution when entering and traveling over the fill area. The safest approach is to load the loader bucket about half full, and then slowly move the front tires into the fill. Watch the fill material carefully as the tires enter the area; if they begin to sink deeply into the fill material (Fig. 10-27), the bucket can be lowered as the operator backs the machine up. This will fill the depression caused by the front tires, and prepare the area for the next wheel rolling cycle.

This fill-compact-fill process is continued until the area is stabilized enough to hold the weight of the TLB. Then, the loader bucket may be loaded as full as possible, for added weight. (Remember that wet material is much heavier than dry, and

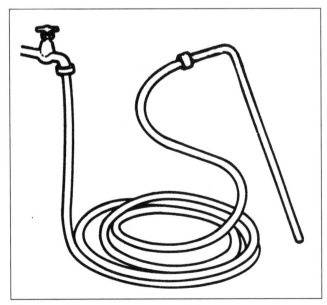

**Fig. 10-23** *Typical jetting tool and hose.*

## Jetting

***Fig. 10-24*** (below) – Here a trench Is back-filled to the existing grade with loose spoil. Water is introduced at the lower end of the trench; as that area becomes flooded, the jet is moved to the other sections of the trench.

As the trench is compacted from the bottom, the back-filled material will gradually sink. The water level is then raised by bringing up the end of the jet. Again, the jet is moved around to various sections of the trench so that the lower levels are thoroughly saturated. If the water seeps quickly into the material and no puddles accumulate on the surface, the fill material can be saturated to within twelve inches of the existing grade. If the water does not soak in easily, then the saturation level should not be raised higher than twenty-four inches from the existing grade.

***Fig. 10-25*** (next page). – By keeping the top layer of the fill area from being saturated, the area can then be safely wheel-rolled with the TLB without becoming unstable. However, if the ground does not accept the water easily, then

wheel rolling will force it to the surface, and the area will become mucky and unstable. If the material accepts water easily, this usually won't be a problem.

***Fig. 10-26***. (next page) – Here we see an area with clay soil being jetted. The most important consideration when introducing water into this type of soil is to remember that the water will not be easily absorbed into the sides of the excavation. Water will instead become trapped within the fill material, and if weight is applied to the area, it will rise to the surface, making the area unstable for the support of wheeled vehicles. if jetting is done correctly, however, the area will support the TLB without sinking in.

In order to achieve stability in these situations, water must be injected in such a way that the lower levels will not be flooded, and the top three feet of the fill area should be moistened only if the soil is very dry. This way the dry section near the surface will provide a "cap" on the moistened level underneath, and will provide adequate support for wheel-rolling.

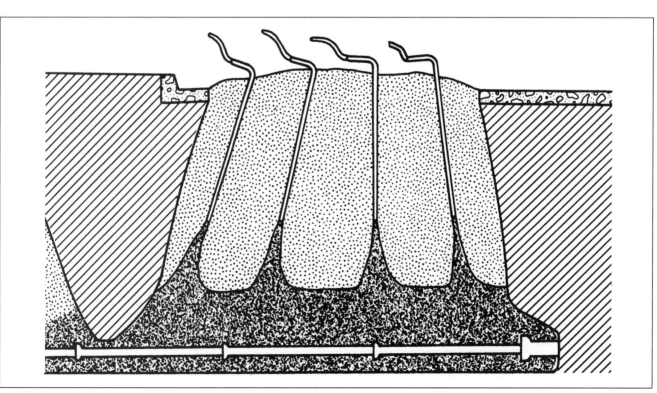

**Fig. 10-24**

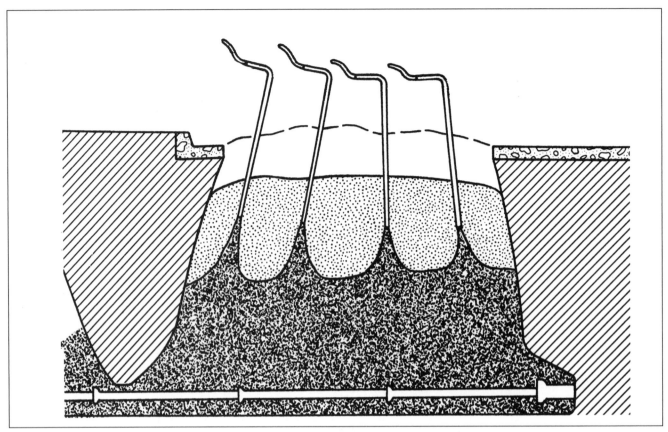

**Fig. 10-25**

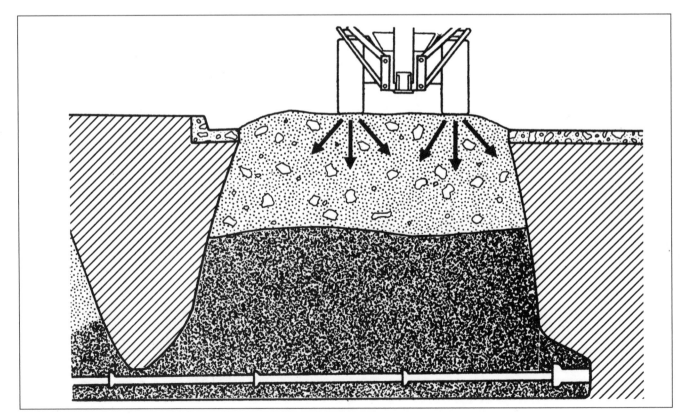

**Fig. 10-26**

therefore will achieve greater soil compaction.) Then the TLB is repeatedly driven forward and backward over the area, until the desired results are achieved (Fig. 10-28). Once compaction is completed, the area is finish graded, as seen in Fig.10-17 (see **Finish Grading**).

## Compaction Attachments

Because soil compaction is such an important element in structural stability, it is usually given much attention during the construction process. The contractor has several options available to him to ensure proper compaction; the TLB, equipped with any one of several compaction attachments, is one of these options. There are several types of attachments available, and some are more effective than others.

The most common type of attachment is basically a large "vibrator," consisting of a hydraulic motor mechanically attached to an eccentric weight. When actuated, the spinning weight causes the attachment to vibrate very forcefully.

Another type in common use is a "hoe-ram" or hydraulically operated jackhammer attachment. A plate is attached instead of the hammer point, and the force of the repeated blows compacts the soil very effectively.

These two types of compactors aren't capable of compressing large areas efficiently, but are useful in a variety of potential problem situations. For example, when plumbing and electrical contractors are required to compact trenches or other excavations, a TLB with a compaction attachment is an excellent choice. With labor costs skyrocketing, and with the manpower required for manual compaction, the TLB also becomes an economical choice.

In addition, when deep excavations require compaction, the TLB may be the only choice from a safety standpoint. The vibration caused by most compaction methods makes it unacceptable to put laborers into the excavation. The TLB, however, can work from the top, in a safe setup, and be out of danger in case a cave-in occurs.

**Fig. 10-27** *When backfilling a trench, the trench is filled, and loader is used to compact that material.*

**Fig. 10-28** *More material is added to fill in the low areas.*

**Fig. 10-29** *This process is then repeated until the area is brought up to grade with the surrounding area.*

## Questions – Chapter 10 **Grading and Compaction**

**1. Grading consists of:**

_____ a. Cutting down the high places

_____ b. Filling in the low places

_____ c. Both of the above

**2. The cut and fill areas of a grading job will become clear to the operator by visualizing the desired grades and comparing them to the existing grades.**

_____ a. True

_____ b. False

**3. Filling often requires compaction of the earth and then refilling and leveling to the desired grade.**

_____ a. True

_____ b. False

**4. The attitude or angle of the machine and the loader bucket (level or not, left to right) is determined by the angle of the ground where the front tires are making contact.**

_____ a. True

_____ b. False

**5. A bucket level check is used to:**

_____ a. Check the accuracy of the bucket level indicators

_____ b. Determine the level position of the bucket

_____ c. Both of the above

_____ d. None of the above

**6. A cutting pass that is too deep or not deep enough can be corrected on the next several passes.**

_____ a. True

_____ b. False

**7. In order to allow for compaction in a fill area, the material should be dispersed:**

_____ a. Lower than the desired grade

_____ b. At the desired grade

_____ c. Higher than the desired grade

_____ d. None of the above

*Notes:* _____

_____

_____

_____

_____

_____

_____

_____

_____

_____

_____

_____

_____

_____

_____

_____

_____

_____

_____

_____

_____

_____

_____

_____

_____

_____

_____

_____

_____

_____

_____
_____
_____
_____
_____
_____
_____
_____
_____
_____
_____
_____
_____
_____
_____
_____
_____
_____
_____
_____
_____
_____
_____
_____
_____
_____
_____
_____
_____

**8. Dispersing the material can be done:**

_____ a. In front of the bucket going forward

_____ b. Behind the bucket going backward

_____ c. Both of the above methods

_____ d. Neither of the above methods

**9. Using a full loader bucket and compacting the area under the TLB's front tires will result in the highest degree of compaction.**

_____ a. True

_____ b. False

**10. When finish grading, the loader bucket should be flat or nearly flat so that the cut and fill can be adjusted to very fine degree.**

_____ a. True

_____ b. False

**11. For the best results when back dragging with the loader, the operator should use:**

_____ a. Downward pressure on the bucket

_____ b. The bucket slightly off the ground

_____ c. Loader in the float position

_____ d. None of the above

**12.  To achieve the final polished results, the operator should back-drag the entire area in one direction, and then:**

_____ a. Repeat in the same direction as the first passes

_____ b. Back-drag the entire area in another direction 60 to 90 degrees from the first passes

_____ c. Repeat in the opposite direction from the first passes

_____ d. Repeat in the same direction as the first passes with the bucket tipped down slightly

**13. Back-dragging with the front of the bucket slightly tipped up will produce a filling action.**

_____ a. True

_____ b. False

**14. When back-dragging, the cutting abilities of the loader can be increased:**

_____ a. With down pressure on the loader

_____ b. By adding material to the bucket

_____ c. Both of the above

_____ d. None of the above

**15. When back-dragging and a fill is desired, the front of the bucket is:**

_____ a. Tipped up slightly from the level position

_____ b. Tipped down slightly from the level position

_____ c. Both of the above

_____ d. Neither of the above

**16. When a fine finish grade is desired in a large area the operator should:**

_____ a. Back-drag the entire area in one direction

_____ b. Change direction from 60 to 90 degrees and back-drag again

_____ c. Both of the above

_____ d. None of the above

**17. When fine grading an area, the procedure is to cut off the high spots on the forward pass and use the accumulated material to fill the low areas on the backward pass.**

_____ a. True

_____ b. False

**18. Under what circumstances would the operator use the backhoe for grading?**

_____ a. Poor access or the work area is too small to use the loader

_____ b. Ground conditions too soft

_____ c . Where slopes or differing elevations are present

_____ d. All of the above

**19. Swinging the backhoe bucket into a solid object could cause severe damage to the backhoe.**

_____ a. True

_____ b. False

_____

_____

_____

_____

_____

_____

_____

_____

_____

_____

_____

_____

_____

_____

_____

_____

_____

_____

_____

_____

_____

_____

_____

_____

_____

_____

_____

_____

_____

**20. Soil that has been dug up by the backhoe will be loose and will require compaction when filling or back filling.**

_____ a. True

_____ b. False

**21. Compaction is accomplished by applying great weight or impacts to the area to be compacted.**

_____ a. True

_____ b. False

**22. When soil is too dry, compaction is resisted due to friction between the soil particles.**

_____ a. True

_____ b. False

**23. Jetting is a technique that is most useful in clay or silty soils.**

_____ a. True

_____ b. False

# 11. Backhoe Techniques

Up until now we have explored various aspects of TLB operation and issues relating to operation, such as maintenance and safety. In the next two chapters, however, we will dig into the specifics of the TLB operator's day-to-day excavating work.

The TLB is designed to perform a number of different tasks and is capable of some applications even the manufacturers probably didn't think of. The bulk of the work to be performed with the TLB, however, is basic earth-moving, and this is accomplished with one or the other of the two buckets. In this chapter we will discuss techniques involved in the use of the backhoe as an earth excavating and transporting tool, and how the operator can master its use in the completion of whatever job he is asked to perform.

## Purpose of the Excavation

Because of the wide range of tasks which the TLB is able to perform, there is also a wide range of different job requirements the operator will need to be familiar with. When any digging job is begun, the most obvious task is the movement of the earth that will be required. Although this may seem to be the most important aspect of a digging job, it is often the part of the procedure that will require the least amount of attention. There are many other aspects that are more important to achieving safe,

professional results, depending on the type of excavation, and we will discuss them here.

***Movement of the earth.*** Even the simple task of removing the amount of earth necessary for an excavation includes other important, but less obvious, considerations. In fact, digging is only half of the process – the other half is correct placement of spoil. While this may not be a vital element of completing an excavation, it is critical to the completion of the job as a whole.

If, for example, an excavation must be backfilled after a section of pipe has been laid, then the spoil should be placed so it can be easily backfilled using the loader. Or, if spoil is to be removed from an area and stockpiled elsewhere, it must be placed in such a way that picking it up with the loader will be easy. If, on the other hand, the excavation will be a working area for other workers, the spoil must be placed far enough away from the excavation so the weight of the pile won't cause a cave-in.

These are all examples of how the operator must think about the entire scope of a job, from beginning to end. Adequate planning can save the operator time and work, and the job will generally proceed more easily and with fewer problems.

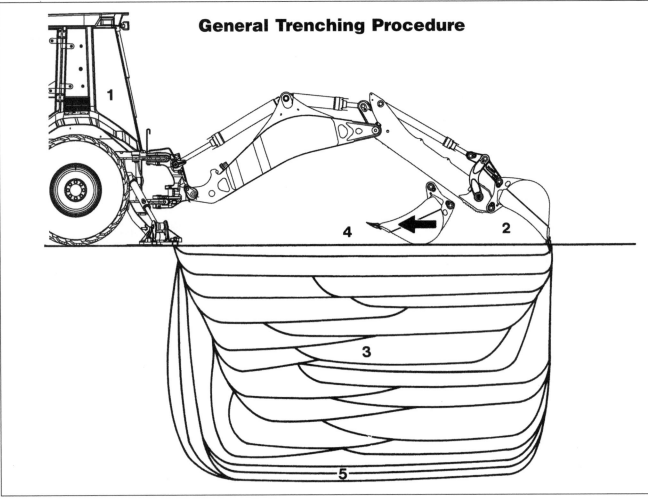

**General Trenching Procedure**

**Fig. 11-1**

*1. Check the Set-up* for safety and alignment with the trench.

*2. Surface Cut* – *The first cut of each section should be shallow, with the operator concentrating on the bucket, making sure the cut is in the exact location desired. This cut will guide the bucket during the rest of the excavation process, so by cutting the first pass in exactly the correct place, the remaining passes will also be correct.*

*3. Bulk Spoil Removal* – *Dig the trench down to within six inches of the desired grade. Depending on the possibility of utilities in the area, this digging may proceed as quickly as possible, or may demand that digging proceed slowly, with great caution.*

*4. Prepare the excavation area* – *At this point, the operator should clean the sides, or "sidewalks," of the trench. By sliding the bucket flat on the surface area next to the trench, the accumulated spoil will either be pushed back away from the trench, or fall back into it, to be removed in the final grading. Also, any rocks, concrete, or any object which may pose a hazard to other workers should be cleared from the area.*

*Rocks exposed in the sides of the trench should also be checked and dislodged and removed if they are not securely in place. Any other tasks that need to be done before moving the machine forward to the next section should be taken care of at this time. The area is then ready for final grading of the trench bottom.*

*5. Fine Grading the Trench Bottom* – *The operator will now make a series of long, grading passes on the bottom of the trench, and also remove any spoil pushed back into the trench during step 4, along with the remaining few inches of dirt. As the trench bottom nears the desired grade, the operator and/or the workers assisting him will check the grade with a measuring tape, builder's level, or whatever grade-checking method is being used for the excavation procedure. After getting the go-ahead signal from the grade-checkers, the operator makes the necessary remaining cuts until the trench reaches the desired grade. He will also remove any accumulated material in the near end of the trench and make more cuts if necessary to complete the trench as close to the machine as possible.*

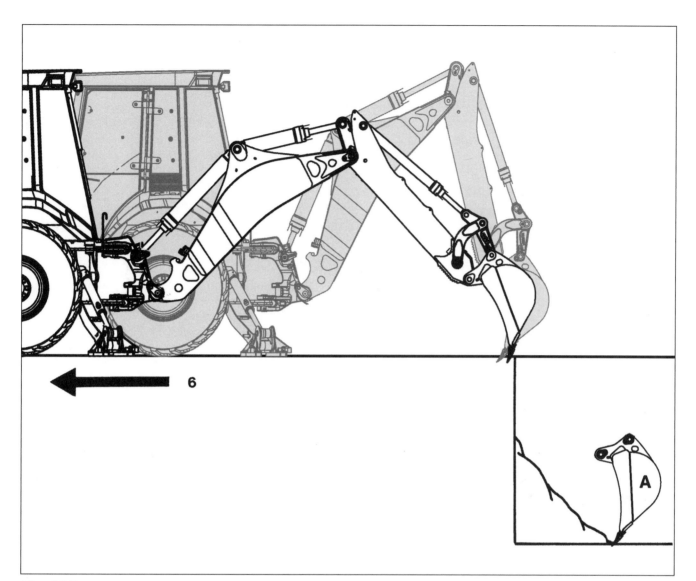

**Fig. 11-2**

***6. Move To The Next Set-up —*** *At this point, the TLB is moved forward to the next trench section, either by using the drive wheels, or by propelling the machine with the hydraulic power of the backhoe. If the latter method is used, the bucket is first drawn in close to the machine and lowered until the teeth penetrate into the soil and the machine is held firmly in place. If the tripod set-up is being used, the loader bucket is then lifted off the ground slightly, as well as the stabilizers. Then check the direction of the front tires and turn them in the desired direction, if necessary. Check the area for safety aspects, and warn workers in the area to stand back from the TLB.*

*Now, by using the crowd and the boom, the machine is slowly and carefully propelled forward. The operator should check the bucket to make sure it doesn't raise up out of the soil, which could cause him to lose control of the machine.*

*The point of this procedure is to correctly position the TLB for the next setup, and therefore, the distance that the machine is moved forward is very important. The machine should be moved as far as possible while still being able to reach the farthest point in the trench where removal of dirt is necessary (A).*

*The operator should also understand that the deeper the excavation, the shorter each section will be. This is because the bucket's "reach" behind the machine is reduced as it is lowered deeper, and the length of the "flat bottom" the machine is able to dig will be less as well.*

*As the TLB reaches the next setup, the entire six-step trenching procedure is repeated, beginning with step 1, the setup check.*

**183**

***Safety of other workers.*** The safety of any procedure is, of course, the most important aspect of any TLB job, and the operator is responsible for many of the safety aspects of a job. Leaving aside for a moment many of the other ways the operator is responsible for safety on the job, let's examine how he can provide a safer working area in and around the excavation.

Some of the safety measures the operator can take include: sloping the sides of the excavation when necessary; smoothing the sloped area and dislodging any exposed rocks, chunks of dirt or any other materials which may present a hazard; cleaning the top of the excavation of loose spoil, rocks or other materials that could fall back in; and monitoring the soil conditions, warning other workers of possibly dangerous situations.

***Precise excavation.*** As explained in the chapter on footings, precision digging requires that the excavation be dug in an exact location to an exact elevation and, usually, with a flat, level bottom. This kind of precision is usually only necessary for footings.

***Level final grade.*** This is a requirement common to excavations and trenches. The finished bottoms of excavations for septic tanks, electrical or telephone vaults, leach fields, etc., must always be level. In addition, trenches for footings, leach lines, and many types of pipelines must also usually have level bottoms.

***Required depth.*** Utility lines are commonly buried to a predetermined depth to make locating them easier. Depending on local regulations, company policies, job standards or requirements called for in the blueprints, the only trench requirement may be one of depth, as measured from the ground surface. For example, electrical mains may be required to be four feet deep, while a gas main might only be required to go down thirty inches. In such cases, the trench will be dug to the desired depth, and will follow the contour of the surface – even up or down slopes, if they are present.

***Gravity flow trench.*** This is a common requirement for sewer lines, drain pipes and drainage ditches. Some jobs are very exacting, while others will have plenty of "fall" and will be less exacting.

By studying these different job situations, it is easy to see that all excavations have a definite purpose, and a set of different requirements to achieve that purpose.

### The Purpose of the Excavation

In order to put all of this knowledge to use, the operator must ask certain questions before starting work:

• What is the purpose of the excavation; what will it be used for?

• Will the excavation later be a working area for other personnel, and if so, what can be done to ensure their safety?

• Will the excavation require precision digging? What tools and assistance will be needed in order to achieve the desired results?

• Will the trench require a level bottom? What procedure should be followed to achieve this result?

• If the only trench requirement is that it be dug to a certain depth, what tools or procedures can be used to accomplish this?

• Will the trench serve as a drainage ditch, or be used for a sewer line or other gravity flow application? What digging procedure can be followed to get the desired results?

• How much material must be removed? Will there be enough room for a stockpile? Will the spoil be used for backfill soon? If not, will it have to be stockpiled elsewhere?

## Extendable Dipperstick Procedure.

The extendable dipperstick models can ease the digging process greatly and can speed the work of digging by reducing the number of set-ups necessary. There are several ways the work of the TLB is affected when the extendable dipperstick is used:

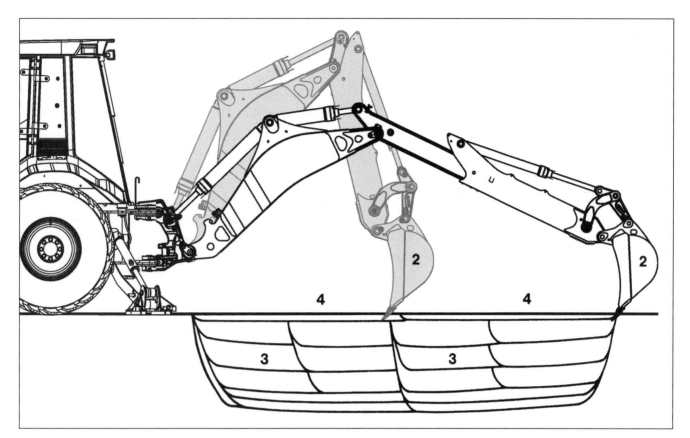

**Fig. 11-3** *The extendable dipperstick procedure is the same as the standard hoe procedure, except it is divided into two stages, the first with the stick extended, and the second with it retracted. The numbers refer to the same steps as the standard hoe procedure.*

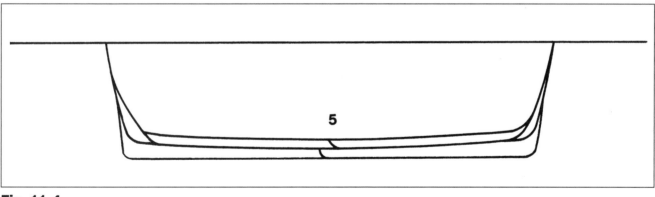

**Fig. 11-4**

• The **reach** of the machine is increased. This means the TLB can not only dig **deeper** and **farther**, but the **stockpiling range** is also increased, which is often very helpful.

• When the unit is extended, the **precision** capabilities of the TLB and the operator are **decreased**.

• As the stick is lengthened, the **digging power** of the machine is **decreased**. The farther it is extended, the less power the machine produces at the bucket.

• When the unit is extended, the **stability** of the machine is **lessened**, especially when swinging the load to the side.

It is apparent that while the extendable dipperstick can be a useful feature, it does have some drawbacks. In order to use it most effectively and safely, it should be positioned in the **shortest position possible.** Of course, this doesn't mean the operator should avoid extending it, but he should extend it only as far as absolutely necessary to perform the task at hand.

The digging procedure, when using a TLB equipped with an extendable dipperstick, is very similar to that of a standard hoe. In order to limit the repeated extending and retracting of the unit, steps 2 through 5 in the general trenching procedure are shown in Figs. 11-3 and 11-4.

As the TLB is moved forward for the next setup in the trenching procedure, the dipperstick should be retracted to its shortest position, as the operator checks the set-up. Then, it is extended outward about halfway, and the **surface cut** and **bulk removal** steps are carried out at the far end of the trench section (Stage 1). After the bulk of the material is removed from this section, the unit is retracted and steps 2 and 3 of the trenching procedure are repeated at the **near end of the trench** (Stage 2).

At that point, steps 2 and 3 are complete, leaving steps 4 and 5 – preparing the area and fine grading the bottom – to complete the procedure. These steps are also divided into two stages – the first being with the unit extended, cleaning and fine grading the far section of the trench and the second stage with the unit retracted, cleaning and fine grading the near section.

Using this procedure will get the best results from the TLB equipped with an extendable dipperstick and will result in a clean, professional excavation in the shortest time.

## Soft Ground Conditions

When working in soft ground, it is easy to fill the bucket quickly while digging. Since there is little resistance against the cutting edges, the bucket can be filled quickly by digging to nearly any depth per cut that the operator desires. If there is little or no chance of utilities being present in the area, digging the soil in deep cuts is acceptable.

The areas where utilities are usually not a problem include open, undeveloped tracts, or on a demolition job where all the utilities are "dead" or out of service. TLB operators don't always have the luxury of knowing positively there are no utilities present, however.

Because of the **threat of utility damage** on the larger percentage of jobs, digging in deep cuts is usually not recommended, regardless of ground conditions. (See chapter on *Utilities*.) In many other instances, **producing a flat, level bottom is important**.

These situations involve such a large portion of the TLB's **problems**, and the operator's **desired results**, that learning the correct digging technique is absolutely necessary to achieving professional results. In short, digging in soft ground gives the operator two options: he can gouge the soil deeply, filling the bucket quickly. Or, when nearing the desired grade, finish grading, or in areas where utilities are a concern, he can fill the bucket gradually, in long, grading-type passes.

## Hard Ground Conditions

Hard ground conditions sometimes cause problems when excavating. These problems can be compounded by using a large bucket, or worn bucket teeth, or an underpowered machine.

The most effective method of digging in this situation is to make long, scraping passes, taking as much material as possible without **stalling** (or stopping) the bucket. When ground conditions are very hard, the operator may only be able to take an inch or two at a time, scraping from as far as the bucket can be filled with accumulated material prior to dumping.

Hard ground conditions also require the operator to understand the geometry of the TLB and the ways in which the machine produces the most power at the cutting edge. In most digging situations, the bucket should be positioned so that the teeth make contact with the ground at an angle from 30 to 45 degrees (Fig. 11-5A). When hard ground is a factor, this angle should be reduced nearly to the point where the back of the bucket makes contact with the bottom of the excavation (Fig. 11-5B). In this position, the teeth become more effective as they cut through the ground with less resistance.

It should also be understood that the power generated by the TLB in this flat cutting attitude is at a maximum, again due to geometric advantages. In fact, the pulling force produced by the machine when positioned this way is the highest the machine is capable of producing.

## Stabilizer Usage and Technique

As we have seen in the chapter on *Set-up*, learning to use the TLB's stabilizers correctly and effectively is a key ingredient in productive, safe backhoe set-ups. If the machine was limited to digging simple trenches in flat, open fields, there would be little need to discuss stabilizer techniques or their applications. As it is, however, with the exception of the TLB that is used only to dig farm drainage ditches and the like, very few TLB operations are that simple.

One of the most commonly used set-ups is the **tripod set-up**, which involves using the loader bucket and the stabilizers to create a three-point platform from which the TLB may work and maneuver. The two stabilizers are by far the most important elements in providing a safe, stable

setup. To provide this stability, they are designed to extend out from, and behind, the machine itself. This extension feature can often cause a space problem, however. In situations where a trench is close to a wall, for example, the stabilizer (when lowered) prevents the center pivot of the swing from being positioned closely enough to dig a straight trench. If the trench is to be used as a footing, the results must be precise. We will discuss how to avoid these problems and how the desired results can be obtained in spite of them.

*Stability.* As their name indicates, the prime function of the stabilizers (or "outriggers") is to provide stability when operating the backhoe. This stability is "engineered" into today's modern TLB, and in common working situations, they do an adequate job of stabilizing the machine. There are, however, many situations where machine stability can be suddenly lost. When performing tasks such as lifting, material handling, or using the extendable dipperstick, the machine can become overloaded and lose balance and overturn (Fig. 11-6). Although there is little chance of the TLB actually rolling over, the operator could be thrown from the machine or tossed violently within the cab, causing injury. Because of this risk, the operator must constantly monitor the weight of the load and the weight distribution of the machine plus the load.

There are other factors which can affect machine stability during operation. One is the ability of

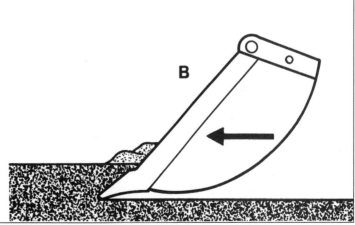

**Fig. 11-5A** *This is the desired bucket attitude for standard digging procedures.*

**Fig. 11-5B** *When hard ground is encountered, the angle should be lowered to increase the digging ability of the machine.*

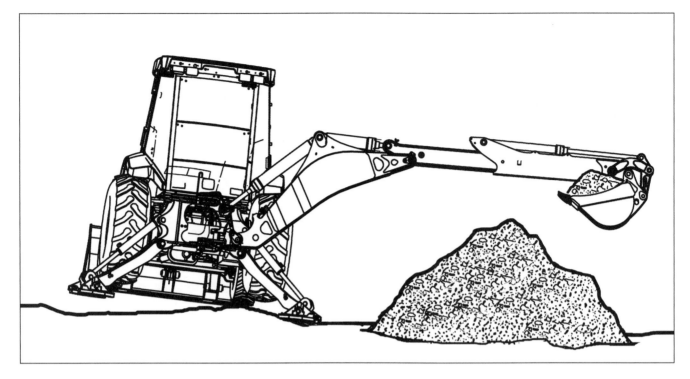

**Fig. 11-6** *CAUTION! When using an large bucket, lifting, material handling, or using the extendable dipperstick, the machine can become overloaded and lose stability.*

the ground to support the weight of the machine plus the load through the stabilizers. Another is the working width of the stabilizers during operation, which is determined by how far they are lowered. When lowered only to ground level, the width from pad to pad is 10 feet (Fig. 11-7). When lowered all the way, the width – and the stability – are reduced (Fig. 11-8). Here we also see that the stabilizers play a part when leveling the machine. When working on a slope or other uneven ground, one stabilizer must be lowered farther than the other, resulting in decreased stability on the lower side. The operator must be aware of these different situations, and how they affect overall machine stability.

***Tilting the machine to work around an object.***
This is a procedure that is used rather infrequently, but can eliminate a problem situation. It is most often needed when the surface cut has been predetermined, and an obstruction is encountered beneath the surface. As illustrated in Fig. 11-9, one stabilizer is lowered farther than the other and the machine is tilted slightly. Stresses in the tractor

and loader can be lessened by lowering the loader so that only one side contacts the ground.

***Note:*** Using this technique will produce an excavation in which one side will have a negative slope. An area such as this should be considered unsafe, and workers should not enter the excavation until it has been properly shored.

## Digging Near a Wall or Fence
Digging against a fixed structure like a wall or fence is a common task for the TLB when working in urban areas. In a few situations, the trench can be moved away from the wall a few feet to simplify the excavation process. However, relocating the trench will be unacceptable in most situations. Footings, for example, must be dug in an exact location, to the exact width and depth.

To achieve results which reflect these exacting standards, the hoe's swing pin must be positioned directly above the center of the ditch. (The closer it is, the more exact the excavation will be.) It is obvious why this could pose a problem for a

**Fig. 11-7** *When the TLB stabilizers are lowered to the ground, the width of the spread is about 11.5 feet (3.53 m)*

**Fig. 11-8** *When stabilizers are lowered all the way, the spread is reduced and machine stability is lessened.*

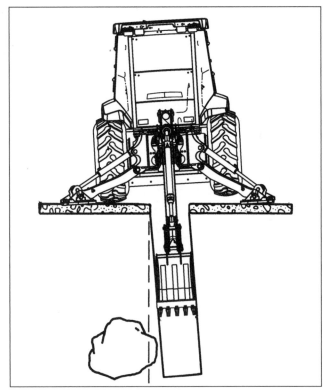

**Fig. 11-9** *When an object is encountered underground, tilting the machine will often allow the bucket to work around the object.*

standard TLB. To ease the excavation of footings and similar procedures adjacent to walls, the side-shift or offset hoe was developed. This machine is designed in such a way that the swing pin can be shifted to either side of the machine, to aid the operator in lining up the machine over the trench.

These machines, however, are still less versatile than the standard center-mount hoe, and are not commonly found in the United States. In Europe, however, where tight working conditions are the rule rather than the exception, the side-shift hoe is a common sight, and the center-mount is a rarity. Digging next to walls is a fairly straightforward task with the side-shift hoe, so we will instead concentrate on methods that can make these types of excavations easier when attempting them with the standard center-mount hoe.

It should be noted that not all situations are the same, and it won't always be possible to get a proper set-up. If the excavation is for something other than a footing (i.e., less exacting), it can usually be dug without having the swing pin aligned exactly.

In this case, during the digging process, the swing may have to be used as the bucket is pulled toward the machine to keep the ditch straight. If the trench width is predetermined by a pavement cut, or if it must not end up wider than the desired dimension, a narrower bucket can be installed to make this operation easier.

In another example, let's say a trench needs to be dug next to a chain link fence. Sometimes the fence can be loosened and raised to allow the stabilizer underneath, greatly easing the set-up and digging processes.

There are some great dangers involved in this type of excavation. When digging near walls, the one thing that should never be done is to take away the support or stability of the wall or structure next to the excavation. Never undermine an existing footing! Because of the danger of collapse, this is a major consideration whenever digging next to a wall or building.

**Set-up techniques.** As we noted, the major aspect of setting up for this type of excavation is the placement of the swing pin. Basically, there are three methods that permit correct placement of the machine. The most common set-up problem here is the stabilizer, which sticks out too far to position the machine close enough to the wall.

**Method #1.** Angle the machine enough so that the swing pin moves closer to the wall (Fig. 11-10). The greater the angle, the closer you can position the pin to the wall (Fig. 11-11). However, as the angle is increased, the arc of the swing is reduced (Fig. 11-12). When this happens, spoil placement can become a problem. Because of the stockpiling limitations of this approach, deep or large excavations will usually be difficult. If no better method is available, the spoil will continuously have to be pulled back to prevent it from falling back into the excavation. This is a tedious process at best. In most circumstances, however, the excavation will be shallow enough so that large quantities of spoil won't be produced, and the swing area will be adequate to complete the job.

## Digging Against A Wall

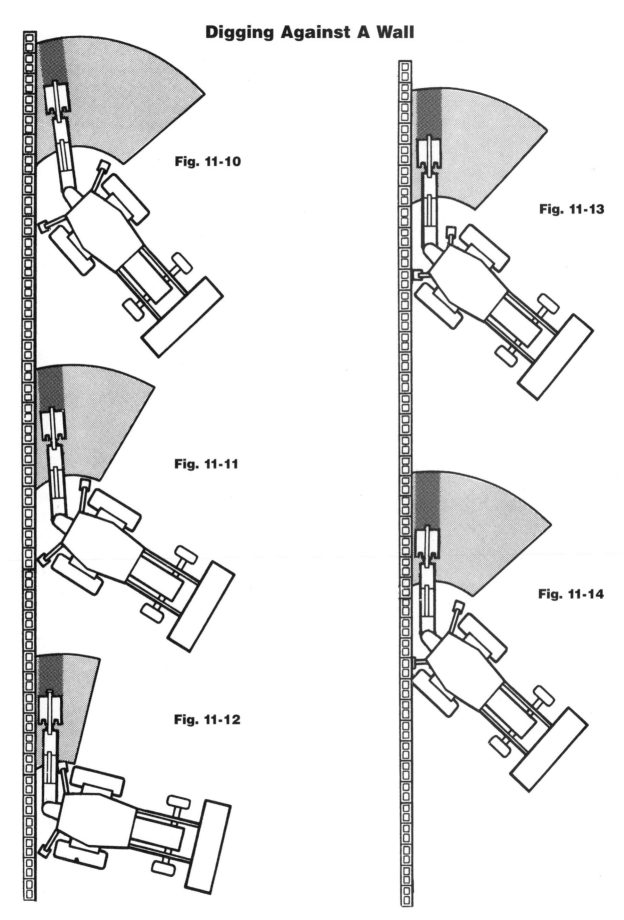

Fig. 11-10

Fig. 11-11

Fig. 11-12

Fig. 11-13

Fig. 11-14

**Method #2.** Another way to place the pin closer to the wall is to reduce the width of the stabilizers spread by lowering them all the way. By combining this maneuver with method #1, the TLB can usually be positioned at less of an angle relative to the wall, increasing the arc of the swing and thus improving the stockpiling range. (Fig. 11-13).

**Method #3.** The last and least desirable method involves raising the stabilizer next to the wall and angling the machine slightly (Fig. 11-14). In this position, the lowered stabilizer will provide the necessary digging support to the machine. The trade-off is that stability is reduced greatly. Although there is little chance of rollover, the machine will shake more and overall control will be affected.

Under some circumstances, where there is no question about the strength of the wall, the stabilizer can be extended to align the swing pin correctly **and** stabilize the machine at the same time. (See **Digging against a bank**.)

**Procedure.** When proceeding with the excavation using a combination of methods #1 and #2, the set-up is repeated continuously; achieving this repetitive set-up requires precise placement of the front loader bucket for the purpose of a pivot. This will allow the operator to pivot the machine easily toward the wall, and into the desired set-up.

Once the operator is ready to start, his first step is to determine the angle necessary to allow proper placement of the swing pin. Once the angle has been determined, the machine can be backed into the correct position, or the front loader bucket can be lowered in the correct spot, and the pivot method can be used to move the rear of the machine.

There are basically two ways of proceeding with an excavation against a wall. One way is to propel and maneuver the TLB with its hydraulic power. The other way is to set up the machine using the loader drive at each setup point.

**Digging against a bank.** This procedure is similar to digging near a wall as far as the set-up is concerned. Because the task is performed with the "inside" stabilizer raised, the machine can be positioned more easily, and closer to the edge. Another advantage here is that the machine may be positioned at a lesser angle relative to the bank, allowing a greater range of spoil placement.

This type of work is most common when excavating hillside foundations. Before attempting such an operation, the slope should be checked carefully for stability. The operator should also check height, angle of the slope, and the safety of the procedure in general.

## Specialized Job Tasks

**Lifting.** Although the backhoe is designed mainly as an excavating machine, it has a wide variety of other, more specialized applications, one of which is lifting. However, lifting requires special care to be done safely. As has been stated earlier, any procedure new to the operator, or one that is rarely performed, should be executed slowly and should be well thought-out ahead of time. Lifting falls into this category of procedures for most TLB operators. Because it usually involves the help of a laborer for the chain or cable hookups, the chance of injury is increased. These operations cannot be rushed; they must proceed at a pace which ensures absolute safety for everyone involved.

Either chains or cables can be used in lifting operations and generally should be rigged as short as possible to prevent the load from swinging out of control. The hook-up should be made in such a way that chain slippage or load shifting during lifting are prevented. A few good and bad chain set-ups are illustrated in Figs. 11-15, 11-16 and 11-17.

## Tunneling

Tunneling with the backhoe may be required in any situation where disturbing or defacing the surface must be kept to a minimum. This could include obstacles such as sidewalks, driveways, curbs and gutters, or street pavement, all of which may have to be preserved undamaged. Or, in some cases, an obstruction such as a pipe may prevent digging straight through as planned. In any event,

**Fig. 11-15** *This lifting hook-up is recommended.*

**Fig. 11-16** *NEVER hook a chain over the teeth as shown. There are several reasons why this is method is unsafe.*

**Fig. 11-17** *NEVER hook the chain like this! During the lifting procedure the chain can slip around the bucket and the load could drop.*

the dirt must be excavated while working around the object.

Sidewalk areas, for example, are city property in most locations. It is common for gas, water and electrical mainlines to be located under them. As a result, unless utility locations have been positively identified, tunneling under sidewalks is usually better accomplished by hand, not with the TLB.

Another point to remember is that the operator's sense of "feeling" with the bucket is diminished as the bucket moves in closer to the machine. When tunneling, or any time the bucket is underneath the machine, it is almost impossible to detect a pipe, and avoid breaking it. This is complicated even further as the operator cannot actually see the bucket or what it is doing, because it is underneath him. This takes some getting used to and requires experience and the ability to control the bucket.

Sometimes the operator thinks the bucket is full, and raises the boom, only to discover he has over-curled the bucket and the spoil has nearly all fallen out.

The operator will get better with practice in this procedure. He will be able to "sense" the position of the bucket and whether it is full or not.

Another approach to this situation is to have someone direct the operator from a position where the bucket is visible. This method is slow, but the amount of material to be removed in most tunneling jobs is relatively small. When the only alternative is hand digging, the key here is cooperation and patience.

As seen in Fig. 11-18, tunneling is best accomplished by digging under the machine. Caution and common sense must be used in any TLB operation, but especially when undermining the area the machine sits on. Generally, tunneling is safe because the stabilizers support the machine's weight, by extending past the undermined area. Any time a safe set-up is impossible, or when the excavation is eight feet deep or more, however, extra caution is advised, and the operator should consider alternatives to undermining the support area.

## Potholing

Potholing is a technique most often used where trenching is required in paved areas, but damage to the surface is to be kept to a minimum. This occurs on a fairly small percentage of jobs, usually in areas where local regulations limit the amount of pavement that can be dug up. Some cities, in fact, charge contractors by the square foot for removed pavement.

Potholing is utilized in one of two ways: 1) it may be a series of holes dug using the same methods described under tunneling, or 2) it may be a series of holes dug at intervals to provide access for boring a tunnel or pushing a pipe with the aid of specialized equipment.

The first method is sometimes used to reduce the need for shoring, usually in sewer line installations of medium range depth (five to ten feet). In most instances, however, this application is totally unsafe and is not recommended in areas where soil is sandy, or contains sand and rocks, or gravel, or any unstable consistency. This technique is more useful in areas where the soil has clay or plastic characteristics. (See Fig. 11-19).

Even in the best soil conditions, however, potholing is not a foolproof procedure. If the area has been excavated previously, the old trench

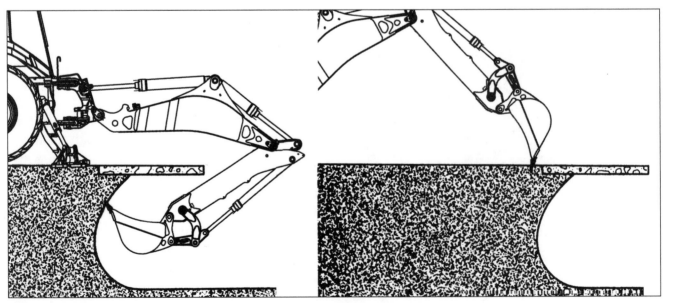

**Fig. 11-18** *When tunneling, the backhoe can actually dig under the machine.*

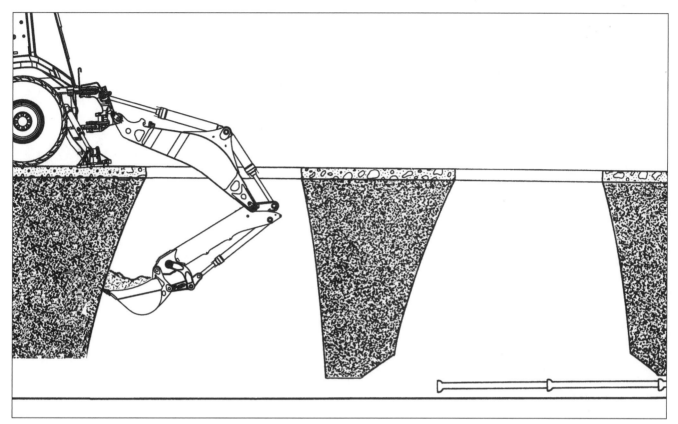

**Fig. 11-19** *This illustration shows the rarely-used potholing procedure as it is used for a sewer line installation.*

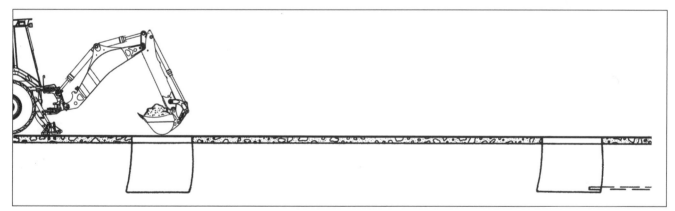

**Fig. 11-20** *The use of potholing during a pipe-pushing procedure.*

presents a hidden, yet very real, danger. With what we learned in previous chapters about the dangers of cave-ins, it is easy to see why care and caution must be used in potholing operations. Shoring or sloping any excavation over five feet is still recommended. When excavating potholes, sloping is obviously not possible, which leaves shoring as the only viable alternative.

Using the potholing method allows the operator to dig a continuous trench while only removing pot-

holes five to eight feet long, with the remaining sections between cuts ten to twelve feet in length. Having a TLB equipped with an extendable dipperstick is often useful in this type of excavating.

The second potholing application is used in conjunction with pipe-pushing, boring or other specialized equipment. It consists of digging small holes spaced at intervals that depend on the type of equipment being used (Fig. 11-20).

## Cribbing Technique – Railroad Applications

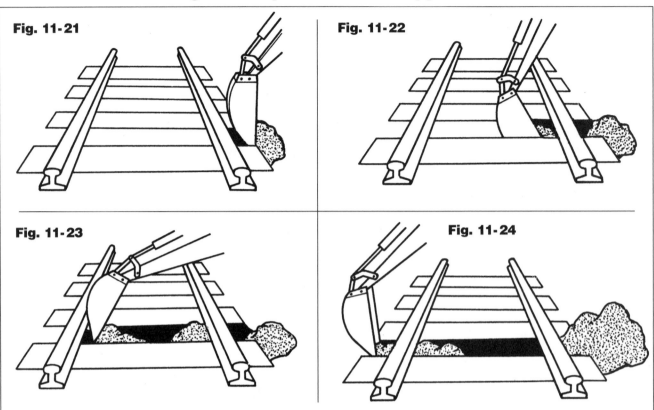

Fig. 11-21

Fig. 11-22

Fig. 11-23

Fig. 11-24

## Cribbing

Cribbing is a technique commonly used by TLB operators involved in railroad bed repairs. However, it is also useful in many other situations, such as when digging and cleaning around pipes. As we discuss the railroad applications of cribbing, the method's usefulness in other situations will become more apparent.

*Railroad applications:* This procedure is used in either of the following two situations: 1) where dirt or mud has filled the spaces between the slag or rocks in the railroad bed, preventing proper drainage and loss of the bed's stability; 2) where spot replacement of ties is necessary. In these applications, the use of a specially made bucket is necessary to fit between the ties. There are several different styles of buckets, but all are very narrow (usually about eight inches) to fit between the ties.

Cribbing can only be done in areas allowing roadway access along the sides of the track for machine setup. Throughout the job, care must be taken to position the machine so that it can always back away from the tracks if and when necessary, in as quick and safe a manner as possible. The operator must also be careful not to damage the tracks themselves. Working around railroads is one of the most dangerous TLB operations, and an extra emphasis must be placed on safety at all times, by everyone involved in the operation.

*Cribbing procedure:* Start by digging down on the near side of the track, from the rail out to the edge of the bed (Fig. 11-21), digging and cleaning both sides of the desired tie at the same time. Then move over the first rail and continue to pull the material to the rail and then push it under (Fig. 11-22). The key idea here is to start near the machine, excavating a "trench" between the ties that will serve as a sort of transfer point for material that is being removed, without piling it on top of the ties. Continue working away from the machine, pulling the material under the near rail (Fig. 11-23). Then, as the area up to the far rail is cleaned, the other side is started (Fig. 11-24), and that new material is pushed under the far rail.

When the digging has proceeded to the farthest point desired, final cleaning and grading is started at the far point, and proceeds toward the machine until completed.

***Cribbing Technique*** – The technique surrounding cribbing actually involves the motion of the bucket. In this case, the bucket is the focus of all movement, and once it is positioned correctly, the operator simply repeats the bucket motion until all spoil has been pushed under the rail. The most effective approach is to push a small pile of spoil to the rail, and then force it underneath by repeated bucket movements (Fig. 11-25). The effectiveness of this move is enhanced slightly by pulling the bucket to the rail in a straight, even motion. This is most useful when forcing the bulk of the material under the rail.

Then, when making the final grading and cleaning passes, push the material as far under the rail as possible, so that it can be handled effectively and the work continued on the near side of the rail. This technique will obviously require some practice in order to be used effectively.

***Other Cribbing Applications*** – Admittedly, most operators will never use their TLB in railroad applications. Why so much emphasis, then, on a technique that will rarely be needed? Because the technique itself is useful in many other situations which are encountered by all operators. For example, cribbing can be a useful procedure when excavating around utilities. Once a line is located, the cribbing procedure is put into practice. This kind of application, however, requires a very light touch. Utility lines obviously are not as strong as a rail. When the lines or pipes are small, or made of plastic or cast iron, it is wise to clean around them by hand, not with the TLB.

## Loading Trucks with the Backhoe

Depending on the hardness of the soil, loading trucks with the backhoe can be quicker and easier than loading with the front end loader. When soil is hard, bucket penetration with the loader may be difficult. In this situation, the soil can be loosened with the backhoe (Fig. 11-26). Or, if a safe set-up is available, the truck can be loaded "pit" style, by positioning the hoe above the truck (Fig. 11-27). When using this technique, the depth of the cut should range from six to eight feet. A cut of this depth will provide a safe set-up, and provide enough material so that time will not be wasted by frequently moving the machine forward.

When soil is soft, such as loose sand or gravel, or when the earth is moist and muddy, maneuvering the loader may be very difficult. When the loader bucket is full, the weight of the load has two effects: 1) The weight will force the front tires into the ground, and 2) the amount of weight on the rear tires will be reduced. This, in turn, will cause the rear wheels to lose traction. This is another situation where loading with the hoe may be more efficient, as well as safer.

To ensure efficiency, the machine should be fitted with the largest size bucket available, up to three feet. Also, the bucket adjustment should be set to

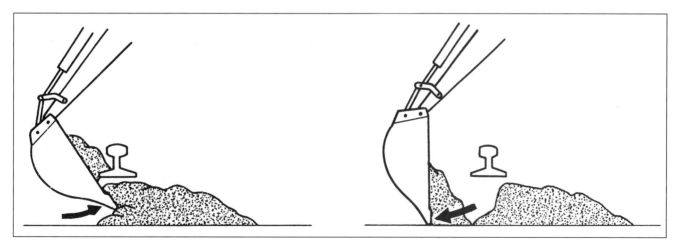

**Fig. 11-25** *A pile of material is pushed to the rail, and by repeating the motion shown, will be effectively "pumped" under.*

**Fig. 11-26** *When soil is too hard for the loader, the backhoe can usually loosen the material adequately.*

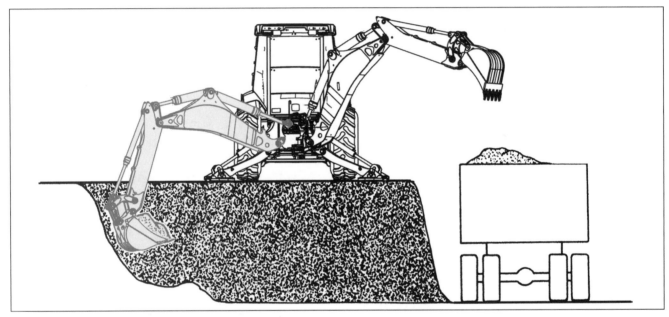

**Fig. 11-27** *Loading trucks with the hoe can also be effective for "pit style" loading.*

allow for maximum curling. Using a larger bucket, it should be pointed out, can cause a stability problem. If this happens, either position the truck closer to the backhoe, or use a smaller bucket.

### Loading trucks while digging an excavation.
This is a fairly common procedure. When the operator knows that spoil is to be trucked out of the area, he should try to load it as it is removed from the excavation. Proceeding with the job in this manner will greatly ease cleanup, and the job will be completed more quickly. When the backhoe is used for trenching, and will be moved forward several times before filling the truck, Fig. 11-28

illustrates a useful set-up for the truck and the backhoe. In this set-up, the truck can move forward easily with the hoe, and the two vehicles work as a team.

If the hoe is digging a large excavation, and can fill the truck from a single set-up without moving forward, Fig 11-29 illustrates a set-up that will help the operator distribute the load evenly in the bed of the truck. One prime consideration, of course, is to prevent damage to the truck (see Figs. 11-30 and 11-31).

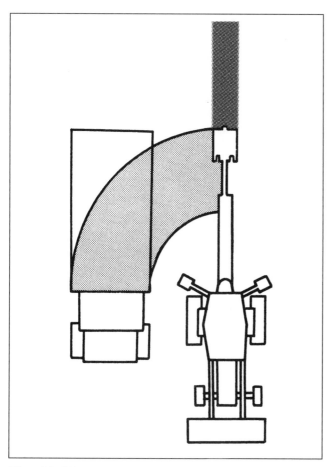

**Fig. 11-28** *By using this truck setup, the truck can easily move forward with the machine as the work progresses.*

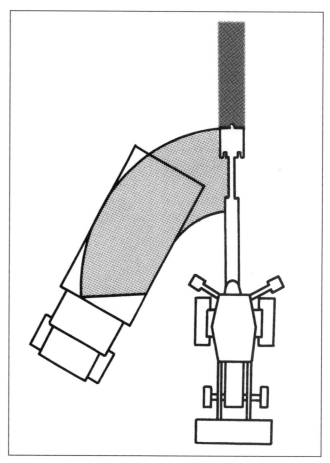

**Fig. 11-29** *Using this truck setup will ease the distribution of the material in the truck.*

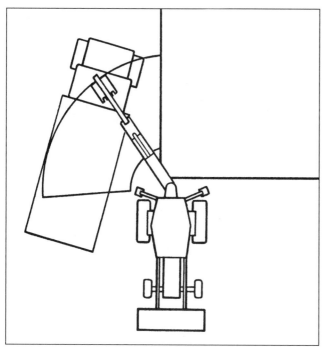

**Fig. 11-30** *Never swing a load over the cab of a truck.*

**Fig. 11-31** *When lifting and swinging the load, be careful to clear the corner of the truck.*

## Material Handling

Sometimes, while on the job site, the TLB operator will be asked to move, load or maneuver an object or objects. Any large object too heavy or awkward to be moved by hand could be included. When such a request is made, the operator should study the entire scope of the task, from beginning to end. The operator is responsible for the safety of himself and others, to the machine, and to the work area. And he alone knows what his machine is capable of. Here again is an example of a situation new or unusual to the operator, and thus the dangers are increased.

Most of the objects which the TLB operator is asked to move will be relatively simple to handle but some will be difficult and dangerous. Some objects should not even be attempted. It is up to the operator to determine the degree of difficulty in each material handling job.

The main element of avoiding problems, once again, is control. Controlling an object means moving it exactly as the operator desires. This is best accomplished by maneuvering the bucket directly under the object's center of gravity and pinching it tightly between the bucket and crowd. The object will then be securely held and controlled by the operator.

When handling odd-shaped concrete chunks or large rocks, moving these objects smoothly is very important to prevent shifting of the load and losing the machine's grip on it. This is especially true when handling or loading out concrete. As the boom is raised, the bucket naturally slants down and the piece must be gripped firmly to prevent it from falling out.

Handling these types of materials requires a very delicate touch on the controls to slowly and smoothly move the object. Whenever the operator

**Fig. 11-32** *In this situation, the operator needs to transport an log down a narrow road.*

tries to pick up any object, whether a piece of concrete, a rock, or even a telephone pole, he must consider its center of gravity. Think about how the object's weight is distributed into the ground where it rests.

Some tricky maneuvering is often required to get the bucket under the object and "grab" it in a way that keeps it from falling out. This type of maneuvering often separates the men from the boys, so to speak, because it requires total bucket control. It's not the same as digging a trench or hole, with the bucket going through normal digging cycles. Digging, scooping, swinging, and dumping are rhythmic operations and smoothness is easy to maintain. When picking up objects, however, there is no rhythm, and maneuvering the bucket and the object often proves jerky and awkward for the inexperienced operator.

**Fig. 11-33** *By swinging the load to the uphill side and lowering the stabilizer, the load can safely be swung to the side and the log can be moved.*

## Land Clearing Procedures

Although the TLB is not the best choice for this type of work, it can be used effectively for small jobs involving the clearing of trees or brush. (Track loaders or bulldozers are better suited for this type of work.) This may include the removal of small shrubs, bushes and other types of low lying vegetation, small trees and saplings, or larger trees up to a foot in diameter. Removing trees larger than this shouldn't be attempted, because they are simply too much for a machine of this size to handle.

The entire procedure should be carried out so that the downed trees and brush won't be in the machine's way as clearing proceeds. Trees should be downed in an orderly fashion, and piled neatly, so removal will be easier when the time comes. Fig. 11-37 illustrates how clearing should progress, and the proper positioning of downed trees. After the first swath has been cut through the area, the procedure will become easier on succeeding passes. The first pass should be twenty to twenty-five feet wide, piling the downed trees on both sides of the cut. Subsequent passes should be slightly narrower (15 to 20 feet), and material should all be downed on the side that has been cleared (Fig. 11-38).

## Clearing Techniques

**Brush and bushes.** This is a straightforward procedure, using the clearing patterns described above. The teeth of the bucket, and the "tooth grab" method, can both be used effectively. The bucket teeth can be used to "comb" or "rake" the area clean of this type of vegetation. Also, the tooth grab is very useful when pulling out bushes without digging up the area and creating unnecessary holes. When clearing this type of material, it is easy to position the spoil on the side of the swath, which simplifies succeeding passes through the area.

**Saplings.** Young trees up to three inches in diameter can be removed by using the same procedures outlined for brush and bushes. Again, the tooth grab method can be useful, as long as the trees aren't brittle. If this is the case, and the trees

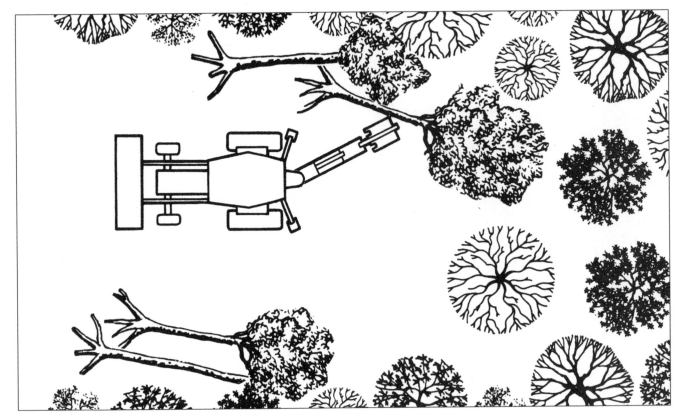

**Fig. 11-37** *When clearing trees, the first pass through the area should be as wide as possible, pushing trees to both sides of the path.*

won't stand being bent to the extent necessary for using the tooth grab method, they can be removed using the push-pull method described. If they are flexible, however, they can be easily removed and stockpiled in one motion, using the tooth grab method.

***Larger trees.*** When trees four inches in diameter and larger are to be removed, the most useful method is the push-pull method. The first step is to push the tree over and away from the machine (Fig. 11-39), and then loosen and free the remaining roots from the ground by pulling at the stump (Fig. 11-40). When using this method, the machine's pushing ability can be increased by rolling the loader bucket down all the way and lowering it firmly to the ground. This will stabilize the machine and prevent it from being pushed instead of the tree. This method is preferable to using the machine's swing to down trees, because the trees can be controlled more effectively, and the push-pull approach is generally safer than using the swing.

The direction in which the trees fall can often be a problem, and the operator must be able to control the direction of the fall, or the procedure can be unsafe. This means the operator must be able to make the trees fall exactly as he desires. If a tree falls in any other way, the operator is not in control and the job can become unsafe. There are several factors that determine where the tree will most likely fall. The operator must take these into consideration and judge the best direction in which to attempt the fall.

If the tree is leaning in one direction, it is very difficult to make it fall in another direction. In this case it is best to fell the tree in the direction of its natural lean. If this isn't possible for some reason, other means may have to be found to bring it down.

Also, if there is any wind on that particular day, the operator must take it into consideration. The strength and direction of the wind can change the plans of the job completely. If possible, the operator can use the wind to his advantage, by planning to down all trees in the same direction, with the wind.

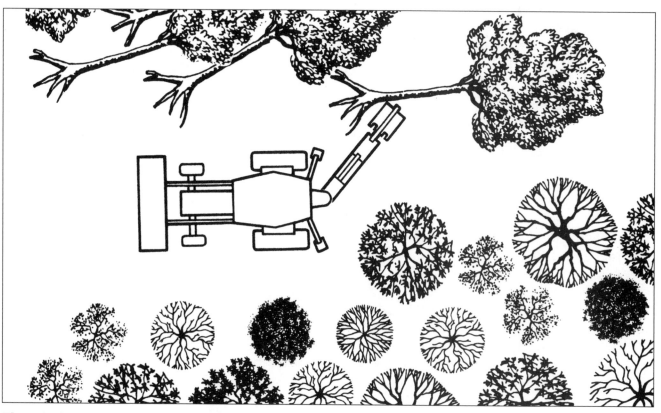

**Fig. 11-38** *On later passes, about half the original width will work well. This will allow the operator to push the trees downed earlier away from those still standing.*

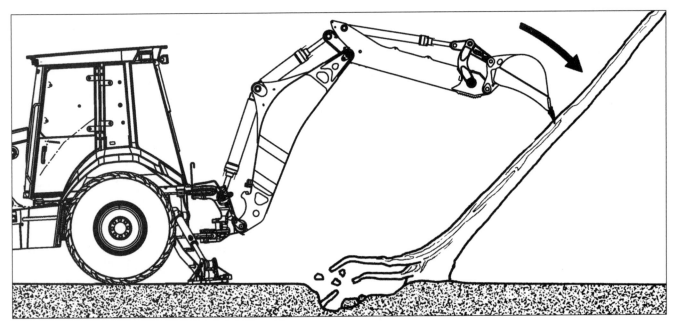

**Fig. 11-39** *PUSH: The tree is pushed away from the TLB and down to the ground.*

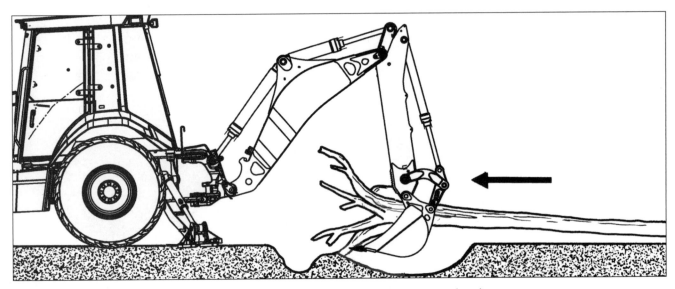

**Fig. 11-40** *PULL: The bucket is used to break the roots and pull the tree toward and around the machine to the side.*

Larger trees (eight inches or larger at the trunk) may be difficult to push over and may require some preparation, such as cutting some of the roots first. However, it is important to cut the roots on the correct side (Fig. 11-41). If the operator wants to push the tree over directly away from the machine, he should cut the roots on the near side of the tree. By doing this, there will be little resistance when he pushes the tree over. Remember: cut the roots on the opposite side of the tree from the desired direction of the fall.

## Stump Removal

Another common land clearing task is the removal of tree stumps. Depending on the type of tree, stumps up to six or eight inches in diameter can be removed with the hoe without having to dig around them. Some types of trees, however, have stronger root systems and will require digging to loosen the stump. If possible, trees of this size and type should be cut higher on the trunk so that the TLB will have more leverage when attempting stump removal. If the tree is cut off five or six feet

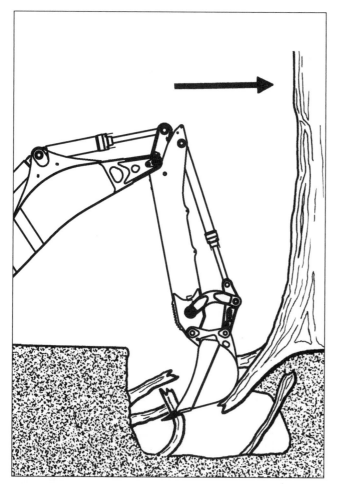

**Fig. 11-41** *Cutting the roots on the near side of the tree will allow it to fall away from the machine.*

from the ground, the remaining stump will provide leverage in the removal process. If the stump cannot be removed using the push-pull method, then digging around it and severing the roots will be necessary.

***Digging out stumps.*** The object of this procedure is to loosen the stump by removing the soil surrounding it, and to cut the roots that hold the stump in place. The rule for this procedure is that the required size of the hole will be about four times the diameter of the stump. So, a one-foot stump will require a four-foot hole in order to loosen it. A stump with a diameter of two feet will usually require a hole measuring eight feet across. It is easy to see that as the size of the stump increases, the project gets much bigger very quickly.

A stump with a diameter of three feet will require a hole about twelve feet across to get to where the

roots can be cut or broken with the backhoe. However, there will often be problems when trying to remove stumps of this size. Even after loosening the stump, the backhoe often doesn't have enough power to lift the stump from the hole.

If this is the case, there are a couple of options open to the operator. One option is to dig an even larger hole next to the stump and simply bury it there. This is probably the easiest alternative, but it is often unacceptable.

Another way to deal with this situation is to fill in under the stump and continue to roll it back and forth. By replacing more dirt back into the hole, and working the stump back and forth, it can be slowly raised until it can be pulled out of the hole. This method is also useful when attempting to remove large boulders from a hole.

## How to Dig an Arc

Although digging in an arc is a task not often encountered, it is one the operator should be familiar with and capable of performing. It is most often called for when curved walls are to be built, or when a pipeline requires a trench to change direction gradually. When the excavation is to be used for a footing (for a wall), the same rules apply as for any other type of footing. The main consideration is the layout, which must be carefully laid down to the exact specifications, and marked on both sides of the footing. As digging begins, the operator should keep in mind the fact that the smaller the radius of the arc, the shorter the section is that can be dug from each set-up.

As shown in Fig. 11-42, by varying the length of the pass in each set-up, the arc can easily be adjusted to the desired radius. After the excavation has been "roughed out," it will almost be down to the desired depth, and will have "corners" and "flats" in the arc. The next step is to make several floating passes with the bucket, using the swing to carve off the corners and slightly round out the flats (or straight areas). Then, after the excavation has been rounded off, the remaining spoil is scraped out and the footing is cleaned to the desired grade.

Another example of a task that will require the digging of an arc, as we noted, is when excavating for a pipeline. This is especially common when electricians are to lay plastic electrical conduit. Here, a very smooth bottom and a gently curved arc will be required. This will eliminate any dips or rises that could cause trouble later, when the wires are pulled through the conduit. Such irregularities could kink the pipe later, after back-filling and compacting the area, so that the wires will not pull through (Fig. 11-43).

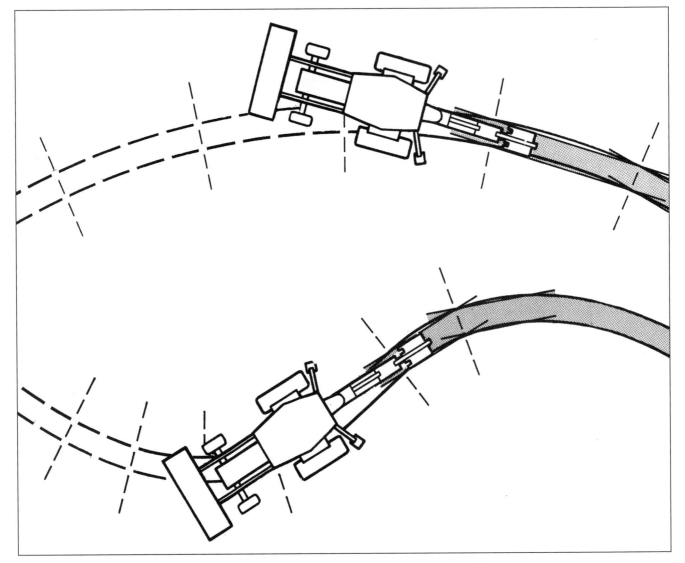

**Fig. 11-42** *An arc is actually dug in short straight sections. The smaller the radius of the arc, the shorter each of these straight sections will be. After the section is "roughed out," the sides are smoothed and the bottom is graded.*

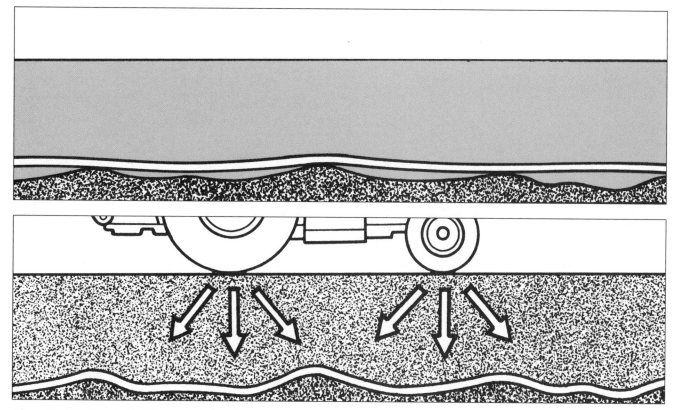

**Fig. 11-43** *Conduit laid in a poorly graded trench will become kinked during compaction.*

## Tooth Grab Method

This is a very useful procedure which can be used in a variety of situations, as we have noted. It can best be used to grab reinforcing steel, small diameter posts and pipes up to two inches in diameter, as well as shrubs, bushes and small trees. Fig. 11-44 shows the exact motion used to "grab" the pipe, tree or other object, while Figs.11-45 through 11-47 demonstrate the strength and effectiveness of this method.

***Note:*** These photos are meant as a demonstration of the effectiveness of this method only; we do not recommend handling concrete in this manner. For more on concrete handling and the tooth grab method, see chapter on **Demolition**.

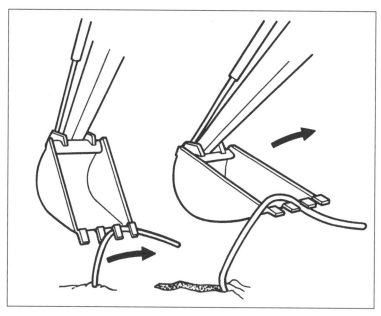

**Fig. 11-44** *The Tooth Grab Method – Starting with the object pointing straight up, the teeth are wrapped around, resulting in a grip that usually won't allow any slippage.*

**Fig. 11-45** *Starting with the rod between the teeth, the bucket makes a circular motion…*

**Fig. 11-46** *…and the rod is gripped securely between the teeth.*

**Fig. 11-47** *This is intended only as a demonstration of this method's effectiveness. Handling concrete in this manner is not recommended.*

## What to Do When No Spoil Placement Area is Available

Although spoil placement can often be a problem, there are times when the trouble can be extreme- there will be no place to put it all, or the work area will be so narrow that the swing cannot be used. These situations are rather infrequent, which is good news since dealing with them can be difficult and time-consuming. There are, however, two methods which can be used to ease job completion in these situations. The first method, using the trench for spoil transport, is illustrated in **Fig. 11-49**, while the second, digging the trench in stages, is explained in **Fig. 11-48**.

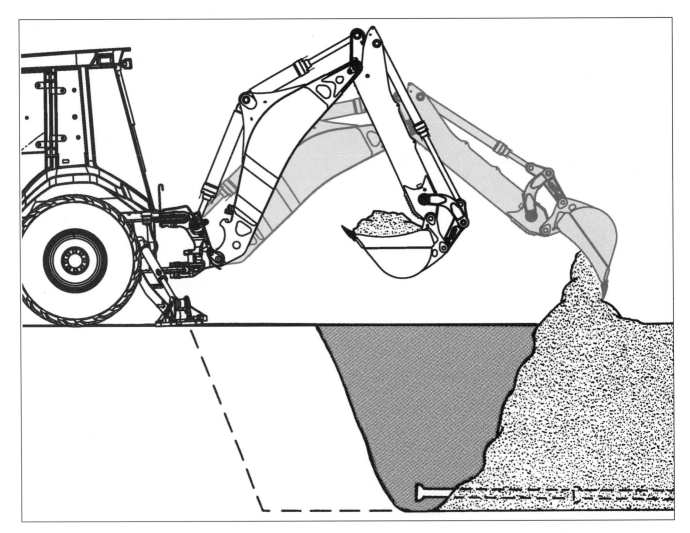

**Fig. 11-48** *When digging a trench in stages, the new spoil is placed over the section of pipe just laid.*

## Using the trench for spoil transport

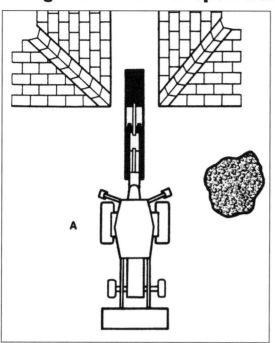

*A). The area dug from this position will serve as the area where all of the spoil from the entire trench will be placed.*

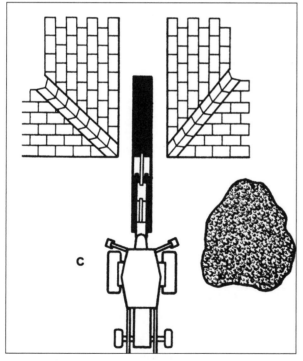

*C) Again, the operator removes the spoil from the trench and places it in the new stockpile area. Then the machine is moved back as far as possible and the trench is dug as far as the backhoe can reach.*

*B). As the operator moves the machine back, the newly dug spoil will be pushed under the machine. When the available space under the machine is full, the machine is moved out to the first position.*

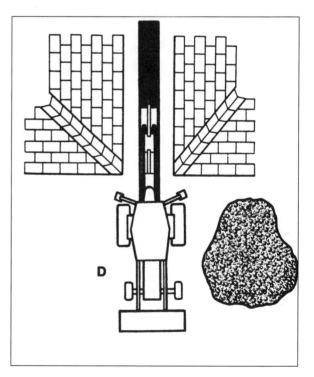

*D). Again the spoil is pulled out into the area where the material can be stockpiled.*

**Fig. 11-49** *Here, the desired trench is to be dug between two buildings which are too close to accommodate the TLB in between. The machine is set up far enough from the buildings to allow for the swinging and stockpiling of the spoil.*

## Crossing Shallow Trenches

**Fig. 11-50**  *This procedure is recommended for trenches two feet deep or less.  When approaching the trench, the bucket is lowered and the weight of the front of the TLB is supported by the bucket.*

**Fig. 11-51**  *Once the weight is supported by the bucket, the machine can be moved forward until the rear wheels approach the trench.*

**Fig. 11-52**  *The stabilizers are then lowered and will support the rear of the machine until it is moved forward.*

212

**Fig. 11-53**  *The machine is then pushed forward with the backhoe until…*

**Fig. 11-54**  *…the weight is supported by the rear wheels and the stabilizers can be lowered to support the backhoe when it is pulled…*

**Fig. 11-55**  *…to the loader use position.*

## Connecting Shallow Trenches

This is a common TLB procedure, and involves starting a trench from both ends and digging toward a meeting point at the center (Fig. 11-56). The need for this approach occurs most often when a trench is being dug between two buildings, or when digging footings for a large structure.

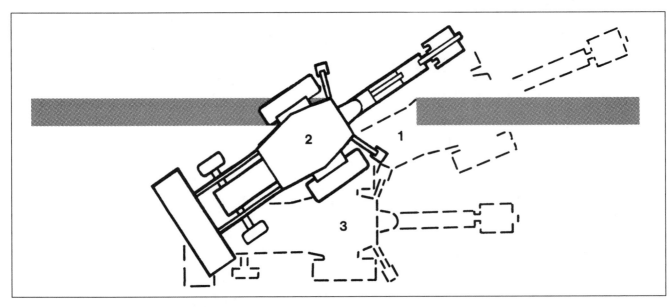

**Fig. 11-56A**  *1) When approaching the opposite trench, the machine will angle so that it can drive past the trench to the side.  2) This position is as far forward as possible so that the remaining area will be as short as possible.  3) Here the machine is pivoted away from the trench to the side. The loader bucket is used to stabilize the machine.*

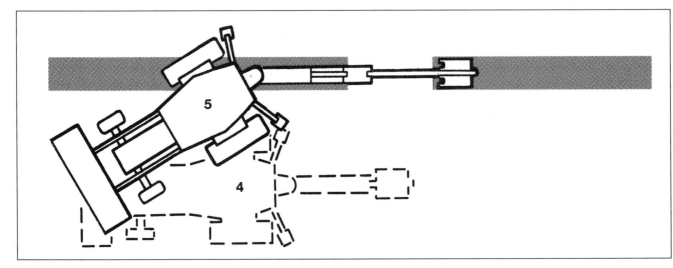

**Fig. 11-56B**  *4) From position #3, the machine is moved forward to a point where it will pivot back across the trench in the exact desired position for the last section, (5).*

## Questions – Chapter 11 **Backhoe Techniques**

**1. When beginning any digging job the most important aspect to consider is the movement of the earth that will be required.**

_____ a. True

_____ b. False

**2. When digging a ditch, placement of the spoil is not an important consideration.**

_____ a. True

_____ b. False

**3. The most important aspect of any TLB procedure is:**

_____ a. Production

_____ b. Speed

_____ c. Safety

_____ d. The depth of the excavation

**4. The operator should provide a safer working area in and around the excavation by:**

_____ a. Sloping the sides of the excavation when necessary

_____ b. Dislodging exposed rocks and chunks of dirt

_____ c. Cleaning the top of the excavation

_____ d. All of the above

**5. Precision excavation is usually only necessary for footings.**

_____ a. True

_____ b. False

**6. Excavations with a level finish grade are usually required for:**

_____ a. Septic tanks

_____ b. Electrical or telephone vaults

_____ c. Footings and leach lines

_____ d. All of the above

_Notes:_ _____

_____

_____

_____

_____

_____

_____

_____

_____

_____

_____

_____

_____

_____

_____

_____

_____

_____

_____

_____

_____

_____

_____

_____

_____

_____

_____

_____

_____

_____

_____

_____

**7. Utility lines, such as water, gas, electric or telephone, are often dug to:**

_____ a. A level final grade

_____ b. Two feet deep

_____ c. The same depth

_____ d. A predetermined depth

**8. Sewer lines, drain pipes and drainage ditches are dug:**

_____ a. With a level final grade

_____ b. As shallow as possible

_____ c. With a sloping or "gravity flow" trench

_____ d. None of the above

**9. Different trades such as concrete, plumbing, and electrical require excavations for different purposes and have different requirements.**

_____ a. True

_____ b. False

_Questions 10–14 concern extendible dipperstick procedures._

**10. When the stick is extended:**

_____ a. The reach is increased

_____ b. The machine can dig deeper

_____ c. The stockpiling range is increased

_____ d. All of the above

**11. When the stick is extended, the precision capabilities of the backhoe are increased.**

_____ a. True

_____ b. False

**12. As the stick is extended, the digging power of the TLB is decreased.**

_____ a. True

_____ b. False

**13. When the unit is extended, the stability of the machine is:**

_____ a. Increased

_____ b. Decreased

_____ c. Remains the same

_____ d. None of the above

**14. As a general rule, the extendible dipperstick should be positioned in the shortest position possible to do the job at hand.**

_____ a. True

_____ b. False

_Questions 15–20 concern general trenching procedures._

**15. After each move, the set up should be checked for:**

_____ a. Safety

_____ b. Stability

_____ c. Alignment with the trench

_____ d. All of the above

**16. The first surface cut is important because it serves as a guide for the bucket during the rest of the excavation process.**

_____ a. True

_____ b. False

**17. When the excavation is nearing the desired depth, the operator should clean the area by:**

_____ a. Cleaning the "sidewalks" of the trench with the bottom of the bucket

_____ b. Dislodging and removing rocks from the excavation area

_____ c. All of the above

_____ d. None of the above

_____
_____
_____
_____
_____
_____
_____
_____
_____
_____
_____
_____
_____
_____
_____
_____
_____
_____
_____
_____
_____
_____
_____
_____
_____
_____
_____
_____

**18. When completing a section of trench, the operator will:**

_____ a. Make a series of long grading passes on the bottom of the trench

_____ b. Have the grade checked at both ends of the trench

_____ c. Clean the end of the trench closest to the machine

_____ d. All of the above

**19. When digging a trench with the backhoe, the distance between setups:**

_____ a. Can change depending on the job at hand

_____ b. Will be shorter when digging a deep trench

_____ c. Will be longer when digging a deep trench

_____ d. All of the above

**20. When digging a deep trench the distance between each backhoe set up will be:**

_____ a. The same as a shallow trench

_____ b. Shorter

_____ c. Longer

_____ d. All of the above

**21. Hard ground conditions slow the digging process. The effects of hard ground conditions can be made worse by:**

_____ a. Using a large bucket

_____ b. Worn bucket teeth

_____ c. An under-powered machine

_____ d. All of the above

**22. When digging in hard ground, digging speed can be increased by: (choose two answers)**

_____ a. Raising the angle of the bucket

_____ b. Lowering the angle of the bucket

_____ c. Making short, deep passes

_____ d. Making long, scraping passes

**23. The stability of the backhoe can sometimes be overloaded during which procedure?**

_____ a. Craning

_____ b. Material handling

_____ c. When using the extendible dipperstick

_____ d. All of the above

**24. Instead of loading with the loader, loading trucks with the backhoe may be better when:**

_____ a. The soil is hard

_____ b. The soil is muddy

_____ c. The soil is sandy

_____ d. All of the above

**25. When an operator faces a situation or task that is new or unusual, danger is increased, and extreme caution should be used.**

_____ a. True

_____ b. False

**26. The operator is responsible for the safety of:**

_____ a. Himself and others

_____ b. The machine

_____ c. The work area

_____ d. All of the above

**27. Digging an arc shaped trench is accomplished by using the swing to move the bucket from side to side.**

_____ a. True

_____ b. False

**28. The rule of thumb for stump removal is that the size of the required hole will be about:**

_____ a. 2 times the diameter of the lower trunk

_____ b. 3 times the diameter of the lower trunk

_____ c. 4 times the diameter of the lower trunk

_____ d. 5 times the diameter of the lower trunk

**29. Using this rule of thumb, a stump diameter of 2 feet will require a hole of _____ feet to remove it.**

_____ a. 2 feet

_____ b. 4 feet

_____ c. 8 feet

_____ d. 10 feet

**30. To remove a very large stump or rock from a hole, an operator could:**

_____ a. Use a large stick to pry it

_____ b. Fill the hole with water

_____ c. Use the loader to push it out

_____ d. Add dirt to the deepest parts of the hole and roll it back and forth until it rises up to the ground level

**31. Using the trench for spoil transport is useful:**

_____ a. During normal digging operations

_____ b. When there is no area for spoil placement

_____ c. When working in dusty conditions

_____ d. When digging a deep trench

**32. Connecting trenches is an operation that most backhoe operators will rarely face.**

_____ a. True

_____ b. False

# 12. Loader Techniques

## Introduction

Unlike most other types of heavy equipment which require the mastering of only one set of controls, the TLB consists of two machines in one – each with separate functions, controls, and required operating skills. Sometimes operators tend to ignore their loader skills while concentrating on backhoe skills, which is unfortunate because use of the loader is just as important as use of the backhoe. In on-the-job situations, operators who have made it their goal to master **total machine usage** will quickly stand out as being more valuable. When this type of operator is at the controls, the TLB becomes possibly the most useful all-around excavation machine in general construction.

## Principles of Operation

The loader is basically simpler to operate and easier to get accustomed to than the backhoe. The hydraulics which control the lift arms and bucket position are also simpler to operate than the four backhoe controls. The hydraulics of the loader, however, provide only the **breakout force** of the bucket (Fig. 12-1), and the **lifting force** supplied by the two lift cylinders (Fig. 12-2). The real power that determines the usefulness of the loader bucket comes from the rear wheels. As a result, the amount of power available at the bucket is determined, in large part, by the amount of **traction** available in the area.

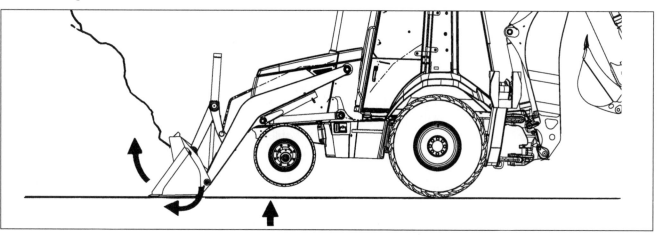

**Fig. 12-1** *BREAKOUT FORCE: The action and power of the bucket when rolling the bucket up, or back. Breakout force is a commonly used specification for rating the power of a loader.*

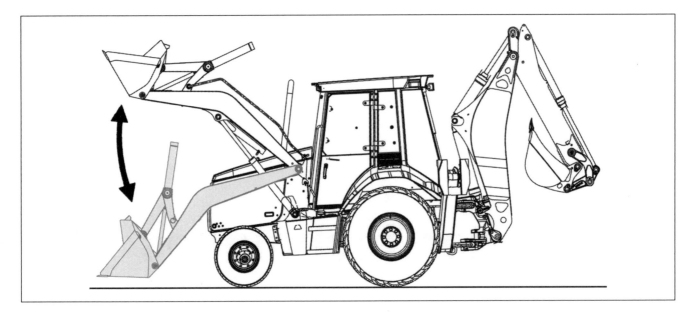

**Fig. 12-2** *LOADER LIFT FORCES: A demonstration of the hydraulics which lift and lower the bucket.*

***Traction –*** There are many forces and conditions which determine how much traction will be provided for the rear wheels. The most basic factor affecting traction is the amount of weight on the wheels, with traction increasing as the weight is increased.

As a forethought to this section, we should be reminded of Newton's law which says that for every action, there is an equal and opposite reaction. In any case where movement or forces are involved, there will be an effect on the machine and often, traction will be affected.

***Driving forces.*** When the driving forces, or torque of the engine, is transferred into the ground, traction can either be increased or decreased. Fig. 12-3 illustrates how torque affects the machine when it is moving forward, while Fig. 12-4 shows the effect when traveling in reverse.

***Hydraulic forces.*** Fig. 12-5 demonstrates that when pressure is applied to the lift of the loader, the weight on the rear wheels – and therefore the traction – is reduced.

The opposite is true when down pressure is applied to the loader – the weight of the rear wheels is increased, as well as the available traction (Fig. 12-6).

***Load weight.*** The weight of the load being carried in the loader bucket will also reduce traction on the rear wheels (Fig. 12-7).

***Ground conditions.*** Surface conditions on the job site can vary from a desert-dry dust bowl to a muddy, soupy mess. Also, soil conditions can range from hard-packed clay to loose sand or gravel. Depending on all these variables, the TLB can either be an effective excavating machine, or it can become awkward, cumbersome, or simply stuck. Because these conditions have a direct impact on TLB performance, the operator must monitor them, and be able to predict, and prevent, potential problems or dangerous situations. Optimum ground conditions that may have provided excellent traction can become dangerous and even deadly after a rain shower, for example.

***Tire pressure.*** One easy way of increasing traction in soft or sandy conditions is to lower the air pressure in the rear tires. This can improve maneuverability greatly, but the operator should take care to refill the tires before using the machine on hard surfaces.

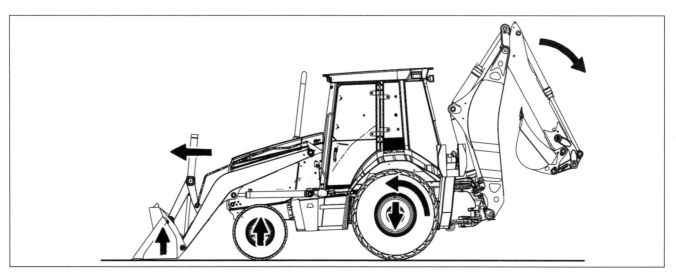

**Fig. 12-3** *FORWARD DRIVING TORQUE* will remove weight from the front wheels and add weight to the rear wheels.

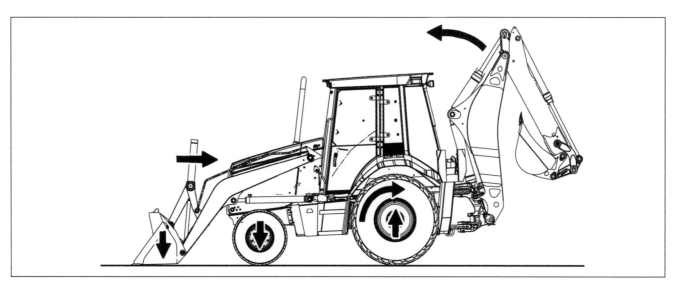

**Fig. 12-4** *REVERSE DRIVING TORQUE* will remove weight from the rear wheels and add to the front. This effect is greater when the machine is operated in low gear.

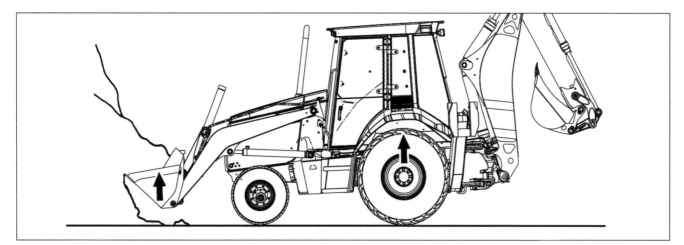

**Fig. 12-5** *LOADER LIFT:* When using the hydraulics to lift in a pile, the weight on the rear wheels will be reduced, as well as traction.

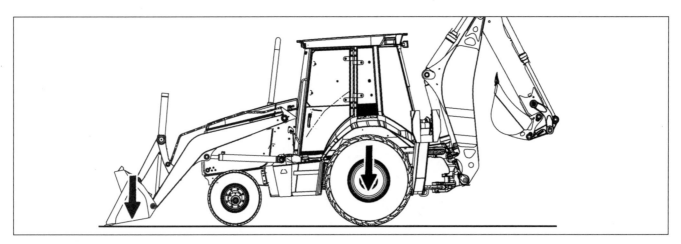

**Fig. 12-6** *LOADER DOWN PRESSURE: When down pressure is applied to the loader, weight and traction on the rear wheels is increased.*

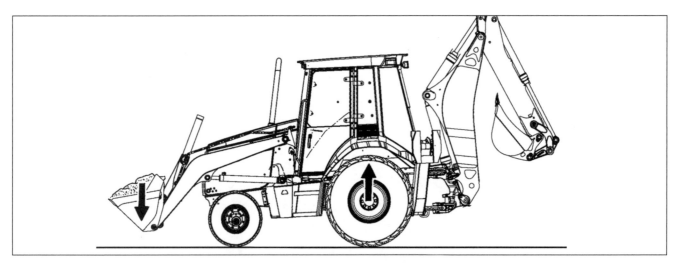

**Fig. 12-7** *LOADER WEIGHT: When carrying a load in the loader bucket, weight and traction on the rear wheels is reduced.*

## Stability

*Slopes.* As discussed in previous chapters, the TLB can often be an awkward machine to maneuver. The machine must be operated in a manner that maintains stability. When the TLB must be operated on a slope, the weight distribution should be adjusted by either **altering the dimensions** or filling the loader bucket. Once again, **do not** attempt any move you are unsure about.

*Load height.* Probably the most basic rule, whenever operating the loader, is to **carry the load as low as possible**. A filled loader bucket, carried low, will stabilize the machine (except when traveling forward down a hill). As the load is raised, stability decreases rapidly. The simple solution would seem to be to always keep the bucket positioned close to the ground – except that one of the loader's most common tasks is the loading of trucks, which requires raising the bucket high above the ground. As long as ground conditions are stable and level, there won't be a problem. Truck loading on any area where stability is compromised should not be attempted. Any necessary corrections should be made prior to truck loading. If the entire area is slightly sloped, the most stable approach to the truck is the one shown in Fig. 12-8. Do not operate in a manner illustrated by Figs. 12-9 and 12-10.

By reviewing the points highlighted in the discussion of traction and stability, it becomes clear that the effectiveness of the loader is affected by weight considerations. As the operator becomes

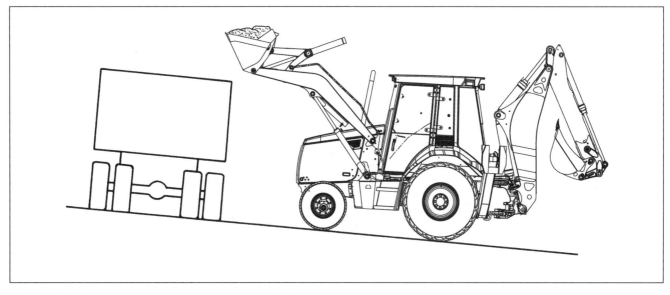

**Fig. 12-8** *When the entire loading area is slightly sloped, the safest approach to the truck is the one shown here. The machine will be stable during both the approach and the dumping stages of the loading process. After the load is dumped, the front of the machine may tend to lift. The TLB should then be carefully backed up and the loader lowered to increase stability.*

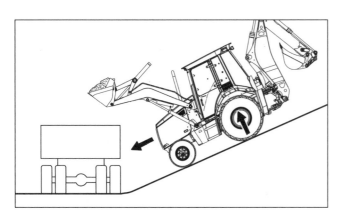

**Fig. 12-9** *Never load a truck on a downhill slope, as TLB control could easily be lost.*

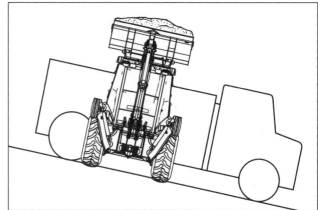

**Fig. 12-10** *Never load on a side slope. Raising the bucket under these conditions could cause a rollover.*

more familiar with the unit and what it can and cannot do, he will also learn how to work around the machine's limitations.

He will be able to complete the job using only those techniques that work well for the TLB.

## Filling the Bucket

Nearly all tasks involving the loader require repeated filling and dumping of the bucket. The ability of the operator to get full buckets without wasting time will determine the effectiveness of many operations.

***Back-ups.*** As mentioned in other chapters, providing a stable back-up is the single most important factor when loading either the loader or the backhoe bucket. By understanding this concept, the operator can often provide a back-up simply by the angle at which he "attacks" the pile, and he can maximize his efficiency by stockpiling in an area where a back-up is available, for example.

***Corners of the bucket.*** In order to get full, even loads in the bucket, **the corners of the bucket must contact the pile at the same time**. If one side of the bucket contacts the pile at an angle, the bucket will not be filled to capacity.

First, the operator must select the area of the pile he wishes to "address" with the bucket. Then he should take note of the points at which the bucket will make contact, and the angle of approach should be one that ensures that the corners of the bucket will contact the pile at the same time. Fig. 12-11 illustrates four different situations and the correct approach for each.

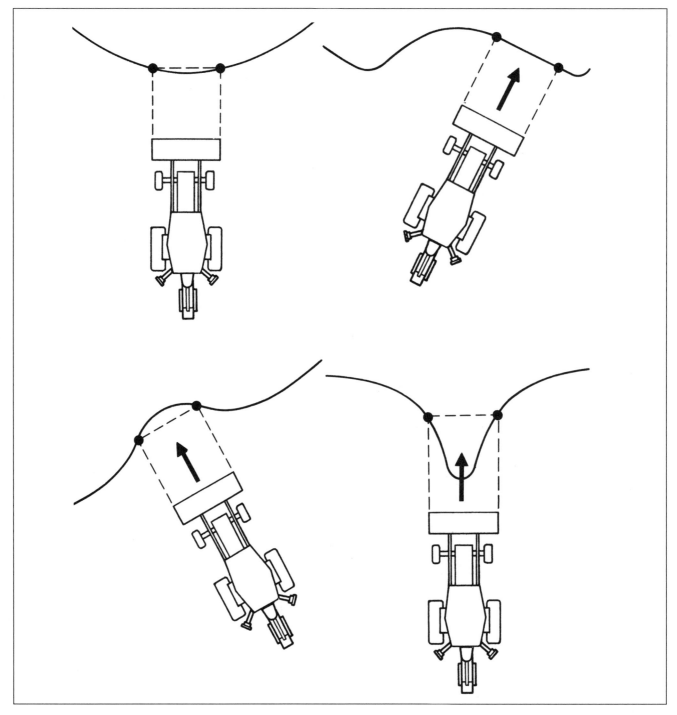

**Fig. 12-11** *Regardless of the contour of the pile, the corners of the bucket should contact it at the same time.*

## Soft Material

When beginning to work a new pile of soft material, it is even quicker to take the first bucket from high in the pile. With the bucket tilted slightly down, the bucket will be forced down and deeply into the pile. Then a full bucket can be achieved by rolling the bucket upward (Fig.12-12A).

The next pass will also be easier, since the weight has been removed from the lower material (Fig. 12-12B).

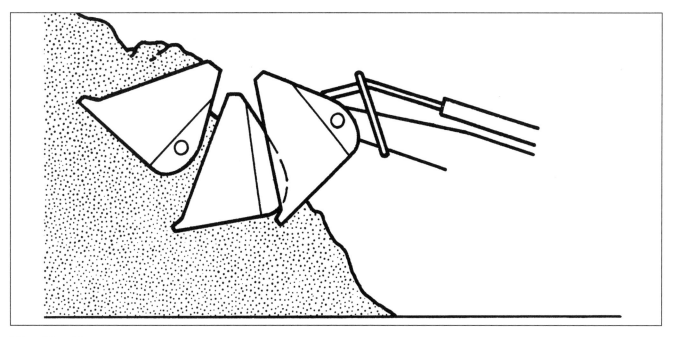

**Fig. 12-12A** *When loading from large, soft piles, start from high in the pile. Drive the bucket down slightly, and deep into the pile.*

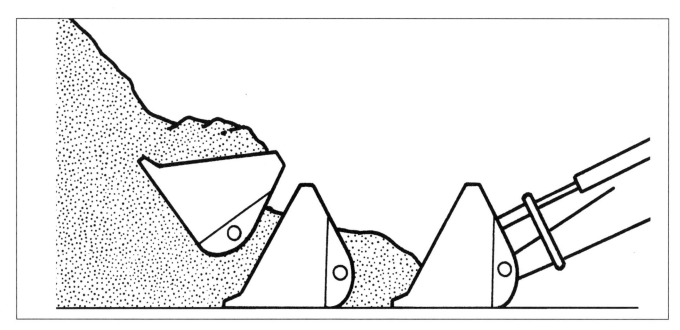

**Fig. 12-12B** *With the extra weight removed the second bucket will fill easily.*

## Bucket Loading Technique

This photo sequence shows in detail how a loader can use maximum power and hydraulic force to fill the bucket. While the material shown in this sequence is very soft, the purpose of studying these motions and forces is to examine techniques that are useful when loading in more difficult conditions.

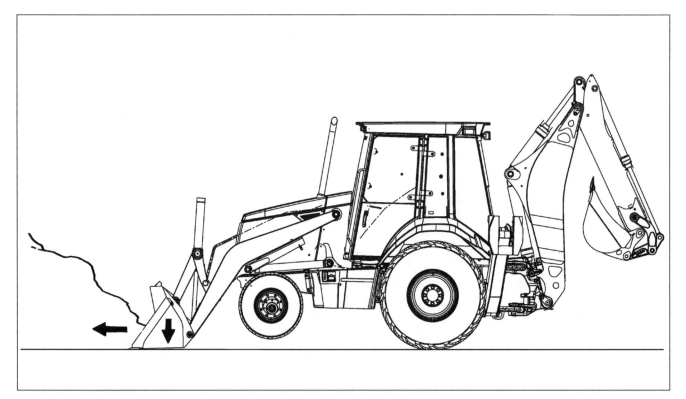

**Fig. 12-13** *Two-Wheel drive machine*
*To maximize the forward driving force and the bucket penetration into the pile, apply **down** pressure to the loader bucket. This will put more weight on the drive wheels, increase traction, and force the bucket into the pile with much more force.*

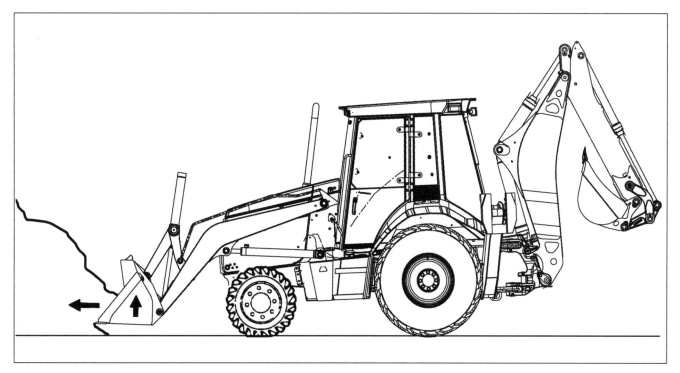

**Fig. 12-14** *Four-Wheel drive machine*
*To maximize the forward driving force and the bucket penetration into the pile, apply **up** pressure to the loader bucket. This will put more weight on the drive wheels, increase traction, and force the bucket into the pile with much more force.*

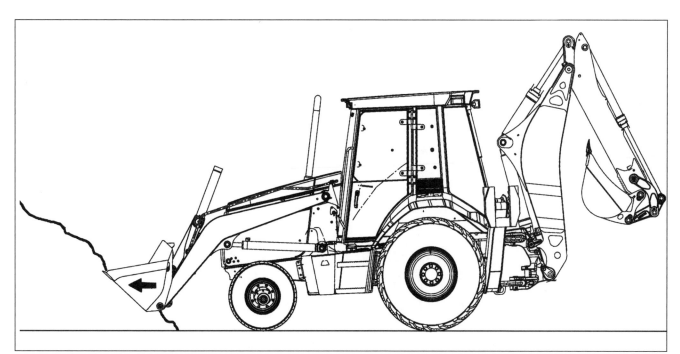

**Fig. 12-15** *Most common mistake for beginners*
*Most inexperienced operators tend to curl the loader bucket too quickly when entering the pile. At this point, the forward driving force only pushes the bottom of the bucket against the pile, and no more material can go into the bucket.*

☞ *The correct method would allow the bucket to penetrate deeply into the pile before "working" the bucket up and down slightly and then curling it up all the way.*

## Hard Material

The loader is much less effective when attempting to load in hard ground conditions. It really doesn't have the traction capabilities or the breakout force necessary to handle such materials.

If the working area provides good traction, then it may be possible to penetrate the material. If the

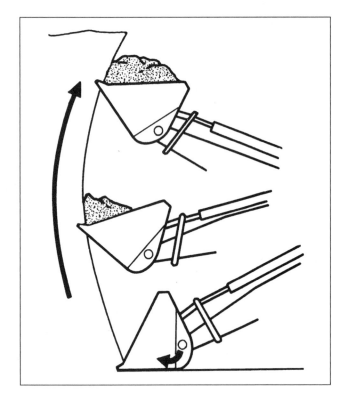

**Fig. 12-20** *A thin scraping action can work well in some harder materials.*

traction is poor, or if the ground is soft, bucket penetration will usually not be possible.

The best approach, when dealing with tough ground conditions, is to use the driving forces in combination with the hydraulics to make a scraping motion similar to the one shown in Fig. 12-20. If this method is ineffective, then the hoe can be used to loosen the material, making the loader's work easier (Fig. 12-21).

## Loading Trucks

When the task of loading material onto trucks is at hand, the operator must first evaluate the loading area. What position should the truck be in? What loading patterns will work best? If there is a wind present, in what direction is it blowing? Does the area provide adequate stability for loading operations?

In selecting the loading area, the operator should look for an area that will allow the trucks to drive through – that is, where they won't have to back up in order to drive out. When they have to back up, the loading process can be very slow.

If conditions are dry and dusty, the operator should consider the wind direction. If possible, trucks should be set up and loading patterns chosen in such a way that the wind will be coming from the rear as the load is being dumped. This will keep dust out of the operator's eyes and make the entire operation more efficient, not to mention more comfortable. Whenever possible, the TLB operator

**Fig. 12-21** *The backhoe can be used to loosen hard material so the loader can pick it up easier.*

**Fig. 12-22** *Avoid contact between the bucket and truck bed…*

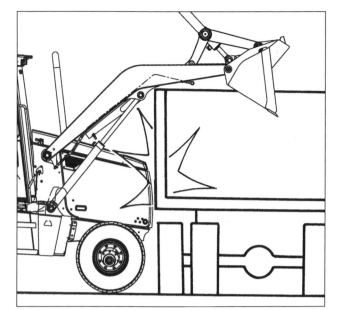

**Fig. 12-23** *…and the front of the machine, and the truck body.*

**Fig. 12-24A** *As the truck fills, the load will need to be pushed across the truck bed in order to even the load. As the leading edge of the bucket passes the sideboard of the truck, the bucket is rolled down quickly.*

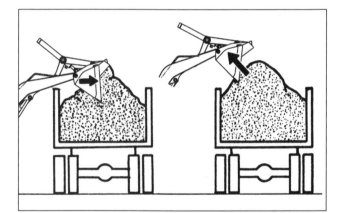

**Fig. 12-24B** *The load is then pushed across the truck. By raising the bucket and backing up slowly, the load will be distributed evenly across the bed. Be careful to watch the bucket, making sure it clears the sideboards of the truck bed, and also be careful not to strike the truck with the front of the tractor.*

should assist the truck driver in locating the truck correctly, depending on the loading pattern.

***Truck loading considerations.*** During the loading process, the operator will need to keep several extra factors in mind. One of these is preventing damage. There are many ways in which the truck may be damaged during the loading process, such as damage to the sideboards of the truck bed (Fig. 12-22), or dents in the bed itself, caused by striking the truck with the front of the tractor (Fig. 12-23).

Another consideration is how the load's weight will be distributed when filling the truck. An improperly loaded truck can become unstable when driven and could overturn on a curve or if the wheels go off the road onto the shoulder. Because of the height and reach limitations of the TLB, the load will tend to pile up on the near side of the truck, or at the rear, if the TLB is loading from that direction. To correct this, the load can be pushed across the truck bed as shown in Fig. 12-24A. This will also help to fill the corners of the truck bed, ensuring a maximum load.

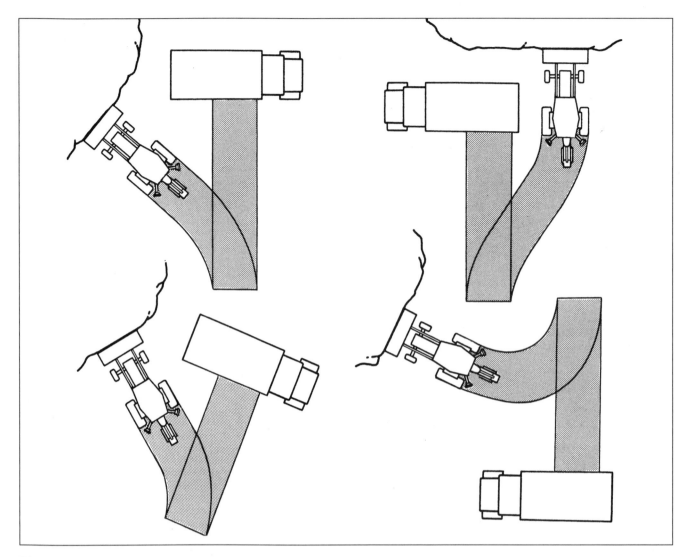

**Fig. 12-25** *Efficient truck loading patterns*

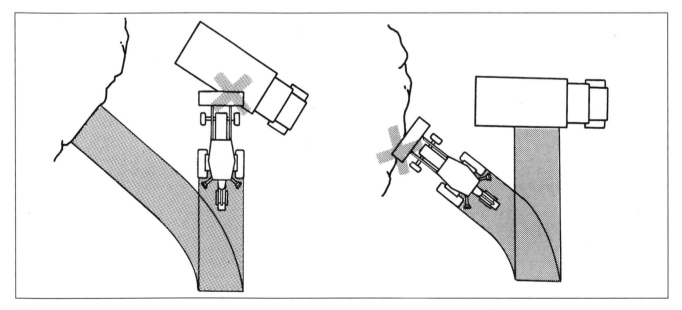

**Fig. 12-26**. *Always choose a loading pattern that will allow for the bucket to enter the pile and dump into the truck evenly.*

## Stockpiling

As we've seen throughout the book, stockpiling is a common task or perhaps the most common loader procedure. Depending on the situation, anywhere from one-third to one-half of all jobs will require removal of spoil generated by the backhoe during excavation. Stockpiles are a common sight on many construction sites during the early phases of work. When footings are dug, spoil is often removed from the area where construction will take place, creating working space as well as a smooth working area. In instances where trenches are dug within the walls of a structure, the spoil will be replaced by sand or other materials that will ensure stability. And, of course, the stockpile will also provide fill materials needed for grading or back-filling.

It is easy to see that the crucial element when stockpiling is **access**. When selecting a stockpiling area, the operator should be mindful of the fact that the TLB will travel to and from the area many times. Free access is a prime consideration, but the chosen area must not cause interference with other aspects of the job in progress.

Another helpful hint is to select a stockpiling area that contains available back-ups, as mentioned earlier. This is most helpful when the amount of material to be stockpiled is small, or if cleanup is to occur soon.

## Ramp Stockpile

Although building a ramp stockpile is usually called for when larger types of heavy equipment are being used, it can be very useful to the TLB operator, particularly when stockpiling large, immeasurable quantities of material, and when the stockpiling area is limited. **If the stockpiling area is adequate for the amount of material involved, the ramp method provides little advantage.**

If, however, the available area is small, and a large amount of material is to be removed, then the ramp stockpile is clearly a better approach. By using this method, the pile can be built into a "two story" pile, and a much greater quantity of material can be stockpiled than by using the standard method.

Another advantage to using the ramp method is that the TLB's shuttle cycle will be the shortest and quickest possible for that particular job situation.

This method is not without some disadvantages and potential problems. If the ramp is too steep, machine stability can be compromised, and steering control can be lost. To avoid this, the ramp must have a low degree of slope (Fig. 12-28).

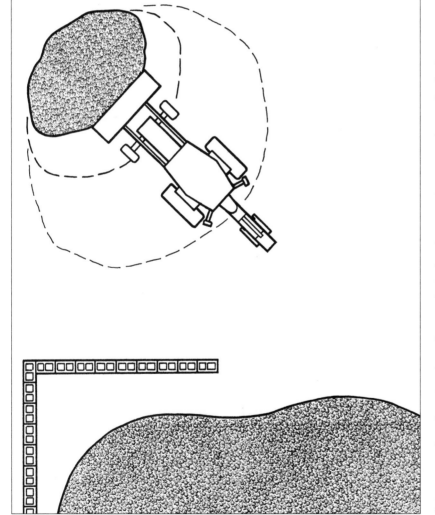

**Fig. 12-27** *When using the **standard stockpiling procedure**, the pile is started at the farthest point available, or the point necessary for the area and the amount of material involved.*

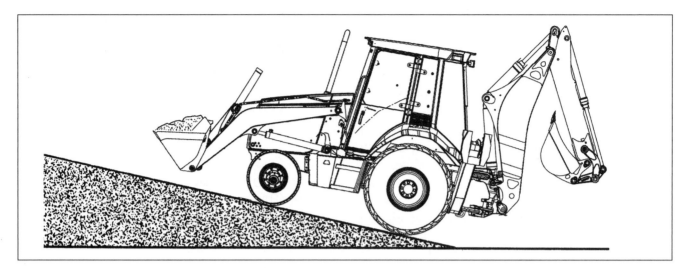

**Fig. 12-28** *The ramp should be formed at a low angle to ensure stability during shuttle operations.*

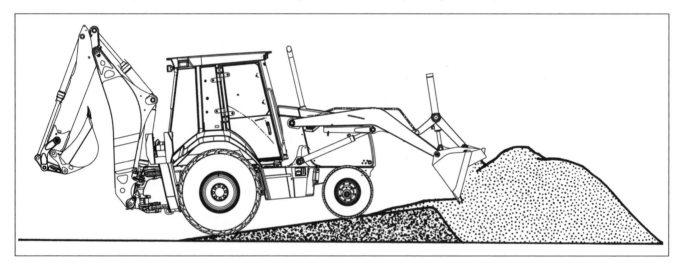

**Fig. 12-29** *As the ramp is enlarged, material is added over the end.*

Also, the "edges" of the ramp, and the "platform" area on top of the pile can be loose and may not support the machine's weight. It may appear to be safe and stable, but it may be. It is most important to keep the rear wheels away from the edges; if the rear wheels were to sink only a little at the edge, the weight distribution immediately shifts to that wheel, causing even more sinking.

To avoid these problems, the ramp should be built to a minimum of one and a half times the width of the machine. After this wide area is compacted and graded, the operator should keep the TLB in the center of the "roadway," and away from the edges.

Another disadvantage of this technique becomes apparent when the stockpiled material is removed. The hundreds of passes over the material will compact it to the point where removal with the loader may be difficult. In this case, the pile may have to be loosened with the backhoe before removing it with the loader.

***Ramp building technique.*** Unlike the standard stockpiling technique, which is started at the farthest point required for the amount of material expected to be stockpiled, the ramp stock pile is started very close to the work area. Basically, the pile is started by building a ramp and adding material over the end (Fig. 12-29). As the ramp is formed and the material is added, the operator grades and smooths the ramp during the shuttling of material to the ramp area. After a load is dumped in the desired place the loader bucket is then used to back-drag the ramp as the machine returns to get another load.

As the ramp grows, it should be raised to the desired height and gradually leveled off. Then the piling is continued with more material added over the end until it reaches the limits of the stockpiling area (Fig. 12-30). As material is added, the pile on the top will grow to the edges of the original pile, and then the "second story" pile will be made in the same manner as the standard stockpiling procedure (Fig. 12-31).

## Related Techniques

Due to the usual lack of space found on most construction sites, the stockpile may have to be moved or condensed into the smallest area possible.

***Moving small stockpiles short distances***. It is not uncommon during the course of construction that stockpiles will need to be relocated, either to provide better access to the area, or to create space for a new excavation. The technique, which is illustrated in Figs. 12-32 through 12-35, is also useful for back-filling trenches.

***Condensing the stockpile.*** During the general cleanup of the job site, gathering spoil from various excavations and piling it all into one or more stockpiles, the material may need to be consolidated or condensed into a single pile. By doing so, the job site is cleared of smaller spoil accumulations and the area becomes more accessible for the other trades on the job, which facilitates the entire construction process.

In another situation, material that has been trucked in may have to be condensed. When the trucks dump the material, it is usually piled low and spread over a large area. To save space the material should be pushed into one large pile as high as possible. The method used to accomplish this task is illustrated in Fig. 12-36.

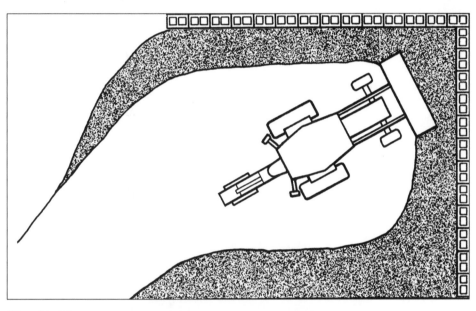

**Fig. 12-30** *When the available stockpiling area is used…*

**Fig. 12-31** *…a "second story" is added to the pile.*

**Fig. 12-32** *When moving or condensing stockpiles, the pile is entered with the bucket flat.*

**Fig. 12-33** *The bucket is raised and tilted down as power is applied...*

**Fig. 12-34** *...until the top of the pile gives way...*

**Fig. 12-35** *...and the bucket is driven forward. From this point, the process is repeated, starting with the bucket flat on the ground (as in Fig. 12-32).*

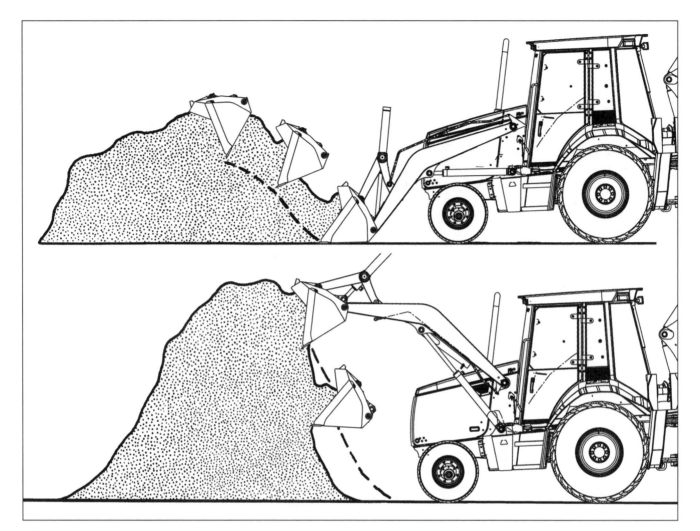

**Fig. 12-36** *A large, flat pile may be condensed using the motion shown here.*

## Shuttle Operations

"Shuttle" is defined as "to move or go back and forth rapidly or frequently." And that is exactly what the TLB does during shuttle operations. Up to this point, we have divided the discussion on loader operation into several categories: principles of operation, including loading the bucket; various job tasks, such as loading trucks and stockpiling; and so on. The one element that combines all of these various operations, linking them together in a workable progression of TLB functions, is the shuttle operation. Shuttling binds the otherwise separate loader operations together into a smooth, efficient job.

Essentially, shuttling consists of moving buckets of materials from one point to another. This material will usually be dirt, but it may also be sand or gravel, other building materials, or any materials which are difficult to remove by hand.

Shuttling is also involved during cleanup of the job site, consolidating spoil piles into a central stockpile area, as noted earlier.

Another very common shuttle operation is the procedure of loading trucks. Actually, truck loading involves three basic elements of loader operation: filling the bucket, the actual loading of the truck, and – linking these two procedures – shuttling back and forth from the truck to the loading area.

Because shuttling is involved in nearly every loader job, it is easy to understand why safe and efficient shuttling is important to loader operation.

***Efficiency.*** The greatest single thing that will ensure efficient shuttling is **a smooth, well-graded shuttle route**. Without a smooth route the TLB's stability can be adversely affected. The TLB is affected by bumps in the work area to a much greater degree than other types of heavy equipment due to its uneven weight distribution. If the operator does not smooth the area, the front tires can bounce into the air by a bump when traveling with the loader bucket empty (Fig. 12-37). A rough shuttle area will also cause materials to fall out of the bucket along the way, creating even more bumps.

In order to keep the shuttle area smooth, the operator should back-drag the route when traveling back to get another bucket. Also, before leaving the pile area with a full bucket, the operator can give the bucket a couple of short, quick shakes. This will leave any loose excess material at the pile and will also settle the remaining material in the bucket. This can also be helpful when the shuttle path travels over paved surfaces that will require cleanup at the completion of the job.

***Length of the shuttle.*** By examining the **efficiency** of any shuttle operation, we can see that it is determined by the amount of material moved within a given time period. Obviously, this means that a shorter shuttle run will be more efficient and productive over the course of the job. So, when planning the shuttle route, try to use the shortest possible path between the two endpoints, as well as one that provides for easy filling and dumping of the bucket.

**Fig. 12-37** *A rough shuttle route or unexpected bump could cause the front tires to bounce into the air.*

***Bucket volume.*** Here the length of the shuttle is again a determining factor. When the shuttle run is **short** (twenty to fifty feet from the point where the bucket is loaded to the point where it is dumped), less than full buckets are acceptable. The object of filling the bucket is to get as much as possible without wasting any time. Entering the pile a second time would surely be a waste of time.

When the shuttle run is **long** (100 feet or more), the operator should fill the bucket as completely as possible. In this situation, a second pass to completely fill the bucket is preferable to traveling the entire distance with a half-full bucket. When filling the bucket for a long shuttle run, follow this two-step procedure:

1) Enter the pile and fill the bucket as much as possible. This should require only one pass, but if the bucket is not completely full, take the extra time to fill it.

2) As the bucket is lifted from the pile, prior to backing away from it, shake the bucket quickly to remove excess material to keep the shuttle route clean. The actual shaking action is accomplished by rolling the bucket out slightly from the fully-curled position and then quickly rolling it back against the bucket stop position.

By following this procedure, the bucket will be completely full and it will also be "well groomed" for the long shuttle run.

In order to better grasp the principles behind shuttle operations, we will exam-ine a long, but not unusual, shuttle procedure. Fig. 12-38 illustrates a shuttle pattern that might be used on any common construction site. This pattern might be repeated several times, or hundreds of times over several hours, or even all day. Here are some important tips and pointers that will help the operator better cope with this type of work.

***"Radar."*** One thing an operator can always expect on any job is a set of certain restrictions. Any object in the work area can be considered a restriction, such as grade stakes, building materials, cars and trucks parked on the site, fences and

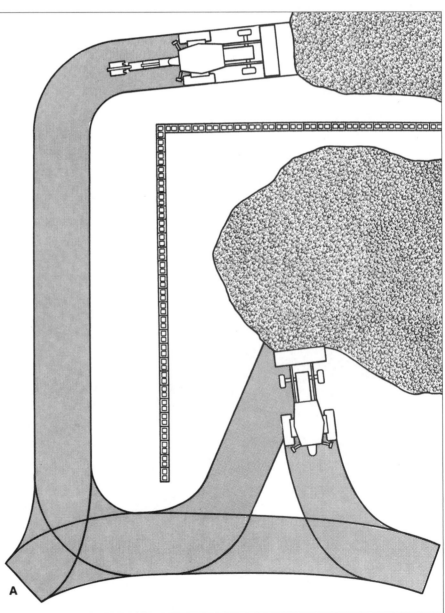

**Fig. 12-38**. *Shuttle operations will often stretch from one end of a job site to the other. Position "A" is detailed in Fig. 12-39.*

walls, trees, buildings, utility lines, building overhangs, overhead wires, etc.

On the first several trips along the shuttle route the operator will note where such restrictions could pose problems. Moving slowly and carefully through and around these hazards, and noting the clearances, will enable the operator to reposition the machine through the areas where obstacles pose a problem. After several passes, the hazard areas will become part of the overall shuttle cycle and the TLB will follow an exact route that will avoid them. As this procedure is repeated many times, the operator will develop a sense of "radar" and will know his position at all times when traveling the shuttle path.

It is important to note that this "radar" system works only on inanimate objects and doesn't apply to people working on the site, moving vehicles, or other heavy equipment.

***Use corners well.*** When space becomes a problem while traveling the job site, the "corners" of the work area can become useful when maneuvering the machine. As seen in position A in Fig. 12-38, the operator can use the corner to change the machine's direction. Fig. 12-39 gives a more detailed view of the motion used in this maneuver.

***Direction of travel.*** When traveling the shuttle path the first few times, the operator will develop a pattern that will be repeated many times. If there are any slopes within the shuttle path, the operator should decide which direction (forward or reverse) he should drive the machine in order to maintain the greatest control over it.

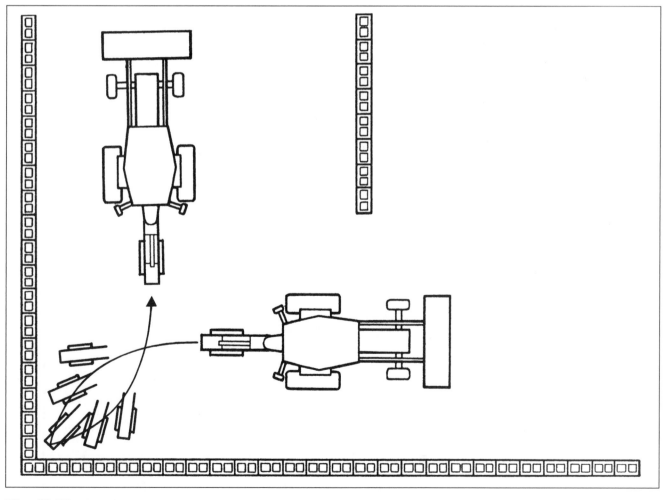

**Fig. 12-39** *This illustration shows in detail how the operator can maneuver the TLB in tight situations using the "corner" of the work area.*

## Safety

***Traveling in reverse.*** Because of the size and position of the backhoe attachment, the vision of the operator can sometimes be obstructed **(Fig. 12-40)**. To overcome this problem the operator must turn his body to one side and lean slightly in the same direction. Then, after surveying the situation on that side of the machine, he shifts around and does the same thing on the other side **(Fig. 12-41)**. By following this procedure the operator will get the full view of what is behind the machine.

***People.*** Extra attention will be required any time there are workers in the shuttle area. People often get so involved in whatever they are doing that they don't think about what is going on around them. **Do not assume** that people will not walk into the path of the machine. Watch out for them and be prepared to stop or take other action to avoid accidents or injuries.

## Related Techniques

***Road building and leveling.*** This technique applies mainly to those times when ramps, driveways and shuttle paths must be built on the job site. The procedure is similar to the cut-and-fill technique described in the chapter on ***Grading and Compaction***, particularly the section on "starting the cut" (see Figs. 10-3 and 10-4 on page 159, and 10-5 on page 160).

The key to easy road leveling is to provide and maintain a level area for the TLB to work from. Once the machine is positioned properly in a level area, the grading and leveling can be accomplished correctly because the bucket will cut at the desired angle.

As the cut-and-fill sequence takes place, the fill side should initially be graded higher than the cut side. This will allow for compaction and will ensure

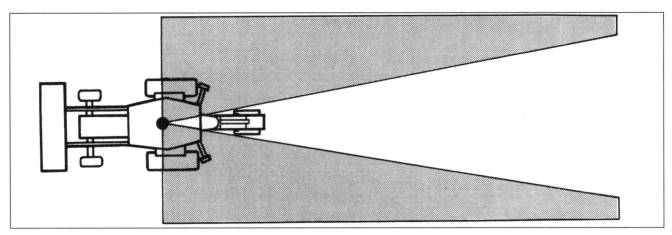

**Fig. 12-40**

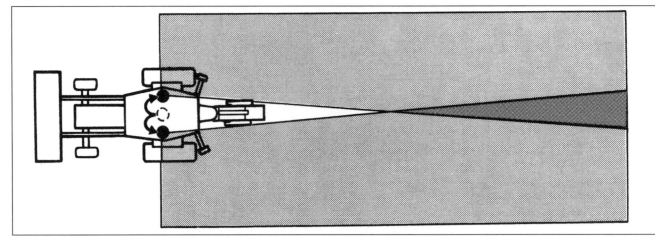

**Fig. 12-41** *Make sure the machine's reverse warning alarm is operational.*

242

the procedure is carried out safely. After the new roadway has been thoroughly compacted, it can be regraded and smoothed until level, if desired.

Another safety reminder when building a roadway: always try to widen the road to the point where it is at least one and a half times the width of the TLB. This will allow easy maneuvering and reduces the risk of running the machine off the edges.

***Circular grading patterns.*** Although this technique may not be called for frequently, it can be very useful when the operator faces a grading job in a tight situation, such as back-filling and grading a trench that is adjacent to a fixed structure, such as a wall or a house.

The basic procedure involves positioning the TLB at the most comfortable angle relative to the trench, with one corner of the bucket contacting the pile of back-fill material. Then, as the operator backs up, away from the trench, he engages the brake on the rear wheel farthest from the trench so that the TLB begins to move in an arc. By carefully engaging and releasing the brake, the operator can make the front bucket move in a circular pattern, pushing back-fill material into the trench in a sideways motion, either left-to-right or right-to-left. Figs. 12-42, 12-43 and 12-44 illustrate the correct procedure and the desired results.

The most common applications of this technique include: back-filling or grading next to buildings and walls; grading close to houses or delicate surfaces; back-filling against basement walls, where keeping the machine's weight back away from the structure is important; grading small or narrow areas that won't support the machine's weight; or when working in small areas where grading may be otherwise restricted or inhibited.

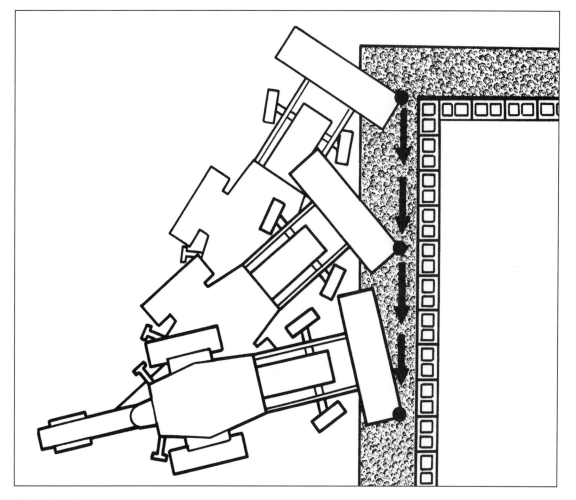

**Fig. 12-42** *When grading a circular pattern the loader bucket is located far from the weight of the machine, and can be controlled easily for grading next to delicate structures.*

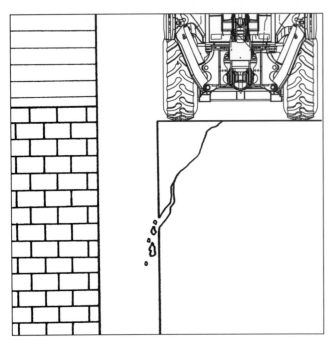

**Fig. 12-43** *Positioning the TLB next to the excavation, as shown here, would be unsafe.*

**Fig. 12-44** *Positioned at an angle the weight will be supported on stable ground.*

**Fig. 12-45** *When cleaning trench sides, the TLB is positioned at about 45 degrees relative to the trench, with at least half of the bucket over the edge of the trench.*

**Fig. 12-46**  *By applying the left brake, the bucket will be slid quickly across and away from the trench...*

**Fig. 12-47**  *...resulting in a clean trench side and little or no material pushed back into the excavation.*

**Fig. 12-48** *When "sanding" a newly laid pipe in a trench, the sand should "fall like rain", to slowly build up around the pipe to support it in place, and to avoid knocking it out of position.*

## Questions – Chapter 12 **Loader Techniques**

**1. Like all types of heavy equipment, the TLB requires mastering one set of controls.**

_____ a. True

_____ b. False

**2. The TLB is considered to be the most useful machine in all-around construction.**

_____ a. True

_____ b. False

**3. Generally speaking, the loader is more difficult to operate than the backhoe.**

_____ a. True

_____ b. False

**4. The amount of power available at the loader bucket is delivered by:**

_____ a. Breakout force

_____ b. Loader lift forces

_____ c. Driving forces of the tractor

_____ d. All of the above

**5. When down pressure is applied to the loader bucket, the amount of traction at the rear wheels:**

_____ a. Is increased

_____ b. Is decreased

_____ c. Stays the same

_____ d. All of the above

**6. When maneuvering the loader with a full bucket, the first and most basic rule is:**

_____ a. Keep the bucket above the top of the tires

_____ b. Keep the bucket rolled up

_____ c. Keep the bucket raised up

_____ d. Keep the bucket low

**7. The higher a fully loaded bucket is raised, the more stable the machine becomes.**

_____ a. True

_____ b. False

_Notes:_ _____

_____

_____

_____

_____

_____

_____

_____

_____

_____

_____

_____

_____

_____

_____

_____

_____

_____

_____

_____

_____

_____

_____

_____

_____

_____

_____

_____

_____

_____

_____

_____

_____

_____

_____

_____

_____

_____

_____

_____

_____

_____

_____

_____

_____

_____

_____

_____

_____

_____

_____

_____

_____

_____

_____

_____

_____

_____

_____

**8. When loading trucks, the work area should be:**

_____ a. Sloped

_____ b. Bumpy and rutted

_____ c. Stable and level

_____ d. It does not matter

**9. The ability of the operator to get full buckets without wasting time will determine the effectiveness of many operations.**

_____ a. True

_____ b. False

**10. In order to get full even bucket loads:**

_____ a. The operator should use first gear

_____ b. The operator should use second gear

_____ c. The corners of the bucket should contact the pile at the same time

_____ d. Full power must be used

**11. The loader is more effective when loading in hard ground conditions.**

_____ a. True

_____ b. False

**12. An improperly loaded truck could become unstable and overturn when driven.**

_____ a. True

_____ b. False

**13. Which of the following are true of "ramp stockpiles"?**

_____ a. The ramp must be built at a low degree of slope

_____ b. The ramp must be 15 feet wide or more

_____ c. Can be built in "two levels"

_____ d. All of the above

**14. When using efficient truck loading patterns the loader:**

_____ a. Will approach the pile squarely

_____ b. Will approach the truck squarely

_____ c. Will usually have a "V" shaped pattern

_____ d. All of the above

**15. Shuttling consists of moving buckets of material from one point to another and is involved in nearly all loader applications.**

_____ a. True

_____ b. False

**16. The greatest single thing that will ensure efficient shuttle operations is:**

_____ a. Using third gear

_____ b. Not overloading the machine

_____ c. Keeping people out of the area

_____ d. A smooth, well-graded shuttle route

**17. When planning a shuttle route, it is important to:**

_____ a. Choose a short, smooth path

_____ b. Provide for easy filling of the bucket

_____ c. Provide for easy dumping of the bucket

_____ d. All of the above

**18. Because of the size and position of the backhoe, the vision of the operator can sometimes be obstructed.**

_____ a. True

_____ b. False

**19. When using the loader, it is okay to assume that people will not walk into the path of the machine.**

_____ a. True

_____ b. False

**20. When the weight on the drive wheels increases, the traction decreases.**

_____ a. True

_____ b. False

**21. Circular grading patterns are most commonly used when:**

_____ a. Back-filling or grading next to buildings or walls

_____ b. Grading close to houses or delicate surfaces

_____ c. Back-filling against basement walls

_____ d. All of the above

_____
_____
_____
_____
_____
_____
_____
_____
_____
_____
_____
_____
_____
_____
_____
_____
_____
_____
_____
_____
_____
_____
_____
_____

**22. When the loader is carrying a heavy load of soil, the traction at the rear wheels is increased.**

_____ a. True

_____ b. False

**23. When the shuttle route is long, the operator should fill the bucket as completely as possible.**

_____ a. True

_____ b. False

**24. After filling the loader bucket, a quick shake of the bucket will remove excess material to prevent loose spoil from falling out of the bucket during shuttle operations.**

_____ a. True

_____ b. False

**25. When traveling in reverse, blind spots created by the backhoe assembly can become a safety hazard.**

_____ a. True

_____ b. False

**26. When backfilling along a basement wall, a circular grading pattern will keep the weight away from the fill area.**

_____ a. True

_____ b. False

**27. The "radar" system works only on inanimate objects and doesn't apply to people working on the site.**

_____ a. True

_____ b. False

**28. The power that determines the usefulness of the loader bucket is generated by the drive wheels.**

_____ a. True

_____ b. False

# 13. Demolition

## Introduction

Up until now, we have focused primarily on the TLB's many applications in construction, and the preparatory work leading up to actual construction. In this chapter, we will discuss the TLB's role in demolition of existing structures such as sidewalks, driveways, walls, parking lots, curbs and gutters.

Breaking and removal of concrete, asphalt, etc. is a very specialized area of TLB operation; while nearly anyone can break up and remove concrete, it takes technique, experience and good judgement to do it efficiently. This type of work often calls for the operator to use common sense to find solutions to unusual problems. The TLB is, however, an excellent choice for many small breaking and removal jobs.

**Fig. 13-1**. *The TLB can be extremely effective when used for breaking and removal of many types of common structures, as shown here.*

# Preparation and Planning

Like any other type of TLB work, the demolition job must be planned, step by step, and the operator must have a clear job sequence in mind. Before beginning, the operator should walk the job site to get a clear idea of the scope of the work to be performed. There are many elements common to most demolition jobs, and they are interrelated. The concepts which the operator must consider include:

- **Efficiency of job completion,** which is determined by how many times the material being removed is handled.

- When material is to be handled two or more times, there are several **stockpiling** considerations to be made.

- As in any loading or material handling operation, providing an adequate **back-up** ensures efficiency.

- In many job situations, **separation of different materials** is an important consideration.

- Cleanup is either carried out at the end of the job, or planned in stages as work progresses.

Let's examine each of these factors individually.

## Efficiency of Job Completion

When removing material from a demolition site, efficiency is determined by how many times the material is handled. The best method, obviously, is to handle the material only once. That is, it should be loaded onto trucks immediately as it is removed from the site. This is accomplished with the backhoe, working along with a truck that is positioned to facilitate loading.

In many instances, using this method will mean that the truck will have to be moved often as work progresses. This approach may seem slow and difficult, especially to beginning operators. However, if we examine the alternative – first removing the material to a stockpile, breaking it into pieces small enough for the loader to handle, and **then** loading the truck – it becomes clear that spending a little extra time loading the material as it is removed will really be quicker in the long run.

The key to the one-step method is patience, because the operator will often have trouble positioning the pieces in the bucket. Also, the operator shouldn't waste time trying to get an extra piece onto the load. Productivity is determined by how much material is loaded within a given period of time. By trying to jockey one more chunk into the bucket, however, the operator will usually end up losing the pieces he has already positioned correctly. The actual loading techniques used in this procedure are explained later (see **Loading with the Backhoe**).

There are many situations where one-step removal won't be possible. For instance, space sometimes won't allow the truck to be positioned alongside the TLB. In other cases, material removal will be so time-consuming that stockpiling it for later loading may be the best approach.

The main point here is to avoid stockpiling the material and load it immediately. Anytime stockpiling is involved, it means that material will have to be handled at least twice, or even three times. When planning job efficiency, plan to handle the material the fewest possible number of times.

## Stockpiling

When stockpiling becomes necessary, the main considerations are how the material will eventually be loaded out and how to stockpile in such a way that loading will proceed quickly and easily. There are several things to consider when choosing the stockpiling method:

**The area.** When deciding **where** material will be placed, the area chosen must be large enough and accessible enough to permit loading and maneuvering of the trucks.

**The size of the pieces.** Generally, when the loader is used to load concrete, the larger the pieces are, the more difficult the loading process will be. One rule of thumb when loading concrete with a machine of this size is that the pieces should be small enough to move by hand. This is accomplished by breaking the concrete into pieces of the desired size **as it is removed**. This will ensure full buckets when loading, and will also make cleanup easier.

**Keeping the pile low.** Because of the irregular shape and great weight of the concrete pieces, piling them high tends to result in friction, causing the pieces to become "tangled" in the pile. Loading from a highly stacked pile is difficult and frustrating. To avoid this, keep the stockpile low – no more than two feet high – and spread out over a larger area. This makes it much easier to get full buckets, and provides a constant **back-up** for the operator.

**Providing a back-up.** A back-up is anything the operator can use to push the load against to get it into the bucket. A back-up is an important element in any loading operation and also an important consideration when choosing the stockpiling area. Back-ups will be discussed in more detail later in this chapter.

## Material Separation

A general rule of thumb to follow when removing material is to keep dirt separate from concrete or other demolition materials at all times. This is especially true in cases where the concrete is to be removed but the dirt remains on the job site for back-filling or some other future use.

One example would be a job where concrete is to be removed from an area especially saw-cut for a trench which is then dug for a sewer or utility line to be laid. In this situation the best approach would be to pile the broken pavement on one side of the trench, and the dirt on the opposite side. Or, the concrete could be removed first and stockpiled to one side before digging.

There are a number of other instances where the operator will be asked to remove a layer of paving material and then dig an excavation of some type. Unless otherwise requested, **always** keep dirt separate from other materials.

We will now examine separately some demolition and removal techniques that are used with the backhoe and the loader.

## Backhoe Techniques

**Removal of Concrete.** When the backhoe is used to remove concrete, the first thing the operator looks for is an opening or some other space where the bucket teeth can be worked underneath the concrete, such as the edge of a sidewalk or driveway. On many jobs, however, there is no access to an edge, so the operator must create his own starting point by breaking a hole through the concrete where the bucket can gain hold. This is usually easy where the material is three inches thick or less (Fig. 13-2); when it is thicker than three inches, however, breaking with the backhoe could damage the teeth or other machine parts, and is **not recommended**. When it becomes necessary to break thick materials, other equipment should be used, such as a pneumatic pavement breaker, stomper or hydro-hammer (Fig. 13-3), hoe-ram or another tool designed specifically for breaking concrete.

In places where the operator can gain access to an edge, however, concrete as thick as six to eight inches can be removed with the backhoe, depending on whether reinforcing steel is contained within the slab. By using the prying method, the material can be lifted and broken at the same

**Fig. 13-2** *Using the breaking technique illustrated in Fig. 13-7, the bucket teeth may be used to break through materials up to three inches thick.*

**Fig. 13-3**. *When thicker material is encountered, access to an edge must usually be created with other types of equipment specially designed for concrete breaking.*

time, and then positioned into the bucket for stockpiling or immediate loading.

***Prying method.*** As its name indicates, the prying method is used to loosen, lift and break concrete slabs, curbs, footings, etc. by working the bucket teeth underneath the concrete and then prying it up using the TLB's tremendous hydraulic power.

First, work the teeth under the concrete as far as possible. Once the teeth are in place, the operator exerts downward pressure on the boom and curls the bucket up, while the crowd is extended slightly. Instead of simply trying to lift the concrete, the bucket is used as a fulcrum.

The force used to lift the concrete is dissipated into the ground, not to the machine (Fig. 13-4).

The amount of breakout force created by this method is tremendous. It is generated by combining the forces of three of the backhoe's four main hydraulic cylinders (boom, bucket and crowd), plus the weight of the machine. Once the pieces are lifted, they are either loaded onto a truck or stockpiled. If they are to be stockpiled, they should be broken into pieces of the desired size.

Caution is advised when using the prying method. As noted above, the power generated in the prying action is not transferred into the machine, but directly into the ground, **through the bucket**. Because of the tremendous forces generated, and the generally abusive nature of concrete breaking and removal work, using a **heavy-duty bucket** is recommended. Light-duty, special purpose buckets, or buckets which have worn thin due to age, are not recommended. Severe bucket damage could result.

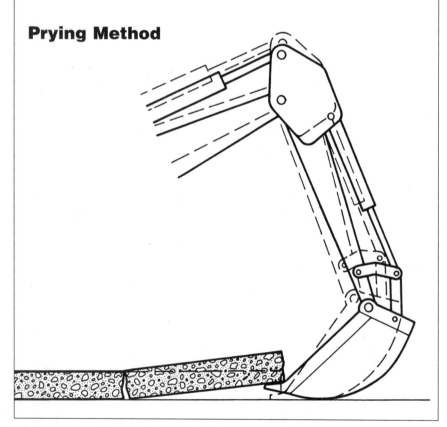

**Prying Method**

**Fig. 13-4** *Once the bucket teeth gain access underneath the concrete the prying method may be used to break and raise material, as illustrated here.*

## Concrete Breaking

In order to complete common concrete breaking and removal jobs effectively, the sections and pieces must be sized properly for eventual loading onto trucks. If the backhoe is to be used, pieces should only be as large as can be safely handled. By the time the loader bucket is used to actually load the material on the truck, pieces should be as small as possible to facilitate the process. As a rule of thumb, concrete pieces should be broken down to the point where they are small enough to load by hand. By breaking the material to this size, the operator realizes two goals: the bucket will load easily and any material remaining behind can then be loaded by hand.

Recall that handling material as few times as possible during removal is an important goal. However, it should be noted that on **more than half** of the breaking and removal jobs involving the TLB, the material will usually be handled two or more times. In order to avoid unnecessary delays during the second (and subsequent) phases of material handling and loading, materials **must** be broken to a size that will ensure easy handling by a machine of this size.

It must be pointed out that breaking concrete can be **very abusive** to the machine. The operator must learn through experience what his machine can and cannot do, as well as the methods by which concrete may be broken **without** abusing the TLB. The operator should always try to prevent unnecessary machine abuse. Here are several methods by which concrete can be effectively broken, with minimal risk of damage to the TLB.

***Dropping***. This simple approach is useful when breaking very large, thick slabs and sections into smaller, more manageable pieces. After using the prying method to loosen concrete, it will frequently break off in large sections – too large for the TLB to handle. By picking up one side or end of such a piece, and then moving the bucket out from under it, it will simply fall and break against the remaining concrete. The point is to utilize the concrete itself to help the machine do the breaking, thereby avoiding machine abuse.

The dropping method is also effective when breaking thinner concrete. Because these sections weigh less than thicker slabs, they can be picked up with the bucket, and positioned directly behind the TLB with the crowd extended outward nearly all the way. Then, starting from a height of about five feet, the boom is then raised and lowered very quickly, rolling the bucket out during the downward motion. This short, quick up-and-down motion, combined with the bucket roll, will drop the piece flatly on the ground. This is one of the simplest, most effective ways to break concrete, but the operator should be careful to use it only in areas where it will be completely safe to do so, and where no damage to other structures or objects will occur.

***Roll-out method.*** This is another good breaking method, because it is easy on the TLB and is done with a motion which is natural to the work cycle. It can be used to break long, narrow pieces by positioning them about two feet above the ground, and then simply rolling the bucket outward (Fig. 13-5).

***Striking.*** This is the least desirable method of breaking concrete and carries the greatest risk of machine damage. It involves using the weight of the backhoe assembly to quickly and forcefully strike the concrete with the bucket. The abusive nature of this method can be minimized, however, once the operator gets to know

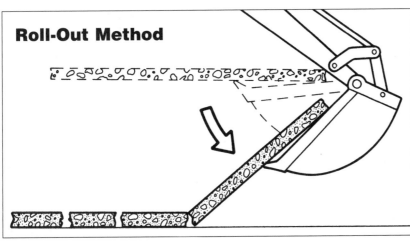

**Roll-Out Method**

**Fig. 13-5**

the TLB's limitations, and works within them. The key to using this method safely and effectively is to **correctly position the pieces prior to striking them**, reducing the force necessary for breaking.

Because concrete is a very brittle substance, a light blow will usually break sections up to five inches thick, **if** they are positioned, and then struck, correctly. To do this, move the piece into a position where it is supported at two points (Fig. 13-6). The piece can then be easily broken at the points indicated by the arrows.

The correct breaking technique involves propelling the boom faster than the hydraulics would normally allow. To accomplish this, position the bucket two to four inches above the precise contact point desired (Fig. 13-7A). Then, raise and lower the bucket as quickly as possible. When done correctly, the maximum distance between the bucket and the concrete at the midpoint between raising and lowering the bucket will be about eight inches (B), and the boom control lever will be returned to the closed position before the bucket contacts the concrete (C). Also, by positioning the crowd at a 90-degree angle to the boom, shocks to the machine will be absorbed by the linkage pins on the bucket and not by the hydraulic cylinders. Correctly

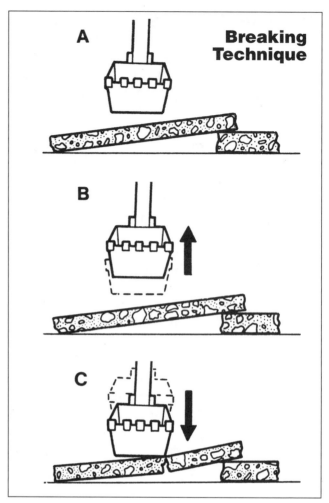

**Breaking Technique**

**Fig. 13-7**

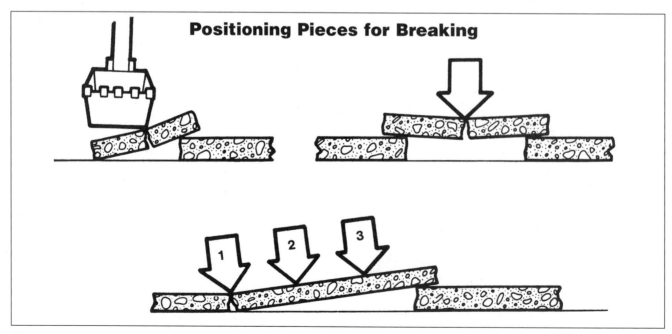

**Fig. 13-6** *Correctly positioning pieces for breaking with the bucket.*

following this procedure will make concrete breaking easier, while preventing pressure surges in the TLB's hydraulic system.

***Thickness limitations.*** It should be clearly understood that all types of equipment have limitations, and that any attempts to exceed those limitations, **especially** when breaking concrete or similar heavy materials, will shorten the life of the machine and could cause immediate, severe structural or hydraulic system damage. The typical breaking limits for the TLB are four to six inches for asphalt and three to five inches for concrete. These figures are based on correctly positioning the pieces between two points of support, as noted above.

**NOTE:** All of the breaking methods discussed here do not take into account the possible presence of reinforcing steel in the material. On jobs where steel is a factor to contend with, other methods will be necessary to break materials of this size, or when sizing the material prior to removal.

***Alternative breaking methods***. There are several types of equipment in common use that are especially designed for breaking concrete, and these may be necessary if the material in question is beyond the limitations of the TLB.

On materials up to one foot in thickness, a "stomper" or hydro-hammer can be very effective. Also, several pneumatic or hydraulically-operated, backhoe-mounted breaking devices are available and are effective in many situations. In addition, the common pavement breaker or jack-hammer is useful, especially for providing an access hole when using the prying method. This is also an excellent choice when breaking concrete or other materials surrounding areas that are to remain paved, thus preventing damage to these areas.

# Loading Techniques

***The importance of back-ups.*** As defined earlier, a back-up can be any object, structure or pile of material that can be used by the operator to push against to facilitate loading. In some applications, the TLB itself can be used as an effective back-up. Providing an adequate backup is an important part of any operation where repeated filling of the bucket is necessary for transport or loading. This includes operations using either the backhoe or the front loader.

Learning to provide back-ups is especially important for the beginning operator. Because of the unusual shapes and sizes of the pieces to be handled, as well as the weight involved, the beginner will often find loading to be very difficult and awkward at first. Back-ups make the job much easier; using them efficiently makes an operator much more productive as well.

## Loading with the Backhoe

In many situations, loading with the backhoe has numerous advantages over alternative loading methods. For example, loading the pieces with the backhoe as they are removed makes one-step removal possible. Loading with the backhoe is also an efficient method of handling large, long or awkward pieces. When handling this type of material, providing adequate backups is especially important. This type of loading requires a high degree of operator concentration, smoothness and safety awareness.

At any time trucks are being loaded, the bucket adjustment must be in the position which provides maximum curl, making it possible to get a good grip on the material. To explain it better, we will separate the loading cycle into two parts:

1) Positioning the bucket, picking up the pieces and gripping the load tightly; and

2) lifting the load, swinging it over the truck and placing it into the truck.

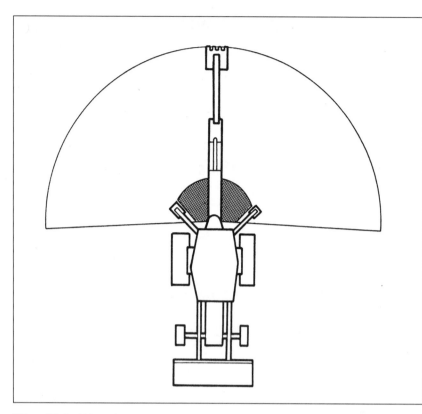

**Fig. 13-8** *When working with concrete or other materials, do not allow pieces to be pushed into the shaded area next to the machine, as machine damage could result.*

## Picking Up the Pieces

The first consideration here is whether the pieces to be picked up are in the **working range of the backhoe** (Fig. 13-8). As loading proceeds, the broken concrete has a natural tendency to be pushed toward the machine. If the pieces are pushed too close to the rear of the machine, they become impossible to pick up. To avoid this, the operator must be aware of this tendency and keep the material away from the area directly behind the machine. Try to keep it pushed back. Notice we said try – it seems that no matter how hard one tries, there are always some pieces that flip over and/or are pushed into that area. Once it gets into the area behind the machine, it can't be pushed out directly with the hoe. It can, however, be maneuvered out by carefully using the swing, pushing the pieces sideways, as

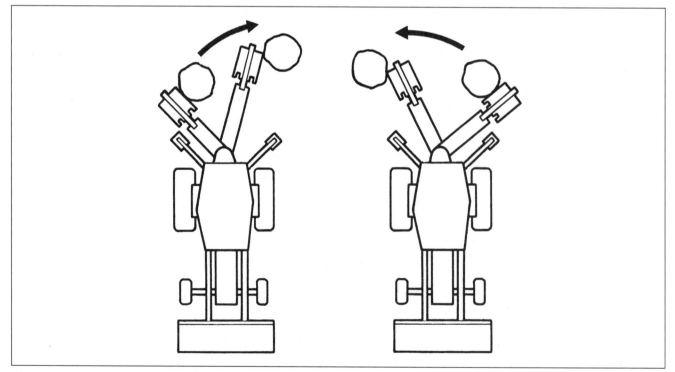

**Fig. 13-9** *By pushing objects sideways with the swing, they will naturally tend to move away from the machine.*

shown in Fig. 13-9. Repeating this procedure two or three times, back and forth, will easily position the piece back into the working area – within the machine's working range.

***Natural back-ups.*** When loading material as it is removed, the operator can take advantage of the natural back-up provided by the remaining pavement. This natural back-up provides a perfect means of positioning the bucket under the piece to be removed. Taking advantage of this principle maximizes efficiency whenever picking up pieces as they are broken. (See Fig. 13-10.)

After the piece is broken, the operator must be careful as he positions the bucket under the piece. If the teeth make contact below the piece's center of gravity, it will be lifted over the natural back-up and slide off the bucket and toward the machine. To prevent this, the bucket is lowered and slid under the piece to a position where the teeth are as close to the near edge as possible (Fig. 13-11). As the teeth make contact, the exact same motion as described in the prying method is used to pick up the piece. That is, down pressure is applied to the boom, while the bucket is curled up and the crowd extended slightly (Fig. 13-12). After the piece is on the bucket, it is clamped tightly between the bucket and the structure of the crowd.

***Positioning the bucket.*** The correct positioning of the bucket is an important element when picking up material. Often, as the material is lifted and broken, the bucket is not positioned under the piece's center of gravity. To position the bucket in such a way that the piece can be picked up, the bucket must be swung sideways under it. Again, due to the material's heavy weight and rough surface characteristics on the underside, this procedure can be somewhat difficult.

There are several ways to approach this situation. One is to carefully lay the piece down and then pick it up again, with the bucket positioned correctly under the center of gravity. Another method is to reduce the friction between the bucket and the piece, allowing the bucket to slide sideways underneath it. When the weight of the piece is resting on the side (cutting edge) of the bucket, the friction will be too great to allow the necessary bucket movement. To effectively reduce this friction, place the weight of the piece on the bucket teeth, and apply pressure to the swing (Fig. 13-13). When the bucket is in the desired position, the weight should be transferred back to the side of the bucket, to prevent the piece from being lifted over the natural back-up.

***Important:*** When the teeth contact the piece, the contact point must be above the piece's center of gravity. Contact below that point may lift the piece over the back-up.

***Positioning the piece.*** This is another method that can be used effectively on pieces that are slightly rounded on the bottom. This enables the piece to roll, slightly re-positioning the bucket directly under the piece (Fig. 13-14).

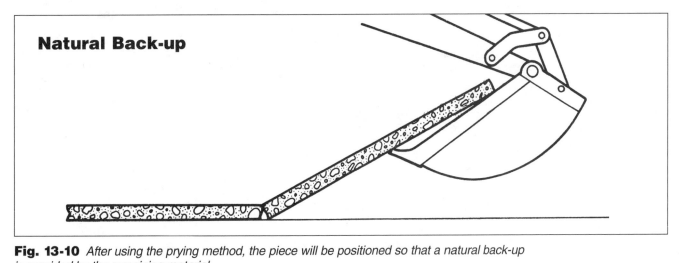

**Natural Back-up**

**Fig. 13-10** *After using the prying method, the piece will be positioned so that a natural back-up is provided by the remaining material.*

**Fig. 13-11**

**Fig. 13-12**

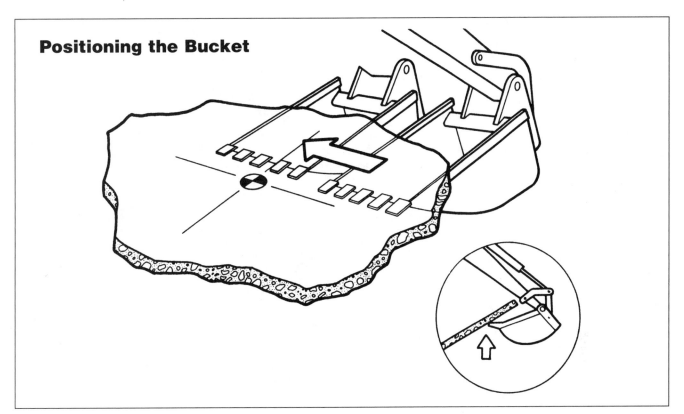

**Positioning the Bucket**

**Fig. 13-13**. *Illustration shows the correct positioning of the bucket in relation to the piece's center of gravity. Inset shows correct angle at which bucket teeth make contact.*

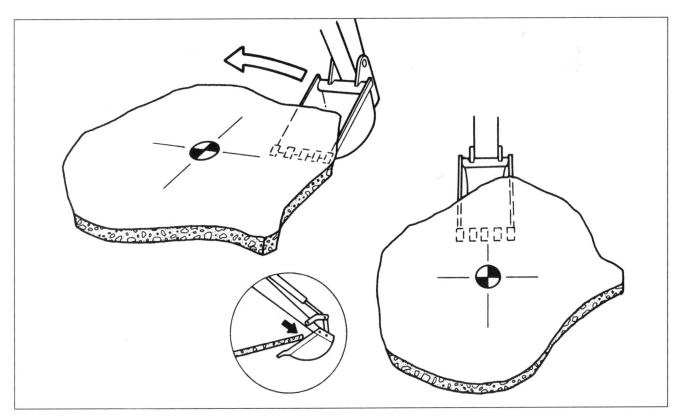

**Fig. 13-14** *POSITIONING THE PIECE:* *If the bucket first contacts the piece incorrectly, the swing can sometimes be used to position the piece correctly on the bucket.*

***Stacking method.*** This method works very well when long, narrow sections are to be removed. This is often encountered where pavement has been saw-cut to allow the excavation of a trench. When the material is less than four inches thick, it can usually be stacked up to three layers and easily loaded onto the bucket. As the operator becomes experienced, this method becomes very efficient for removing pavement from a trenching area (Fig. 13-15). **Note:** When pavement is to be cut for a trench, the width of the cut must be wider than the desired trench. For example, if a trench is to be twenty-four inches wide, the pavement should be cut at least twenty-six inches. If the cut is made exactly to the width of the trench, the bucket simply won't fit into the opening. This in turn means using a smaller bucket, and since it holds less volume, digging will take longer.

***Handling thicker concrete.*** Up to this point, we have referred mostly to handling of slabs four inches thick and less. Thicker material can also be handled effectively with the backhoe (Fig. 13-16). Because thick materials tend to break off in larger pieces, loading is actually easier because the operator will only handle one piece at a time. (It is much easier to handle one large piece than many little ones.) Again, the key to picking up large pieces is to provide a good back-up. When loading large pieces of material, one at a time, the

**Fig. 13-16**. *Thick pieces can also be handled well by loading them into the bucket – one at a time.*

**Fig. 13-17**. *USING THE STABILIZER AS A BACK-UP: Pieces can often be pushed onto the bucket by using the stabilizer as a backup. However, perfect control and extreme caution is required to prevent damage to the ram.*

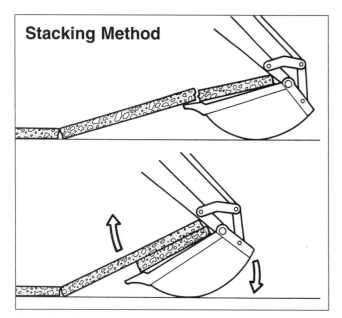

## Stacking Method

**Fig. 13-15** *Long pieces can be broken and stacked for loading in a single motion.*

TLB's stabilizers can be used as a very effective back-up where no other object is available.

***Using the stabilizer as a back-up.*** This procedure can be used in many situations. Because of possible damage to the hydraulic ram however, it is best to find an alternate back-up.

When no other back-up is available, use the utmost care to prevent damage to the ram. To prevent concrete or other heavy, dangerous material from contacting the ram, the material must not be allowed to roll, or slide onto it. This rolling or sliding can be prevented by keeping the ram at least as high as the material which is being loaded into the bucket.

As seen in Fig. 13-17, this maneuver is somewhat difficult and is not recommended for beginning operators. Because of its difficulty and the potential for damage to the TLB, it is easy to understand why this method **should not** be used as standard operating procedure, but as a special, last-resort method. The real beauty of this technique is realized when it becomes necessary to load large or odd-shaped materials, such as curb and gutter sections, poles, railroad ties, stumps, I-beams, large slabs, etc. Its other obvious advantage is that it is always available, and can be used to eliminate many problem situations.

When attempting this procedure, especially with long pieces of material, it is essential to position the material (or the TLB) so that its center of gravity makes contact **at** the stabilizer. This will ensure the piece is balanced when it is loaded into the bucket. With this in mind, it is easy to see why, when loading a number of long pieces, it is important to arrange them in an orderly manner on the ground, with the center of gravity of each piece located at the same place. (Fig. 13-18)

Now that we have discussed the many aspects of getting the load into the bucket, let's examine the second part of the loading process, which simply consists of lifting and swinging the load over the truck and positioning the material in the truck bed in an orderly fashion. This can be done either with

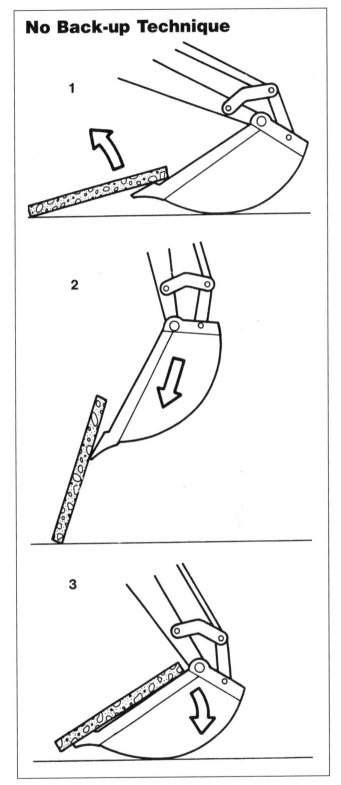

**No Back-up Technique**

**Fig. 13-18** *When no back-up is available, this three-step procedure is recommended:*
*1) The piece is lifted until near vertical.*
*2) The bucket sides carefully down behind the piece by rolling the bucket down and back.*
*3) The piece will be secured on the bucket.*

the backhoe or the loader bucket, and we will consider each separately.

## Lifting and Swinging

We have seen many ways to efficiently manipulate material into the bucket. The reason there are so many methods is because there are so many different shapes and sizes to contend with.

After the load has been picked up, it is best to clamp it firmly in place to prevent it from falling out. However, clamping the load in the bucket is not always possible. Dropping a load of concrete from ten feet in the air unintentionally is not only inefficient, it is also dangerous, posing a hazard to the machine, the truck, the work area and people in the area. The lifting and swinging of the load must **always be very smooth and gentle**, to reduce the risk of accidentally dropping it.

So, when lifting and swinging, the operator must first and foremost **control the load**. This means he must move very smoothly at all times; sometimes he must also proceed very slowly, to prevent loose pieces from falling off.

As the load is lifted, there is a natural tendency for the pieces to fall out of, or off of the bucket. During the course of a day's work, there will be many situations when a load may contain pieces that are not securely held in place (Fig. 13-19). When it appears that all or part of a load may fall as it is swung over the truck, the operator may want to "test" the load to see how securely it is held in place. The purpose is to make sure the load will be safe when swinging it to the side. If it isn't, falling pieces could damage the truck, the TLB's stabilizer arm, or, if the load is very high, it could even fall onto the cab area of the machine. When conducting this test, the load is positioned straight behind the machine, in a manner that would be safe if pieces do fall.

Position the load directly behind the TLB over an area where falling concrete would not present a problem. Clamp it as tightly as possible with the bucket. Then, a very light and quick movement of the crowd will shake the load so that any pieces not securely held will move or fall. The bucket is

**Fig. 13-19** *When loading loose, awkwardly-shaped materials, every move must be made slowly and smoothly to prevent material from falling from the bucket.*

then re-tightened, and the load should be safe to swing, as the remaining pieces are securely gripped by the machine (Fig. 13-20).

As the load swings over the truck and clears the side, it should be lowered with the crowd and placed carefully into the truck (not dropped) to reduce the risk of damage. As the pieces are placed into the truck, the operator should pay attention to the load's **weight distribution** in the bed. The weight of the load should be distributed evenly to both sides.

Another important point is to place the materials in such a way that they won't bind the load when it is dumped later on. After large slabs are placed in the bed, they should then be carefully broken by hand to make sure the load will dump easily.

One way to prevent a load from binding is not to pile it too high, never higher than the tailgate hinge pin. If piled too high, the load will slide back and bind as the bed is raised, making it impossible to lower the bed again until the material if off-loaded by hand.

**Fig. 13-20** *By testing the load, the operator can be sure that it is safe to swing over the truck.*

## Loading with the Loader

When loading out concrete with the loader bucket, the same rules apply as when loading any other type of material. Loading concrete requires a little extra planning and preparation. The two main aspects to be considered are 1) the height of the stockpile, and 2) the size of the pieces.

As stressed earlier, keeping the stockpile as low as possible is the best approach (see Figs. 13-21,22, 23).The lower the pile, the easier it will be to fill the bucket. In general, material should never be piled higher than is absolutely necessary.

The size of the pieces is also very important. The smaller they are, the easier it will be to load them into the bucket. If larger pieces are stockpiled without being broken first, they can be very difficult to load. In contrast, when crushed or broken into pieces less than two inches, the bucket can be filled quickly and easily. Of course, pieces will rarely be broken up that small on most jobs, but

the principle remains: **small pieces are easier to load than large ones**. The only exception is when large pieces are loaded one at a time.

*Large pieces.* Loading large chunks of material with the loader can be a very dangerous operation. There is no way to "grip" them with the loader, as the backhoe can do.

Due to the weight of the large pieces, a smooth and nearly level loading area is a necessity. Because the TLB is designed to lift only as much as it can safely handle, it is fairly easy to avoid trouble as far as overloading the machine is concerned. However, this applies on **level ground only**. Loading heavy material on any sloped surface is extremely dangerous, and should not be attempted.

The recommended method for loading large pieces into the front loader bucket is similar to that for loading the backhoe. First, position the piece

**Fig. 13-21** *Even when a pile like the one shown here is only as high as the bucket, resistance is often so great that getting a full bucket will often be impossible.*

**Fig. 13-22** *Here the pile was back-dragged and effectively lowered so that the material could be pushed easily into the bucket.*

**Fig. 13-23** *When loading from a properly prepared stockpile, getting full buckets will be consistently easier.*

where a back-up can be used to force the piece into the bucket. Then, lift the piece to about a 45 to 60 degree angle (Fig. 13-24). Carefully work the bucket down and under the piece. As the lower edge of the bucket is positioned as far below the piece's center of gravity as possible, the bucket can be rolled back. If the piece does not remain in the bucket, roll the bucket up and down repeatedly, **working it down and under the piece**.

Once the piece is resting in the bucket (Fig. 13-25) (or in the case of large, flat pieces, lying on the outer bucket surfaces), all movements must be smoothly executed to keep the load from shifting during transport or when raising the loader. Just as when loading is done with the backhoe, the pieces must be placed carefully in the truck bed (not dropped) to prevent damage. Before loading large

pieces, a cushioning layer of dirt, or small concrete pieces, should be placed in the bed to further protect it. As before, load distribution is a factor – distribute the material evenly in the truck, during all loading operations.

***CAUTION:*** If a machine is not equipped with a **self-leveling** bucket, it is necessary to pay constant attention to keeping the bucket level in order to prevent the load from falling onto the cab area of the machine.

**Fig. 13-24** *After the piece has been lifted as shown, the leading edge of the bucket is worked down and under the piece as far as possible.*

**Fig. 13-25** *If the top of the piece is heavier than the bottom, it will naturally fall onto the bucket ready to load.*

**Fig. 13-26** *This photo shows a common demolition job site shortly after work has begun.*

**Fig. 13-27** *Here the bulk of the material has been removed.*

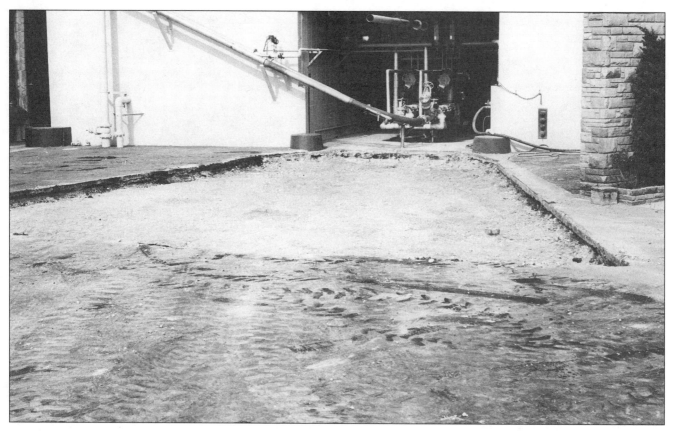

**Fig. 13-28** *Job site is shown following cleanup.*

## Questions – Chapter 13 **Demolition**

**1. The efficiency of job completion is determined by:**

_____ a. What kind of trucks are being used

_____ b. How many different materials

_____ c. How many times the material must be handled

_____ d. The size of backhoe bucket

**2. When stockpiling broken concrete or other materials becomes necessary, the main consideration is:**

_____ a. Keeping the pile low

_____ b. The size of the pieces

_____ c. Providing a good backup

_____ d. All of the above

**3. During the demolition process, dirt should be kept separate from other materials such as asphalt and concrete.**

_____ a. True

_____ b. False

**4. When using the "prying method," the power is generated by:**

_____ a. The boom cylinder

_____ b. The bucket and crowd cylinders

_____ c. The weight of the machine

_____ d. All of the above

**5. Because of the tremendous forces generated by the "prying method", a heavy duty bucket is mandatory.**

_____ a. True

_____ b. False

**6. Breaking and removing concrete is very abusive to the machine and there is no way to avoid abuse.**

_____ a. True

_____ b. False

_Notes:_ _____

_____

_____

_____

_____

_____

_____

_____

_____

_____

_____

_____

_____

_____

_____

_____

_____

_____

_____

_____

_____

_____

_____

_____

_____

_____

_____

_____

_____

_____

**7. The "roll-out" method is "easy" on the machine because it is done using the natural motion of the machine.**

_____ a. True

_____ b. False

**8. When picking up concrete that is still "in place," with the backhoe, the remaining concrete provides a natural backup.**

_____ a. True

_____ b. False

**9. When working with large pieces, why should the bucket be positioned under the center of gravity of the piece?**

_____ a. To prevent breaking it

_____ b. To maintain control while moving it

_____ c. To test the weight

_____ d. All of the above

**10. When digging a trench with a 24 inch bucket, the concrete covering the area should be sawcut to a width of _____ inches prior to the backhoe work.**

_____ a. 22 inches

_____ b. 24 inches

_____ c. 26 inches

_____ d. 36 inches

**11. Using the stabilizer as a backup:**

_____ a. Is a difficult maneuver that could cause machine damage

_____ b. Should not be used as standard operating procedure

_____ c. Should not be attempted by operators under the skill level of a veteran

_____ d. All of the above

**12. When lifting and swinging concrete to load a truck, the operator should:**

_____ a. Move the load smoothly and gently

_____ b. Control the load at all times

_____ c. "Test" the load to dislodge loose pieces before swinging over the truck

_____ d. All of the above

**13. To prevent a load of concrete from binding in the truck bed when dumped:**

_____ a. Only load in the back of the truck

_____ b. Do not overload the truck

_____ c. Do not pile pieces higher than the tailgate hinge pin

_____ d. All of the above

**14. When material is to be handled two or more times, there are several stockpiling considerations to be made.**

_____ a. True

_____ b. False

**15. In many demolition jobs, separation of different materials is an important consideration.**

_____ a. True

_____ b. False

**16. Clean up of demolition materials is either carried out at the end of the job, or in stages as the work progresses.**

_____ a. True

_____ b. False

**17. One of the most efficient methods of breaking and loading concrete is to break and load the material with the backhoe and load it into trucks in one operation.**

_____ a. True

_____ b. False

**18. When using the loader to load concrete, the larger the pieces, the easier the loading process will be.**

_____ a. True

_____ b. False

_____
_____
_____
_____
_____
_____
_____
_____
_____
_____
_____
_____
_____
_____
_____
_____
_____
_____
_____
_____
_____
_____
_____
_____
_____
_____
_____
_____
_____
_____

**19. When loading broken concrete with the loader, the larger the stockpile the easier the loading will become.**

_____ a. True

_____ b. False

**20. On most demolition jobs concrete and dirt can be mixed and hauled away.**

_____ a. True

_____ b. False

**21. A trench is to be dug in an existing parking lot. The concrete has been saw cut to allow the trench to be dug. The spoil from the trench will be reused for backfill, and the concrete will be loaded onto a truck and removed from the site. The fastest and easiest way to accomplish this work is to pile the concrete and dirt together on one side of the trench.**

_____ a. True

_____ b. False

**22. The most powerful break out force created by the TLB is when the backhoe uses the "prying method."**

_____ a. True

_____ b. False

**23. Breaking concrete into smaller pieces can be accomplished by:**

_____ a. Dropping

_____ b. The roll out method

_____ c. Positioning and striking

_____ d. All of the above

**24. Because of the unusual shapes and sizes of broken concrete, as well as the weight involved, the beginning operator can find loading to be difficult and awkward.**

_____ a. True

_____ b. False

**25. Loading heavy material on any sloped surface is extremely dangerous and should not be attempted.**

_____ a. True

_____ b. False

# Natural Gas Dangers

This information has been compiled from recommendations provided by the Southern California Gas Co.

Natural gas is potentially hazardous, but at the same time, it is a very important energy source for our modern society. As a backhoe operator, the more you know about natural gas, distribution systems, piping materials, and how to handle a broken line, the better off you will be. You, your work crew, and general public will be in a safer environment when all workers are informed about the dangers of natural gas.

## General Information About Natural Gas

• Natural gas is lighter than air. It will rise and diffuse rapidly when escaping into an open area.

• Natural gas is not toxic or poisonous. However, if natural gas displaces air in an enclosed space, suffocation can occur because of the lack of oxygen.

• Natural gas is usually odorless in its natural state; therefore, an odorant is added and can be detected by humans in concentrations of as little as 1%. This provides a margin of safety as flammable conditions require between 4 and 14% gas to air mixture.

• The ignition point of natural gas is quite high, being 1100 to 1200 degrees F. However, many common sources of ignition can reach this and higher temperatures.

## Layout of Hand Digging Excavations

When preparing to locate a gas pipe by hand it is important to understand that these pipes can be broken by hand tools. Because of this danger, it is best to position the hand dug area so access is from the side of the pipe, as well as over the top. This improves the ability to safely dig, because once the pipe depth and location is known, the backhoe can dig with more safety and efficiency. However, the pipe must be cleaned off between every bucket of material to keep the pipe visible to the operator at all times. Be aware that other lines may occupy the same general area too, so do not assume the first line exposed is the one that you were looking for. Be safe, always hand expose facilities before using power digging or boring equipment between gas line marks. The risk of injury or damage will be reduced if the location of the pipe is confirmed or found, and the situation can be assessed before it is too late.

## Hand Digging

When hand digging, always consider the inherent inaccuracies in electronic locating equipment, the size and type of the pipe, and the potential force that can be applied by digging tools. The harder the soil, and the more vulnerable the facility, the lesser the blade "bite" that should be applied by the digging tools. To further assist in avoiding damage use "shaving" techniques, and apply digging blades parallel to facilities. Also, make smaller inspection holes and use probes in the area of the dig before taking larger "bites" with digging tools. As practical, use downward blade angles that slope slightly away from suspected locations. Care is always necessary because gas pipes can be damaged by hand digging tools, especially when used by inadequately trained or inexperienced persons, or when used with haste and carelessness. Avoid hazardous situations by leaving gas lines exposed and visible, or re-expose them as power digging, earth boring, and/or installation approaches. This way, safe clearances can be observed and maintained.

## Slight Impacts To Pipe

A "nick" in a plastic pipe, or in a protective wrapper on steel pipe, can cause future leakage. Please notify the gas company directly in these cases so a representative may inspect and take any corrective action. Spot inspections and most minor repairs are free.

## Pipe Size and Type

Gas lines (pipes) come in sizes from 1/2-inch, up to several feet in diameter, and are usually made of some type of plastic or steel.

Steel gas lines are part of a distribution system that includes high pressure transportation lines, as well as medium and low pressure distribution lines. The steel pipe is very prone to rust and corrosion. The resulting danger of future leaks requires that coatings and other means of corrosion protection must be used to protect these pipes. Steel gas lines have a waterproof coating such as plastic, rubber, tar-based coating, or special tape, to prevent the rust and corrosion. This coating is critical to the life of the pipe, and the safety of the area. If this coating is scraped or disturbed in any way, the damaged area must be properly sealed to prevent corrosion and a future leak that could cause an explosion in 8 or 10 years. Gas pipes that have been scraped by shovels or a backhoe bucket should be reported to the local gas company for immediate repair, before backfilling the trench. They appreciate the call and generally do not charge for maintaining the protection of their pipe.

Plastic gas lines have generally small diameters and are used for low or medium pressure installations. They are sometimes installed in conduits, or inside existing steel pipes to ease the installation, or to "replace" a rusted pipe with a new one. Plastic pipe comes in various colors, and in sizes that start at 1/2-inch in diameter and go up from there. The size and type of pipe will determine how the hand digging can proceed.

The size and type of pipe will:

1. determine the width of the "tolerance zone."

2. help you to identify the pipe when it is located, and indicate the vulnerability of the line to outside forces.

3. helps determine the degree of "touch" needed to safely expose the pipe manually.

## Accidental Release of Pressurized Natural Gas

Escaping natural gas usually dissipates harmlessly unless it becomes ignited or is confined. For your safety, remember that only fire departments or gas company personnel are properly equipped and trained to handle escaping gas, particularly with the pressures in our underground piping.

Here are some basic precautions to take if they can be done safely. These include securing the vicinity, notifying the proper entities, and monitoring the area. These three steps are described below in the order of the most common application.

## Vacate & Secure

• If personnel are in or near the excavation, instruct them to exit immediately.

• If a tractor or excavator is involved, and can be shut down immediately and safely, do so.

• Clear the area of personnel and secure the immediate vicinity from intrusion by others. This includes any motorized equipment. Consider roping off the area.

• Call 911 or the local fire department when escaping gas is ignited; has the potential to enter other buildings or substructures; is causing public alarm; or is perceived to be posing a threat to traffic, the work crew, the public, or any habitable buildings.

• Keep ignition sources away. These may include: open flames, smoking materials, generators, electric motors and switches, engines, sparks from digging equipment, welding operations, or electrically controlled equipment.

• Continue to monitor the area. If people become anxious, ask them to remain calm, advise that proper response entities have been notified, and have them stay a safe distance from the site.

• Never attempt to control escaping gas at the break. Do not try to block, plug, or bend over broken pipe ends. Aside from the possibility of being blasted by debris picked up by the gas stream, there could be a lack of oxygen, or an ignition source

present. Any contact, particularly with plastic pipe, can cause a spark. Wait for the gas company or fire department. They are trained and equipped to handle these incidents. If they need your assistance, they will safely direct you.

## About Static Electricity

In some situations, static energy is caused by friction of rapidly escaping gas. This is most likely to occur on plastic pipes! It is not normally a concern unless a static charge is suddenly given a path to ground. If someone or something contacts the broken pipe a spark can result. This is one reason why it is best there be no contact with broken pipes while gas is escaping. Also, be aware that friction between materials, such as found in some types of clothing, can also cause a spark, and is another reason for not entering an excavation or area containing escaping gas.

If ignition occurs, it is usually best to let the fire burn to the extent it is not threatening life or additional property. Putting fires out without stopping the flow of gas can cause more hazard than letting the gas be consumed by fire. Keep in mind that smoldering paint, hoses, or debris in and near excavations can cause re-ignition if gas continues to vent into the area.

Ignition can occur from a variety of sources in the right air-to-gas mixture (4 to 14%). The problem is knowing exactly when or where this mixture exists is nearly impossible. So, always proceed with caution, and never attempt to control escaping gas at the break, or in a gas/air mixture – ignition could occur unexpectedly!

If desired, and if it can be done from a safe distance (e.g. downwind and out of the area of gas odor or concentration), a light spray of water directed on the pipe within the excavation can reduce the likelihood of a static charge build-up. But be careful, flooding the excavation can cause additional problems in repairing the break.

## Other Recommendations and Cautions

• Do not operate gas valves located in the streets or parkways. Turning the wrong valve can create a critical situation elsewhere.

• Never enter a manhole or other confined space near escaping gas. It could be migrating into the vault or area.

• Do not direct water streams on burning gas at its point of escape. If this point is in an excavation, it will fill the hole with mud and water and make the repair slower and more hazardous.

• Never turn any gas valve on once it has been turned off. Only gas company representatives have the expertise to determine when this is advisable.

# Glossary of Terms

**ALTERING DIMENSIONS:** Moving part of the machine into a different position to change the size or shape of the TLB in order to gain an advantage. Some examples would include; to move the center of gravity of the machine, or, to shorten a dimension to fit into a smaller area.

**BACK-UP:** Any object or structure the operator may use to push against, moving material into either the backhoe or loader bucket.

**BOOM:** The main lifting structure of the hoe assembly.

**BREAKOUT FORCE:** The force created by the curling action of the loader bucket.

**CAVE-IN:** The sudden collapse of the excavation wall.

**CENTER OF GRAVITY:** 1. An imaginary point within or near an object that represents the balance point of that object. 2. The position within or near an object that represents the "center of the weight" of that object. 3. The point within the machine around which its weight is evenly distributed.

**COMPACTION:** The compression of soil into a dense state through the application of great weight, usually that of the machine.

**CONDUIT:** Plastic or steel piping through which wires pass underground.

**CONTROL:** The ability to effectively direct the TLB so that it performs exactly as the operator desires.

**CROWD:** The secondary structure of the hoe assembly, to which the backhoe bucket is attached.

**DEMOLITION:** Breaking and removal of concrete, asphalt or other heavy building materials.

**DIGGING CYCLE:** The series of motions used by the operator during excavating, from filling the bucket, to swinging and dumping the bucket, to returning to the original digging position.

**DIMENSIONS:** measure of the size and mass of an object, such as length, height, width and weight.

**DISPERSION:** To distribute or spread material in an orderly manner aiding in job completion.

**DITCH:** See *trench*.

**DOWNHILL FORCE:** The variable force on an object that is produced by the weight of the object… and the pitch of slope.

**ELEVATION:** An established point above sea level or other measured point of reference.

**EXCAVATION:** Any digging operation involving the removal of earth; also, the space created by digging.

**FEATHERING:** Process of manipulating the hydraulic control valves on the TLB so that a smooth, flowing action is created.

**FLOAT:** Position in the loader control valve which allows the loader arms to raise and lower freely.

**FOOTINGS:** The concrete foundation of a building or other structure, requiring excavations of a precise nature.

**FRICTION:** 1. A force that acts to resist or retard motion between two objects that are in contact. 2. Creates resistance in varying degrees to all procedures that involve digging, cutting, or bucket loading.

**GRADE:** A) To cut, fill and smooth a given area. B) See elevation.

**GREASING**: Lubrication of the machines mechanical joints to prevent wear.

**HOSES:** Flexible rubber/steel/fabric pipes which carry fluid through the TLB's hydraulic system.

**JETTING:** Process of injecting great amounts of water through a hose to speed the compaction process.

**JOYSTICK:** Control lever which combines two functions, and which is manipulated in four directions instead of two.

**LAYOUT:** A job plan, usually laid on the ground with lime or other visible material, to indicate the direction and/or trench width for the TLB to follow.

**LEVEL:** A perfectly flat or even surface area, conforming to the surface of still water.

**MOMENTUM:** The result of the weight of an object combined with motion.

**MONITOR:** To periodically check the status of; watch over.

**MOTION:** 1. The action or process of change of position. 2. The act of moving a machine or materials. 3. A requirement for performing and completing any work

**ONE CALL SYSTEM:** An international system designed to coordinate locating existing utilities in an effort to prevent breakage and accidents.

**OVERDIGGING:** Digging too deeply or farther than intended.

**PERCENT:** Measurement used to specify slopes. Refers to the amount of rise or fall in 100 feet horizontally. A 2% slope would rise or fall 2 feet in 100 feet horizontal.

**PIER:** A large concrete platform that supports the weight of a building or other structure.

**PITCH OF SLOPE:** 1. an incline upward or downward. 2. an inclined surface or stretch of ground. 3. a deviation from level or the amount of deviation.

**PIVOT METHOD:** The technique of maneuvering the TLB using the loader bucket as a pivot point.

**PLUMB:** Perpendicular to level.

**RATIO:** Measurement used to specify slopes. 2:1, pronounced ""two to one", means 2 feet horizontal to 1 foot vertical.

**RESTRICTIONS:** Obstacles or other hazards that prevent tree movement or operation of the TLB.

**ROLL-OVER:** Accidentally causing the TLB to tip over violently.

**SET-UP:** Exact positioning of the TLB that will produce the desired excavation results.

**SHANK:** Permanent mounting to which bucket teeth are attached.

**SHORING:** A system of wood or metal restraints which, when placed inside an excavation, hold the walls in place and prevent cave-ins.

**SHUTTLE:** The repeated movement back and forth of the TLB across the job site in a predetermined route.

**SLOPING:** The digging of excavation walls in such a way, and at such an angle, that the risk of cave-ins is eliminated; an alternative to shoring.

**SPOIL:** Material (dirt) removed from an excavation.

**STICK:** See crowd.

**STOCKPILE:** The accumulation of spoil or other materials on the job site, in areas which are accessible to the TLB, trucks, etc.

**SWING:** The hoe function which permits side movement.

**TEETH:** The hardened steel cutting edges which are attached to the backhoe bucket.

**TOOTH-GRAB METHOD:** Technique by which the operator may use the bucket teeth to hook or grab objects such as small trees, pipes, reinforcing rods, etc.

**TORQUE:** The force which produces rotation; in the TLB, the reaction to the force takes the form either of lifting force or down pressure on the bucket or front tires.

**TOTAL OPERATING WEIGHT:** The weight of the TLB itself plus the load it is transporting.

**TRACTION:** The amount of friction between the tires and the surface traveled on.

**TRENCH:** A particular type of excavation, usually no wider than the bucket being used to dig it.

**UTILITIES:** The presence on a job site of lines operated by public agencies, including electrical, telephone, gas or water lines.

**WEIGHT:** 1. A measure of the heaviness or mass of an object. 2. The downward force exerted on an object by gravity.

**WEIGHT DISTRIBUTION:** The manner in which the total operating weight of the TLB is distributed into the area on which it sits; may change depending on a variety of external factors.

**ZERK FITTING:** Common fittings located around the TLB, through which a grease gun may be attached for the injection of grease into the operating hinge joints.

# Index

# Answer Key

## Chapter 1

1. On a two-wheel drive TLB, about how much of the machine's weight is in the backhoe assembly?
   **d. 1/3**

2. Because of its location, high above the ground and far behind the wheelbase, the weight the backhoe attachment transfers the machine's center of gravity upward as well as to the rear when compared to other machines.
   **a. True**

3. Why should the operator alter the TLB's dimensions?
   **a. To improve stability**
   **b. To improve safety**
   **c. To improve maneuverability**
   **d. All of the above**

4. A 32% slope will rise how many feet vertical in 100 ft. horizontal?
   **c. 32 ft**

5. On a two-wheel drive machine, why is it important to keep as much weight and traction as possible on the rear wheels?
   **c. The brakes are only on the rear wheels**

6. If you must drive up or back down a grade with the hoe on the downward end, you should:
   **d. Stabilize the front wheels by filling the loader bucket with dirt or heavy material**

7. Raising the loader bucket will:
   **a. Shorten the machine**
   **b. Shift the weight up and to the rear**
   **c. Decrease the TLB's stability**
   **d. All of the above**

8. Features such as 4 wheel-drive, and large front tires tend to destabilize the TLB.
   **b. False – *The weight of the drive assembly will shift the weight forward slightly, and make the machine more stable.***

9. A machine with a hydraulic breaker attached to the backhoe will have _____ weight on the front tires?
   **a. Less**

10. A 3/4:1 slope is commonly used in stable soils for sloping temporary excavations, when specified by the engineers.
    **a. True**

11. Operating a TLB (or any kind of heavy equipment) is a construction trade that is unique in the construction industry:
    **c. Because of the high weight involved**

12. The universal forces and principles are:
    **a. Constant**
    **b .Variable**
    **c .Both of the above**

13. A slope that rises 1 ft. vertical for every 10 ft. horizontal is expressed as:
    **c. 10%**

14. The great weight of the TLB dictates that the other forces and principles acting on the machine will be minimal.
    **b. False – *The great weight of the TLB dictates that the other forces and principles acting on the machine will also be of great magnitude.***

15. When weight and motion are combined the result is:
    **c. Momentum**

16. When momentum and downhill force combine, they can become stronger than the forces that are keeping the machine under control.
    **a. True**

17. Which of the following are true of a 2:1 slope?
    **a. Commonly used slope for stability between building pads**
    **b. Loader backhoes are almost never used on a slope this steep**
    **c. A 2:1 slope is a 1 ft rise for every two feet horizontal**
    **d. All of the above**

18. Downhill force is the result of the combination of weight and momentum.
    **b. False – *Downhill force is the result of the combination of weight and pitch of slope.***

19. When on a downhill, a bicycle rider will be propelled by the center of gravity.
    **a. True**

20. When operating a TLB, a loss of traction would result in:
    **a. Reduced productivity**
    **b. Loss of control**
    **c. Loss of safety**
    **d. All of the above**

21. Friction usually occurs between the bucket (or cutting-edge) and the ground.
    **a. True**

22. Raising the loader bucket or extending the backhoe will move the center of gravity toward the rear of the machine.
    **a. True**

23. The power or strength of downhill force is determined by the weight of the object and the slope it is resting on.
   **a. True**

24. A 1:1 slope is commonly used in temporary excavations as per OHSA regulations.
   **a. True**

25. There are _____ universal forces and principles that determine the safe operation of a TLB.
   **c. 8**

26. On flat, level ground, downhill force is an important consideration for the operator to consider when planning the job.
   **b False – *On flat, level ground, downhill force is not a factor because there is no slope present.***

27. A 100% slope equals ____ degrees.
   **c. 45**

28. A 1% slope is commonly used for drainage on paved surfaces such as parking lots.
   **a. True**

29. A 50% slope is equal to a 1:1 slope.
   **b. False – *A 50% slope is equal to a 2:1 slope.***

30. A 2% slope is commonly required for sheet flow drainage such as grading around houses to ensure positive drainage.
   **a. True**

31. On a 20% slope, how much vertical rise would there be when the horizontal measurement was 100 feet?
   **c. 20 ft**

32. The center of gravity of an object is determined by:
   **a. The weight of the object**
   **b. The shape of the object**
   **c. How the weight is distributed.**
   **d. All of the above**

33. When using the loader, the base of the machine is the entire area inside of where the tires contact the ground.
   **a. True**

34. The vertical line indicates the force of gravity and where the COG is in relation to the base.
   **a. True**

35. The high weights involved in operating heavy equipment:
   **d. Bring with them with the unbending laws of physics.**

# Chapter 2

1. One common element that should be present in every TLB operation is smoothness.
   **a. True**

2. Smooth operation of the TLB will:
   **a. Improve safety**
   **b. Increase efficiency**
   **c. Lengthen machine life**
   **d. All of the above**

3. Controlling the machine with the brakes is most effective on TLB models equipped with automatic, torque converter transmissions.
   **a. True**

4. Excluding the stabilizers, how many functions are controlled by the main backhoe control valves?
   **c. 4**

5. If two are more valves are opened at the same time, through which valve will the oil flow?
   **a. The valve with the least resistance**

6. Smooth operation can be mastered by a technique called feathering.
   **a. True**

7. Control can only be mastered by making a concentrated effort to be smooth at all times while at the backhoe controls.
   **a. True**

8. What is the fastest way to learn and gain complete control of the backhoe's hydraulics?
   **c. Practice and constant striving for smoothness**

9. The advantages of the two-lever system include less operator fatigue and increased control when using all four functions at once.
   **a. True**

10. The four-lever system gives the operator slightly greater control when propelling or maneuvering the machine with the backhoe itself.
   **a. True**

11. The "floating the bucket" exercise involves following the contour of the ground with the bucket 1 foot off the surface of the ground.
   **b. False – *The "floating the bucket" exercise involves following the contour of the ground with the bucket 1 inch off the surface of the ground.***

12. A machine with improperly functioning or mis-adjusted brakes should be removed from service and repaired.
   **a. True**

13. All TLBs respond the same way to operator input.
   **b. False – *TLBs respond "in their own way" to operator input.***

14. The mechanical response of TLBs can vary greatly. Machine response can differ due to:
   **a. Different manufacturers**
   **b. Age of the machine**
   **c. Weight distribution of the machine**
   **d. All of the above**

15. Weight distribution and the center of gravity stays the same from one machine to another.
   **b. False – *Weight distribution and the center of gravity differs from one machine to another.***

16. An older machine should be operated in a more gentle way to avoid overstressing its individual parts.
   **a. True**

17. In what steering configuration can the operator use the brakes to steer and control the machine?
   **b. 2wd**

18. The machine response in older machines can be degraded by:
   **a. Broken or missing parts**
   **b. Poor or worn brakes**
   **c. Weaker hydraulic power**
   **d. All of the above**

19. The independent brakes of the two-wheel drive TLB can be used to:
   **a. Steer the machine**

b. **Control the machine**

c. **Stop the machine**

d. **All of the above**

20. Proper response and equal adjustment of independent brake systems is critical to safe operation.

**a. True**

21. When the engine is idling, the hydraulic system"

**c. Produces low power and low speed**

22. The hand throttle is commonly used during loader operations.

**b. False – *The hand throttle is commonly used during backhoe operations.***

23. In tight working conditions, or where utilities may be in the area, the operator should lower the RPMs of the engine for slower speed and more precise control over the machine.

**a. True**

24. Because of the technical skills required for loading and unloading a TLB onto a transporter, only experienced operators should carry out the task.

**a. True**

25. If you ever find a mechanical problem on any machine that could compromise safety, notify your supervisor immediately, and take necessary action to maintain safety at all times.

**a. True**

## Chapter 3

1. What is the number one cause of accidents with the TLB?

**c. Getting on and off the machine**

2. You turn the TLB off at the end of a working day and everything is okay. It is all right to start the machine up the next day and start working.

**b. False – *The operator must do a pre-operation check of the machine.***

3. What safety devices should you check?

**a. Reverse warning alarm**

**b. Seat belt**

**c. Guards**

**d. All of the above**

4. When must you wear your seat belt?

**c. All of the time**

5. When loading a machine onto a truck or trailer, the ground conditions should be:

**a. Firm and level**

6. When loading the machine, make sure buckets, blades, forks and other mounted equipment are:

**b. Lowered**

7. Following loading you must:

**a. Lower and secure buckets, booms, all other equipment**

**b. Shut off the engine and remove the key**

**c. Place transmission in park or low and apply brake**

**d. All of the above**

8. When securing the TLB to the transporting vehicle with cables or chains, be sure that they are not in contact with the machine's hydraulic hoses, hydraulic cylinders, valves, rods or tires.

**a. True**

9. One of the designated exit points on all TLBs is at the rear of the machine at the stabilizers.

**b. False – *The designated exit points on all TLBs is at the side of the machine.***

10. Safety systems on the TLB must be maintained in original condition. Which of the following are considered to be safety systems?

**a. Hand holds, steps and railings**

**b. Seat belt, horn and mirrors**

**c. Reverse warning alarm**

**d. ROPS**

**e. Loader arm service lock**

**f. All of the above**

11. The loader arm service lock should always be installed when operating the backhoe.

**b. False – *The loader arm service lock should always be installed when performing maintenance procedures with the loader arms raised.***

12. The neutral start safety system on the starter is designed to prevent:

**c. To prevent the machine from starting while the transmission is in gear**

13. The rollover protective structure (ROPS) was designed to protect the operator from rollover accidents.

**a. True**

14. When operating a machine with a ROPS it is not necessary to use the seatbelt.

**b. False – When operating a machine with a ROPS it is necessary to use the seatbelt.**

15. About one third of all rollover accidents occur when:

**b. The machine was moved too close to the edge of a road or downslope**

16. The risk of rollover can be reduced by monitoring how the machine's weight is distributed as the work proceeds.

**a. True**

17. Cave-in deaths occur primarily due to suffocation or crushing.

**a. True**

18. Ground conditions that appear to be stable may not be, due to previous excavations.

**a. True**

19. According to OSHA, trenches deeper than six feet must be shored or sloped.

**b. False – *According to OSHA, trenches deeper than five feet must be shored or sloped. (This can vary, as some states have their own restrictions.)***

20. Shoring is usually the responsibility of the backhoe operator.

**b. False – *Shoring is usually the responsibility of the contractor***

21. Sloping a trench is usually the responsibility of the TLB operator.

**a. True**

22. Sloping requires the removal of many times the amount of material than would be removed if the trench was simply shored.

**a. True**

23. Always watch out for workers or other people on the job site.
**a. True**

24. If you suspect there are hidden dangers, such as unstable ground conditions you should:
**b. Notify your supervisor immediately**

25. Safety should be the operator's number one concern at all times.
**a. True**

## Chapter 4

1. What are the most important factors which contribute to unusual wear to the TLB's mechanical joints?
**a. Unnecessary stresses, strains or shocks to the structure and bearing surfaces**
**b. Failing to grease the bearing surfaces on a regular basis**
**c. Dirt entering pin and bushing areas of mechanical joints**
**d. All of the above**

2. The best schedule for greasing the machine is:
**d. Lightly and frequently**

3. Weakening of hydraulic hoses will occur over a period of time due to what factors?
**a. Weathering of the rubber coating**
**b. Hitting or rubbing against objects**
**c. Rubbing against machine parts while working**
**d. All of the above**

4. To ensure proper installation and long hose life, what main factors should you check when installing hydraulic hoses? (choose two)
**a. The hose must follow its natural flex**
**c. Must be the correct length**

5. When changing buckets, and the bucket and the boom are properly aligned, the pins can be pushed into place, rather than hammered.
**a. True**

6. There are two "natural positions" which are critical to the bucket changing process. These are: (choose two)
**c. Lying**
**d. Hanging**

7. When removing the bucket from the backhoe, the proper order of pin removal is:
**b. Remove the linkage pin first and then the hinge pin**

8. When putting a bucket on the backhoe, the proper order of pin replacement is:
**a. Replace the hinge pin first and then the linkage pin**

9. What is the best source of information for your particular machine?
**a. The operator's manual that was supplied with the TLB.**

10. Which components require their fluid levels to be checked daily?
**a. The engine**
**b. The transmission**
**c. The hydraulic system**
**d. All of the above**

11. What should you do if you notice a sudden change in the fluid level of any component?
**a. Investigate it immediately**

12. The most common cause of a sudden drop in fluid level is a leak.
**a. True**

13. The design of the pre-cleaner for most air filter systems is:
**c. Centrifugal**

14. To clean a dirty primary filter you should:
**c. Blow it out with compressed air**

15. A dirty secondary filter should be cleaned by blowing it out with compressed air.
**b. False – *A dirty secondary filter should be replaced, never be re-used.***

16. Filling the fuel tank at the end of the work shift will eliminate condensation from forming in the tank.
**a. True**

17. The best source of maintenance information for any machine is the operator's manual.
**a. True**

18. On a sealed component, such as an engine, transmission, or differential, the outer casing provides the structure of the component and keeps lubricating fluids in and the dirt and contamination out.
**a. True**

19. The differential unit on a TLB:
**d. Divides and delivers power to the drive wheels**

20. The oil and filter on a TLB engine should be changed every 500 hours or 3 months.
**b. False – *The oil and filter on a TLB engine should be changed every 200 hours, or every month.***

21. Most TLBs are equipped with a ____stage air filter system.
**c. 3**

22. Secondary air filters are lifetime components and should be cleaned and reused.
**b. False – *Secondary air filters should never be cleaned and reused.***

23. Daily maintenance of the TLB includes:
**a. Greasing the machine**
**b. Checking the fluid levels**
**c. The pre-operation inspection**
**d. All of the above**

## Chapter 5

1. In what year was the first One Call System introduced, and in what city?

**c. 1974, in Rochester, New York**

2. What must be done to the work area before calling the One Call?

**a. Mark out the work area in white paint for concrete or with flags or stakes for dirt areas**

3. Orange paint markings by a One Call representative indicates what type of installation?

**c. Communications,alarm or signal lines, cable TV, or conduit.**

4. In most states, a One Call permit is valid for how long?

**a. 14 days**

5. Existing pipes positioned at an angle to the trench are easy to detect without damaging them.

**b. False – *Existing pipes positioned at an angle to the trench are difficult to detect without damaging them.***

6. Who is legally responsible to call the One Call System?

**c. Anyone about to dig**

7. Most types of pipes are possible to locate through contact when digging with the backhoe.

**b. False – *Most types of pipes will be damaged through contact when digging with the backhoe.***

8. One Call representatives have marked the utilities on the work site. The proposed trenching will cross a telephone line, an electrical main, a water main and a gas main. Prior to digging, the law in most states requires:

**c. The existing utilities must be exposed by hand**

9. The high-level skills developed by operators in the past are not relevant to modern day backhoe operators.

**b. False – *The high-level skills developed by operators in the past are relevant to modern day backhoe operators.***

10. The One Call System and the utility companies have marked your site. You have exposed the marked utilities by hand and are now ready to begin digging. It is now safe to assume that all the underground utilities have been located.

**b. False – *It is never safe to assume that all the underground utilities have been located.***

11. When working on private property the One Call System will provide locations for all of the existing utilities.

**b. False – *When working on private property the One Call System does not provide locations for all of the existing utilities.***

12. When investigating a new job site before digging, there can be telltale signs that will help operators to spot potential underground hazards. Mark any of the following that could alert you to unmarked underground utilities.

**a. Long narrow depressions in the ground**
**b. Water boxes**
**c. Sewer clean outs**
**d. Gas meters**
**e. Electrical vaults and pull boxes**

13. A highly-skilled and experienced operator uses which of the following techniques to detect an unmarked pipe through bucket contact and avoid breaking it:

**a. Bucket movement**
**b. Control**
**c. Total concentration**
**d. All of the above**

14. When digging in hard soil, underground pipes are easier to detect without damage.

**b. False – *When digging in hard soil, underground pipes are more difficult to detect without damage.***

15. White paint markings indicate what type of installation?

**a. Proposed excavation.**

16. A Stage 1 situation is where there should be no utilities in the area, such as farmland and some construction sites.

**a. True**

17. A Stage 2 situation is where information about utilities is limited or incomplete, but there are some utilities believed to be present.

**a. True**

19. Stage 3 exists when it is possible that utilities exist that have not been located and marked by One Call representatives.

**a. True**

20. Red paint markings by a One Call representative indicate what type of installation?

**a. Electric power lines, cables, conduit and lighting cables.**

21. In a Stage 4 digging situation, the operator should:

**c. Use half throttle and proceed slowly and carefully**

22. Services provided by the One Call System covers job sites throughout the United States.

**a. True**

23. The One Call System notifies all contractors in the area of the proposed excavations in the area.

**b. False – *The One Call System notifies utility companies of the proposed excavations in the area.***

24. Yellow paint markings by a One Call representative indicate what type of installation?

**b. Gas, oil, steam, petroleum, or gaseous materials.**

25. The One Call System must be contacted a minimum of _____ prior to starting digging operations.

**b. 48 hours**

26. Blue paint markings by a one call representative indicates what type of installation?

**d. Water, irrigation, and slurry lines.**

27. The greatest concentration of underground utilities is located on public property.

**a. True**

28. Pink paint markings by a one call representative indicate what type of installation?

**c. Temporary survey marking.**

## Chapter 6

1. The operator should walk the job site to consider:
   **a. The types of tasks he will have to perform**
   **b. The order in which he will proceed**
   **c. How to complete the entire job as efficiently as possible.**
   **d. All of the above**

2. The best operators plan out the job sequence well in advance.
   **a. True**

3. Some of the important things to discuss with the person in charge include:
   **a. Utility locations**
   **b. Placement of spoil**
   **c. Bucket size requirements**
   **d. All of the above**

4. In order to avoid digging the machine into an unmaneuverable situation the operator should:
   **c. Plan the sequence of the digging**

5. Shuttle operations are often required to move large quantities of material from one place to another.
   **a. True**

6. The placement and stockpiling of spoil is determined by what will eventually be done with the material.
   **a. True**

7. The best way to avoid misunderstandings about the work to be done is to have the area clearly marked.
   **a. True**

8. Precision layout is most often required when digging footings.
   **a. True**

9. Precise layouts are required in which of the following situations?
   **a. When planning ground floor lavatories**
   **b. Floor spills**
   **c. Any place where pipes or electrical conduits will come up through the concrete in an exact spot**
   **d. All of the above**

10. Marking both sides of the footing is essential if the footing to be dug is wider than the bucket being used.
   **a. True**

11. In addition to determining the digging sequence, the operator should also be mindful of:
   **a. Coordinating the TLB's work with the other trades on the job site**
   **b. Planning locations for stockpiling**
   **c. Plan and prepare a shuttle route to the stockpile area**
   **d. All of the above**

12. When sizing up a job, the operator should consider:
   **a. The nature of the work expected of the TLB**
   **b. The amount of earth to be moved**
   **c. The time available to perform the work.**
   **d. All of the above**

13. Place temporary reference markers to indicate obstacles to be avoided. Use markers such as stakes with colored ribbons or paint, that are easily visible from the cab of the machine.
   **a. True**

## Chapter 7

1. The main elements of a correct set up are:
   **a. The center line of the hoe must be positioned correctly to cut the trench exactly to the lay out lines**
   **b. Positioning of the entire machine in such a way that stockpiling of spoil in the desired area is possible**
   **c. Making sure the machine is level in order to produce a plumb trench**
   **d. All of the above**

2. The backhoe can only be operated efficiently and safely when it is positioned on a solid base. When it is positioned on the solid base the weight of the machine is supported by the tires.
   **b. False – *When it is positioned on the solid base the weight of the machine is supported by the stabilizers and the loader bucket.***

3. The tripod set-up is a working platform for the backhoe and consists of the front loader bucket and the two stabilizers.
   **a. True**

4. If the operator uses the backhoe with the loader bucket off the ground, the machine will bounce slightly on the front tires. What will the effect of this bouncing be?
   **a. Loss of efficiency**
   **b. Loss of safety**
   **c. Loss of resistance to being pulled backward due to digging forces**
   **d. All of the above**

5. When the tripod set up is used and the loader bucket is firmly lowered on flat ground, what is the effect on the backhoe?
   **a. The machine is stabilized**
   **b. The machine does not shake and bounce**
   **c. The operator does not shake and bounce**
   **d. All of the above**

6. The tripod set up has drawbacks when the machine is operated on:
   **a. Concrete or a delicate surface such as tile, masonry or stonework**
   **b. A hillside or anywhere the area under the front loader bucket is not level**
   **c. When there is insufficient area to rest the bucket**
   **d. All of the above**

7. When is the pivot method used?
   **a. When aligning the machine to the excavation**
   **b. When connecting two trenches**
   **c. When crossing trenches**
   **d. All of the above**

8. When the front loader is firmly down on flat ground, the machine is stabilized and tipping is controlled while the rear of the machine moves sideways.
   **a. True**

9. A precision set-up is aligned and confirmed by:
   **a. Extending out the backhoe and touching the bucket to the layout line**
   **b. Placing the bucket on the layout line close to the machine.**
   **c. Both of the above**

10. After the machine is set up properly, the operator must be constantly aware of the machine's alignment with the trench.
   **a. True**

11. The bucket can be knocked out of alignment by obstructions such as:
   **a. Rocks or roots**
   **b. Pipes**
   **c. Pieces of concrete**
   **d. All of the above**

12. In some situations, the backhoe can be pulled out of alignment by hydraulic digging forces.
   **a. True**

13. When using a tripod set-up, a TLB can be pivoted how many degrees in either direction?
   **b. 25 degrees**

14. When digging pier footings, there is only one procedure that can accomplish the desired results.
   **b. False – *When digging pier footings, there are several procedures that can accomplish the desired results.***

# Chapter 8

1. Digging footings is one of the easiest tasks for an operator to perform.
   **b. False – *Digging footings is one of the more difficult tasks for an operator to perform.***

2. When digging footings, an operator is creating a concrete form by the dirt that is removed.
   **a. True**

3. The requirements for trench-type footings are:
   **a. Correct location**
   **b. Correct depth**
   **c. Correct width**
   **d. All of the above**

4. When planning a footing job, the most important consideration is:
   **a. The amount of spoil that will be created**
   **b. Where the spoil will be placed**
   **c. The order in which to proceed with digging**
   **d. All of the above**

5. When the footing is getting close to the desired elevation, the operator should use long level passes with the bucket and check the elevations at both ends.
   **a. True**

6. Cleaning the outer sides of the trench with the bottom of the bucket creates a clean trench area and a safer working environment.
   **a. True**

7. Requirements for pier-type footings include:
   **a. Proper location**
   **b. Straight, smooth sides**
   **c. Level bottom at the correct elevation**
   **d. All of the above**

8. The best approach to digging pier footings is to dig out the center first and then finish by cutting the sides.
   **b. False – *The best approach to digging pier footings is to dig the sides first and then finish by digging out the center.***

9. Layout lines should be extended past the limits of the excavation so that the location is still visible after digging has begun.
   **a. True**

10. Cleaning and smoothing the layout area before doing the layout will:
   **a. Simplify precise layouts**
   **b. Make the operator's task easier**
   **c. Make maneuvering the backhoe easier**
   **d. All of the above**

11. Measuring the depth of the footing from the side is the best method because it is the easiest and most accurate grade check.
   **b. False – *Measuring the depth of the footing from the side will usually not provide information on elevations, which is required for accurate results.***

12. When digging footings, the operator and a laborer should work together for the best results.
   **a. True**

13. If footings are dug too large:
   **c. More concrete will be required**

14. If the footings are dug too small, the reinforcing steel will not fit.
   **a. True**

15. Before starting to excavate any type of footings:
   **a. Consider all aspects of the job ahead of you.**
   **b. Plan the layout as thoroughly as possible**
   **c. Get a good mental picture (plan) of the excavation sequence**
   **d. All of the above**

16. When excavating a trench footing, it is best to dig each section of the trench as short as possible.
   **b. False – *When excavating a trench footing, it is best to dig each section of the trench as long as possible.***

17. Sometimes it may be necessary to start a footing at both ends and work toward the center to a pre-planned meeting point.
   **a. True**

# Chapter 9

1. A smooth well graded work area is the key to safety and productivity when using the loader.
   **a. True**

2. When an area is to be used for shuttle operations of material back and forth it should be graded smooth before starting to transport material.
   **a. True**

3. A smooth work area can help to prevent:
   **a. Loss of control when traveling around the job site**
   **b. Loose material from spilling from the bucket**
   **c. Operator fatigue**
   **d. All of the above**

4. When shuttle operations are not involved, a clean working area is not required.
   **b. False – *A clean working area always makes the job easier.***

5. In general building construction, spoil from excavations is often stockpiled outside of the building area.
   **a. True**

6. The TLB and its function is independent of other workers and trades on the job site.
   **b. False – *The TLB serves other workers and trades and is sometimes dependent on other workers and trades.***

7. Trenches and excavations dug by the backhoe often become the work area for workers in other construction trades.
   **a. True**

8. Methods and procedures followed by the operator can determine the productivity and safety of the work area for the other trades on the job.
   **a. True**

9. When working on sod (grass surface) the main goal is to do as little damage as possible to the surface.
   **a. True**

10. When cleaning up in sod areas the loader bucket should be:
    **a. Flat**

11. The best method of cleaning up dirt areas is to cut the high areas on the bucket's forward passes and fill the low areas while back-dragging.
    **a. True**

12. As the pile becomes smaller the back up:
    **b. Becomes smaller**

13. When back-dragging with the loader, you will get the best results when:
    **b. When the loader control is in the float position**

14. At the end of asphalt cleanup procedures, it is a common procedure to:
    **a. Use a flat shovel to clean the remaining material that the machine is unable to pick up**
    **b. Clean the area with a push broom**
    **c. Both of the above**

15. A bumpy and uneven job site can compromise operator safety. This can affect the operator immediately by:
    **a. Having less control over the machine**

16. A bumpy and uneven job site can compromise operator safety. This can affect the operator before the end of the day by:
    **b. Causing operator fatigue**

17. When filling a loader bucket, the further you push the pile, the more material you get in the bucket.
    **b. False – *When filling a loader bucket, and the pile begins to move, no more material will be pushed into the bucket.***

## Chapter 10

1. Grading consists of:
   **a. Cutting down the high places**
   **b. Filling in the low places**
   **c. Both of the above**

2. The cut and fill areas of a grading job will become clear to the operator by visualizing the desired grades and comparing them to the existing grades.
   **a. True**

3. Filling often requires compaction of the earth and then refilling and leveling to the desired grade.
   **a. True**

4. The attitude or angle of the machine and the loader bucket (level or not, left to right) is determined by the angle of the ground where the front tires are making contact.
   **b. False – *The attitude or angle of the machine and the loader bucket (level or not, left to right) is determined by the angle of the ground where the rear tires are making contact.***

5. A bucket level check is used to:
   **a. Check the accuracy of the bucket level indicators**
   **b. Determine the level position of the bucket**
   **c. Both of the above**

6. A cutting pass that is too deep or not deep enough can be corrected on the next several passes.
   **a. True**

7. In order to allow for compaction in a fill area, the material should be dispersed:
   **c. Higher than the desired grade**

8. Dispersing the material can be done:
   **a. In front of the bucket going forward**
   **b. Behind the bucket going backward**
   **c. Both of the above methods**

9. Using a full loader bucket and compacting the area under the TLB'S front tires will result in the highest degree of compaction.
   **a. True**

10. When finish grading, the loader the bucket should be flat or nearly flat so that the cut and fill can be adjusted to very fine degree.
    **a. True**

11. For the best results when back dragging with the loader, the operator should use:
    **c. Loader in the float position**

12. To achieve the final polished results, the operator should back-drag the entire area in one direction, and then:
    **b. Back-drag the entire area in another direction 60 to 90 degrees from the first passes**

13. Back-dragging with the front of the bucket slightly tipped up will produce a filling action.
    **b. False – *Back-dragging with the front of the bucket slightly tipped up will produce a cutting action.***

14. When back-dragging, the cutting abilities of the loader can be increased:
    **a. With down pressure on the loader**
    **b. By adding material to the bucket**
    **c. Both of the above**

15. When back-dragging and a fill is desired, the front of the bucket is:
    **b. Tipped down slightly from the level position**

16.When a fine finish grade is desired in a large area the operator should:
**a. Back-drag the entire area in one direction**
**b. Change direction from 60 to 90 degrees and back-drag again**
**c. Both of the above**

17. When fine grading an area, the procedure is to cut off the high spots on the forward pass and use the accumulated material to fill the low areas on the backward pass.
**a. True**

18. Under what circumstances would the operator use the backhoe for grading?
**a. Poor access or the work area is too small to use the loader**
**b. Ground conditions too soft**
**c . Where slopes or differing elevations are present**
**d. All of the above**

19. Swinging the backhoe bucket into a solid object could cause severe damage to the backhoe.
**a. True**

20. Soil that has been dug up by the backhoe will be loose and will require compaction when filling or back filling.
**a. True**

21. Compaction is accomplished by applying great weight or impacts to the area to be compacted.
**a. True**

22. When soil is too dry, compaction is resisted due to friction between the soil particles.
**a. True**

23. Jetting is a technique that is most useful in clay or silty soils.
**b. False – *Jetting is a technique that is most useful in sandy or granular soils.***

# Chapter 11

1. When beginning any digging job, an important aspect to consider is the movement of the earth that will be required.
**a. True**

2. When digging a ditch, placement of the spoil is not an important consideration.
**b. False – *When digging a ditch, placement of the spoil is an important consideration.***

3. The most important aspect of any TLB procedure is:
**c. Safety**

4. The operator should provide a safer working area in and around the excavation by:
**a. Sloping the sides of the excavation when necessary**
**b. Dislodging exposed rocks and chunks of dirt**
**c. Cleaning the top of the excavation**
**d. All of the above**

5. Precision excavation is usually only necessary for footings.
**a. True**

6. Excavations with a level finish grade are usually required for:
**a. Septic tanks**
**b. Electrical or telephone vaults**
**c. Footings and leach lines**
**d. All of the above**

7. Utility lines, such as water, gas, electric or telephone, are often dug to:
**d. A predetermined depth**

8. Sewer lines, drain pipes and drainage ditches are dug:
**c. With a sloping or "gravity flow" trench**

9. Different trades such as concrete, plumbing, and electrical require excavations for different purposes and have different requirements.
**a. True**

10. When the stick is extended:
**a. The reach is increased**
**b. The machine can dig deeper**
**c. The stockpiling range is increased**
**d. All of the above**

11. When the stick is extended, the precision capabilities of the backhoe are increased.
**a. True**

12. As the stick is extended, the digging power of the TLB is decreased.
**a. True**

13. When the unit is extended, the stability of the machine is:
**b. Decreased**

14. As a general rule, the extendible dipperstick should be positioned in the shortest position possible to do the job at hand.
**a. True**

15. After each move, the set up should be checked for:
**a. Safety**
**b. Stability**
**c. Alignment with the trench**
**d. All of the above**

16. The first surface cut is important because it serves as a guide for the bucket during the rest of the excavation process.
**a. True**

17. When the excavation is nearing the desired depth, the operator should clean the area by:
**a. Cleaning the "sidewalks" of the trench with the bottom of the bucket**
**b. Dislodging and removing rocks from the excavation area**
**c. Both of the above**

18. When completing a section of trench, the operator will:
**a. Make a series of long grading passes on the bottom of the trench**
**b. Have the grade checked at both ends of the trench**
**c. Clean the end of the trench closest to the machine**
**d. All of the above**

19. When digging a trench with the backhoe, the distance between setups:
**b. Will be shorter when digging a deep trench**

20. When digging a deep trench the distance between each backhoe set up will be
   **b. Shorter**

21. Hard ground conditions slow the digging process. The effects of hard ground conditions can be made worse by:
   **a. Using a large bucket**
   **b. Worn bucket teeth**
   **c. An under-powered machine**
   **d. All of the above**

22. When digging in hard ground, digging speed can be increased by: (choose two answers)
   **b. Lowering the angle of the bucket**
   **d. Making long, scraping passes**

23. The stability of the backhoe can sometimes be overloaded during which procedure?
   **a. Lifting**
   **b. Material handling**
   **c. When using the extendible dipperstick**

24. Instead of loading with the loader, loading trucks with the backhoe may be better when:
   **a. The soil is hard**
   **b. The soil is muddy**
   **c. The soil is sandy**
   **d. All of the above**

25. When an operator faces a situation or task that is new or unusual, danger is increased, and extreme caution should be used.
   **a. True**

26. The operator is responsible for the safety of:
   **a. Himself and others**
   **b. The machine**
   **c. The work area**
   **d. All of the above**

27. Digging an arc shaped trench is accomplished by using the swing to move the bucket from side to side.
   **b. False – *Digging an arc shaped trench is not accomplished by using the swing to move the bucket from side to side.***

28. The rule of thumb for stump removal is that the size of the required hole will be about:
   **c. 4 times the diameter of the lower trunk**

29. Using this rule of thumb, a stump diameter of 2 feet will require a hole of _____ feet to remove it.
   **c. 8 feet**

30. To remove a very large stump or rock from a hole, an operator could:
   **d. Add dirt to the deepest parts of the hole and roll it back and forth until it rises up to the ground level**

31. Using the trench for spoil transport is useful:
   **b. When there is no area for spoil placement**

# Chapter 12

1. Like all types of heavy equipment, the TLB requires mastering one set of controls.
   **b. False – *The TLB requires mastering two sets of controls.***

2. The TLB is considered to be the most useful machine in all-around construction.
   **a. True**

3. Generally speaking, the loader is more difficult to operate than the backhoe.
   **b. False – *Generally speaking, the backhoe is more difficult to operate than the loader.***

4. The amount of power available at the loader bucket is delivered by:
   **a. Breakout force**
   **b. Loader lift forces**
   **c. Driving forces of the tractor**
   **d. All of the above**

5. When down pressure is applied to the loader bucket, the amount of traction at the rear wheels:
   **a. Is increased**

6. When maneuvering the loader with a full bucket, the first and most basic rule is:
   **d. Keep the bucket low**

7. The higher a fully loaded bucket is raised, the more stable the machine becomes.
   **b. False – *The higher a fully loaded bucket is raised, the less stable the machine becomes.***

8. When loading trucks, the work area should be:
   **c. Stable and level**

9. The ability of the operator to get full buckets without wasting time will determine the effectiveness of many operations.
   **a. True**

10. In order to get full even bucket loads:
   **c. The corners of the bucket should contact the pile at the same time**

11. The loader is more effective when loading in hard ground conditions.
   **b. False – *The loader is more effective when loading in medium ground conditions.***

12. An improperly loaded truck could become unstable and overturn when driven.
   **a. True**

13. Which of the following are true of "ramp stockpiles"?
   **a. The ramp must be built at a low degree of slope**
   **b. The ramp must be 15 feet wide or more**
   **c. Can be built in "two levels"**
   **d. All of the above**

14. When using efficient truck loading patterns the loader:
   **a. Will approach the pile squarely**
   **b. Will approach the truck squarely**
   **c. Will usually have a "V" shaped pattern**
   **d. All of the above**

15. Shuttling consists of moving buckets of material from one point to another and is involved in nearly all loader applications.
   **a. True**

16. The greatest single thing that will ensure efficient shuttle operations is:
   **d. A smooth, well-graded shuttle route**

17. When planning a shuttle route, it is important to:
   **a. Choose a short, smooth path**
   **b. Provide for easy filling of the bucket**
   **c. Provide for easy dumping of the bucket**
   **d. All of the above**

18. Because of the size and position of the backhoe, the vision of the operator can sometimes be obstructed.
   **a. True**

19. When using the loader, it is okay to assume that people will not walk into the path of the machine.
   **b. False – *When using the loader, it is never okay to assume that people will not walk into the path of the machine.***

20. When the weight on the drive wheels increases, the traction decreases.
   **b. False – *When the weight on the drive wheels increases, the traction also increases.***

21. Circular grading patterns are most commonly used when
   **a. Back-filling or grading next to buildings or walls**
   **b. Grading close to houses or delicate surfaces**
   **c. Back-filling against basement walls**
   **d. All of the above**

22. When the loader is carrying a heavy load of soil, the traction at the rear wheels is increased.
   **b. False – *When the weight on the drive wheels increases, the traction increases.***

23. When the shuttle route is long, the operator should fill the bucket as completely as possible.
   **a. True**

24. After filling the loader bucket, a quick shake of the bucket will remove excess material to prevent loose spoil from falling out of the bucket during shuttle operations.
   **a. True**

25. When traveling in reverse, blind spots created by the backhoe assembly can become a safety hazard.
   **a. True**

26. When backfilling along a basement wall, a circular grading pattern will keep the weight away from the fill area.
   **a. True**

27. The "radar" system works only on inanimate objects and doesn't apply to people working on the site.
   **a. True**

28. The power that determines the usefulness of the loader bucket is generated by the drive wheels.
   **a. True**

## Chapter 13

1. The efficiency of job completion is determined by:
   **c. How many times the material must be handled**

2. When stockpiling broken concrete or other materials becomes necessary, the main consideration is:
   **a. Keeping the pile low**
   **b. The size of the pieces**
   **c. Providing a good backup**
   **d. All of the above**

3. During the demolition process, dirt should be kept separate from other materials such as asphalt and concrete.
   **a. True**

4. When using the "prying method," the power is generated by:
   **a. The boom cylinder**
   **b. The bucket and crowd cylinders**
   **c. The weight of the machine**
   **d. All of the above**

5. Because of the tremendous forces generated by the "prying method", a heavy duty bucket is mandatory.
   **a. True**

6. Breaking and removing concrete is very abusive to the machine and there is no way to avoid abuse.
   **b. False – *Breaking and removing concrete is very abusive to the machine but there are ways to avoid abuse.***

7. The "roll-out" method is "easy" on the machine because it is done using the natural motion of the machine.
   **a. True**

8. When picking up concrete that is still "in place," with the backhoe, the remaining concrete provides a natural backup.
   **a. True**

9. When working with large pieces, why should the bucket be positioned under the center of gravity of the piece?
   **a. To prevent breaking it**
   **b. To maintain control while moving it**
   **c. To test the weight**
   **d. All of the above**

10. When digging a trench with a 24-inch bucket, the concrete covering the area should be saw cut to a width of ____ inches prior to the backhoe work.
   **c. 26 inches**

11. Using the stabilizer as a backup:
   **a. Is a difficult maneuver that could cause machine damage**
   **b. Should not be used as standard operating procedure**
   **c. Should not be attempted by operators under the skill level of a veteran**
   **d. All of the above**

12. When lifting and swinging concrete to load a truck, the operator should:
   **a. Move the load smoothly and gently**
   **b. Control the load at all times**
   **c. "Test" the load to dislodge loose pieces before swinging over the truck**
   **d. All of the above**

13. To prevent a load of concrete from binding in the truck bed when dumped:

    c. **Do not pile pieces higher than the tailgate hinge pin**

14. When material is to be handled two or more times, there are several stockpiling considerations to be made.

    a. **True**

15. In many demolition jobs, separation of different materials is an important consideration.

    a. **True**

16. Clean up of demolition materials is either carried out at the end of the job, or in stages as the work progresses.

    a. **True**

17. One of the most efficient methods of breaking and loading concrete is to break and load the material with the backhoe and load it into trucks in one operation.

    a. **True**

18. When using the loader to load concrete, the larger the pieces, the easier the loading process will be.

    b. **False –** *When using the loader to load concrete, the smaller the pieces, the easier the loading process will be.*

19. When loading broken concrete with the loader, the lower the stockpile, the easier the loading will become.

    a. **True**

20. On most demolition jobs concrete and dirt can be mixed and hauled away.

    b. **False –** *On most demolition jobs concrete and dirt must be separated before being hauled away.*

21. A trench is to be dug in an existing parking lot. The concrete has been saw cut to allow the trench to be dug. The spoil from the trench will be reused for backfill, and the concrete will be loaded onto a truck and removed from the site. The fastest and easiest way to accomplish this work is to pile the concrete and dirt together on one side of the trench.

    b. **False –** *The fastest and easiest way to accomplish this work is to separate the materials as they are removed.*

22. The most powerful break out force created by the TLB is when the backhoe uses the "prying method."

    a. **True**

23. Breaking concrete into smaller pieces can be accomplished by:

    a. **Dropping**
    b. **The roll out method**
    c. **Positioning and striking**
    d. **All of the above**

24. Because of the unusual shapes and sizes of broken concrete, as well as the weight involved, the beginning operator can find loading to be difficult and awkward.

    a. **True**

25. Loading heavy material on any sloped surface is extremely dangerous and should not be attempted.

    a. **True**

## *Other fine products from...*
# Equipment Training Resources

*Add these quality training materials to your library today:*

### LOADER-BACKHOE BOOK – REVISED EDITION
*Operating Techniques for the Tractor-Loader-Backhoe*

296 pages – over 300 photos & illustrations, and over 300 questions & answers

**Revised Edition** (English) **– $38**

**Revised Edition** (Spanish) **– $38**

PDF files on disk for classroom computer use or projection **– $300**

FILES FOR VIEWING ONLY - NOT PRINTABLE

### LOADER-BACKHOE SAFETY VIDEOS
2 part set – 20 minutes each  OPERATOR SAFETY and WORKER SAFETY are covered for the best protection of the entire crew.

**2-part Set – $195**  DVD ONLY

### LOADER SAFETY & TRAINING VIDEOS
4 part set – 20 minutes each. TRACK LOADERS and RUBBER TIRE LOADERS are covered in depth in the three most important area of operation: SAFETY, MAINTENANCE, and OPERATING TECHNIQUES.

**4-part Set – $395**  DVD ONLY

*For complete detail on any of these products see our on-line catalog at*
## www.equiptrain.com

| TITLE | PRICE | QTY | EXTENSION |
|---|---|---|---|
| **Operating Techniques for the TRACTOR-LOADER-BACKHOE** Revised Edition (English) | $38 | | |
| **Operating Techniques for the TRACTOR-LOADER-BACKHOE** Revised Edition (Spanish) | $38 | | |
| **Operating Techniques for the** NOT PRINTABLE **TRACTOR-LOADER-BACKHOE** PDF files on disk (English) | $300 | | |
| **LOADER-BACKHOE SAFETY VIDEOS** 2-part Set (DVD) | $195 | | |
| **LOADER SAFETY & TRAINING VIDEOS** 4-part Set (DVD) | $395 | | |
| | | | |
| | | | |
| | | | |
| | | | |
| | | | |
| | | | |
| | | | |
| **$10** per order (up to **3** lbs.) **Shipping & Handling** | | | |
| CA residents add 9.75% **Sales Tax** | | | |
| **TOTAL** | | | |

Name_____

Company _____

Address _____

City_____ State _____ Zip _____

Phone _____ Fax _____

☐ BILL US using Purchase Order # _____

☐ CHARGE my ☐ VISA ☐ MasterCard ☐ AMEX   Signature _____

Card # _____ Exp. date _____

**E**QUIPMENT
**T**RAINING
**R**ESOURCES

8340 Chimineas Ave., Northridge, CA 91325
Phone (818) 349-1230 • Fax (818) 349-1241
www.equiptrain.com